1st EXAM → 93%

2nd EXAM → 88%

3RD EXAM → _____

~~Total~~

Ave. →

homework

+ $4\frac{1}{2}$ →

FINAL

PROBLEMS ON
THERMODYNAMICS

HW

1st → chen

2nd → chem

3Rd → chen

4th → chen

5th → chen

6th → chen

7th → chem.

8th → chen.

9th → xchen.

10th → chen.
_____

+ $4\frac{1}{2}$ pts.

VIRGIL MORING FAIRES

Late Professor of Mechanical Engineering
U.S. Naval Postgraduate School

CLIFFORD M. SIMMANG

Professor of Mechanical Engineering
Texas A & M University

ALEXANDER V. BREWER

Late Professor Emeritus of Mechanical Engineering
Texas A & M University

PROBLEMS ON THERMODYNAMICS

SIXTH EDITION

MACMILLAN PUBLISHING CO., INC.

New York

COLLIER MACMILLAN PUBLISHERS

London

Earlier editions entitled *Problems on Applied Thermodynamics* copyright 1938 and 1948 by Macmillan Publishing Co., Inc. Earlier editions entitled *Problems on Thermodynamics* © 1957, © 1962, and © copyright 1970 by Macmillan Publishing Co., Inc.

Macmillan Publishing Co., Inc.
866 Third Avenue, New York, New York 10022

Collier Macmillan Canada, Ltd.

ISBN 0-02-335230-2

Printing: 1 2 3 4 5 6 7 8   Year: 8 9 0 1 2 3 4

PREFACE TO THE SIXTH EDITION

The organization of the problems has been changed to match the rearrangement in *Thermodynamics*, Faires and Simmang, Sixth Edition, hereafter in this book referred to as the *Text*. Although the problem book is especially designed for this sixth edition text, the problems are for the most part also suitable for use with any thermodynamics text intended for engineers. The total number of problems has been increased because two new chapters (14, "Gas Compressors," and 19, "Heat Transfer") have been included in the sixth edition.

As in previous editions, the comprehensive type of problem is favored so that the student has a better opportunity to tie together the various related ideas. Also, the problems are designed to help the student organize his thought processes in a manner to match actual situations in engineering. Many of the problems are the result of notes and data jotted down while the author was on a conducted tour of an industrial plant.

There is a generous balance of problems based upon the SI system of units; however, the number of problems based upon the English system of units is still plentiful. It is believed that the complete transition to the SI system will require a new generation (in time); it is doubtful that the English system will ever pass into complete oblivion.

A large number of problems have answers given, but there are plenty without answers, permitting the teacher to mix such problems in any desired proportion. Most teachers seem to like to assign some without answers, since in practice, engineering problems do not have a known answer.

The attention of all users, students and teachers, is called to the Appendix. Like tables have the same numbers as in the *Text*, and the numerous charts are also similarly identified. The steam tables in this book are in accordance with tolerances established by the Sixth International Steam Table Conference and are reproduced by permission of The American Society of Mechanical Engineers and Combustion Engineering, Inc. Without this kind permission, an adequate set of steam tables could not have been presented here. Answers to problems on vapors are based on the tables in this book. Either the values in the tables have been selected to cover the problems or, as in the case of steam, the problems are usually designed to fit the tables with the minimum of interpolation. I am especially grateful to Professors Keenan and Kaye, and their

v

publisher, John Wiley, for permission to take extracts from various gas tables. There is a greatly increased emphasis on the use of these gas tables in our problems.

A manual giving solutions to many of these problems is available to teachers only. The manual also gives the solutions to most of the problems in the *Text*. For the same problem and its solution, both the *Text* problem and the problem book number are listed side by side for quick and convenient location.

I am greatly indebted to my two late coauthors, Professors Faires and Brewer, who taught and counseled me during my professional growth. To my numerous sources—industry, journals, magazines—I say thanks for your cooperative support. Among my several colleagues who extended specific contributions, I wish to name Professor E. S. Holdredge and Dr. A. B. Alter and give them special thanks.

C. M. S.

CONTENTS

SYMBOLS

With few exceptions, standard symbols have been used; but the choice has been influenced by those used in the ASHRAE *Guide* and in Keenan and Kaye *Gas Tables*.

A — area; mass number; Helmholtz function; ampere.

a — acceleration; acoustic speed.

$\mathscr{A}$ — availability function; $-\Delta\mathscr{A}_{n/o}$, availability, nonflow; $-\Delta\mathscr{A}_{f/o}$, availability, steady flow.

b — $h - T_0 s$.

C — a constant.

C_p, C_v — molal specific heats at constant pressure and at constant volume.

c — clearance ratio in engines, compressors; speed of light; specific heat, Btu/lb-°R. c_p, c_v, specific heat at constant pressure; specific heat at constant volume; c_n, polytropic specific heat.

D — diameter.

d — a dimension; distance.

E — general symbol for energy; E_s, total stored energy of a system; E_e, electric energy; E_{ch}, chemical energy; E_c, energy chargeable against an engine in obtaining its thermal efficiency; E_F, energy dissipated in friction; E_a, available energy; E_u, unavailable energy. Young's modulus.

e — thermal efficiency; e_b, brake thermal efficiency; e_i, indicated thermal efficiency; e_k, combined or over-all thermal efficiency; elementary charge.

$\mathscr{E}$ — electromotive force (emf).

E — electrical field strength intensity.

F — force or total load; F_g, force of gravity.

f — friction factor (pipe flow); fugacity.

f_m — mass fraction.

f_t — temperature recovery factor.

G — Gibbs (free energy) function; gravitational constant; irradiation.

g — local acceleration of gravity; g_o, standard acceleration of gravity.

H — total enthalpy; H_m, enthalpy of a mixture; H_p, enthalpy of products of combustion; H_r, enthalpy of reactants; H^o, enthalpy in standard state.

h — specific enthalpy; Planck's constant; $\bar{h}$, enthalpy of 1 mole of substance; h^o, enthalpy in standard or reference state; h_0, stagnation enthalpy; h^*, enthalpy of ideal gas (where distinction is necessary); h_{rp}, enthalpy of reaction.

h film coefficient (heat transfer).

$\mathbf{H}$ magnetic intensity.

I impulse; irreversibility; intensity of radiation.

$\mathscr{I}$ electric current, amperes.

J Joule's constant ($\approx$778).

K kinetic energy; K_s, spring scale; K_p, equilibrium constant.

k the ratio c_p/c_v; conductivity.

$\mathbf{k}$ Newton's proportionality constant

L distance; length; stroke of piston; represents unit of length; L'', stroke in inches.

$\mathbf{M}$ Mach number; magnetic moment.

M molecular mass; unless otherwise specified, lb/mole = pmole; M_a, molecular mass of gas A, and so on. Moment.

$\mathscr{M}$ momentum.

m mass; percentage steam bled in regenerative cycles; exponent in $pV^m = C$ for an irreversible process.

N number of anything; number of power cycles per minute completed by an engine.

N_A Avogadro's number.

n revolutions per minute (rpm); polytropic exponent: number of moles.

P gravitational potential energy; represents the unit of a pound.

p unit pressure; p_m, mean effective pressure (mep): p_{mi}, indicated mep; p_{mB}, brake mep; p_0, stagnation or impact pressure; p°, pressure in reference state; p_r, relative pressure; p_R, reduced pressure.

Q heat; Q_A, heat added; Q_R, heat rejected; Q_r, radiated heat; etc.

q heating value; q_l, lower heating value; q_h, higher heating value; q_v, heating value at constant volume; $\bar{q}$, heating value per mole of fuel.

$\mathscr{Q}$ electrical charge, coulombs of electricity.

R specific gas onstant, $R = \bar{R}/M = 1545/M$ ($=pv/T$ for ideal gas).

$\bar{R}$ universal gas constant.

$\mathbf{R}$ Reynolds number

r radius; ratios; reheat factor; r_k, compression ratio; r_c, cutoff ratio; r_p, pressure ratio; r_e, expansion ratio; $r_{f/a}$, fuel/air ratio; $r_{a/f}$, air/fuel ratio; r_k, hydraulic radius.

$\mathscr{R}$ electrical resistance.

S total entropy

s specific entropy; s°, absolute entropy in a standard state; $\bar{s}$, entropy per mole.

s_1^a absolute entropy in state 1; and so on.

$\mathscr{S}$ surface tension.

T absolute temperature, usually degrees Rankine; T_R, reduced temperature; T_0, stagnation temperature; T_0, sink temperature; T°, standard or reference temperature.

t temperature, usually in degrees Fahrenheit; time.

U total internal energy; U_p, internal energy of products, and so on; U°, internal energy at standard state.

u specific internal energy; $\bar{u}$, internal energy of one mole of substance; u_{rp}, internal energy of reaction; u°, in standard state.

V total volume; V_D, displacement volume.

v specific volume; v_r, relative volume; v_R, reduced volume; v_{Ri}, ideal reduced volume; $\bar{v}$, volume of one mole.

$\mathcal{V}$ speed, velocity.

W shaft or fluid work; W_I, indicated work; W_B, brake work; W_K, combined work; W_f, flow work; W_p, pump work.

$\dot{W}$ power

w total emissive power.

X volumetric or mole fraction.

x quality of a two-phase system; coordinate.

y percentage (or fraction) of liquid in a two-phase system; coordinate; spring deflection.

Z compressibility factor; atomic number.

z altitude; potential energy of a unit weight.

α *(alpha)* constant in specific heat equation; absorptivity; linear thermal expansion coefficient $(dL/L)/dT$.

β *(beta)* constant in specific heat equation; coefficient of volumetric expansion.

γ *(gamma)* specific weight; constant in specific heat equation; coefficient of performance; angle.

δ *(delta)* angle.

ε *(epsilon)* effectiveness; emissivity; energy of photon, of translation of molecule; unit strain; ε_r, effectiveness of regeneration.

ζ *(zeta)* bulk modulus.

η *(eta)* energy ratios; engine efficiency; combustion efficiency; η_b, brake engine efficiency, turbine blade efficiency; η_c, compressor efficiency (adiabatic if not qualified); η_i, indicated engine efficiency; η_k, combined engine efficiency; η_m, mechanical efficiency; η_n, nozzle efficiency; η_p, propulsive efficiency; pump efficiency; η_r, efficiency of reaction blades; η_s, turbine stage efficiency; η_v, volumetric efficiency.

θ *(theta)* represents unit of temperature; angle.

κ *(kappa)* Boltzmann's constant; κ_d, coefficient of discharge; κ_f, velocity friction coefficient; κ_p, pressure coefficient; κ_s, adiabatic compressibility coefficient; κ_T, isothermal compressibility coefficient; κ_v, velocity coefficient.

λ *(lambda)* wavelength.

μ *(mu)* degree of saturation; absolute viscosity; Joule–Thomson coefficient; micron.

μ_0 permeability.

ν *(nu)* kinematic viscosity; frequency.

π *(pi)* $3.1416\ldots$, Peltier coefficient.

ρ *(rho)* density; reflectivity.

σ *(sigma)* Stefan-Boltzmann constant; unit stress.

τ *(tau)* time; represents a unit of time; transmissivity.

ϕ *(phi)* relative humidity; angle; $d\phi = c_p dT/T$.

ω *(omega)* angular velocity; humidity ratio; angle.

Δ *(delta)* indicates a difference or a change of value, Δt = change of temperature or difference in temperature, in accordance with the context.

Ω *(omega)* thermodynamic probability; electric resistance.

APPROVED INTERNATIONAL PREFIXES

Abbreviations ( ) and meanings are as follows (in accordance with this well-known example : kilo $(k) = 10^3$):

tera (T) = 10^{12}	deka (da) = 10	nano (n) = 10^{-9}
giga (G) = 10^9	deci (d) = 10^{-1}	pico (p) = 10^{-12}
mega (M) = 10^6	centi (c) = 10^{-2}	femto (f) = 10^{-15}
kilo (k) = 10^3	milli (m) = 10^{-3}	atto (a) = 10^{-18}
hecto (h) = 10^2	micro (μ) = 10^{-6}	

ABBREVIATIONS

a	air.
AC	alternating current.
A/F	air-fuel ratio.
AIChE	American Institute of Chemical Engineers.
ASME	American Society of Mechanical Engineers.
ASHRAE	American Society of Heating, Refrigerating and Air-Conditioning Engineers.
atm	standard atmosphere, a unit of pressure.
BDC	bottom dead center.
bhp	brake horsepower.
bmep	brake mean effective pressure.
Btu	British thermal unit.
cm^3	cubic centimeter.
cd	candela.
cfm	cubic feet per minute.
cgs	centimeter-gram-second system.
chu	centigrade heat unit.
CI	compression ignition.
cm	centimeter.
cpm	cycles per minute.
cps	cycles per second.
da	dry air.
DC	direct current.
dg	dry gas.
eV	electron volt.
f	fuel.
F/A	fuel-air ratio.
fhp	friction horsepower.
fpm	feet per minute.
fps	feet per second.
fps^2	feet per second-second.
gm	gram.
gmole	gram mole.
gpm	gallons per minute.
HP	high pressure.
hp	horsepower.
Hz	hertz.
ICE	internal combustion engine.

ID	inside diameter.
ihp	indicated horsepower.
imep	indicated mean effective pressure.
IP	intermediate pressure.
J	joule.
kg	kilogram.
kW	kilowatt.
LMTD	logarithmic mean temperature difference.
ln	natural logarithm (base e). $\ln N = 2.3 \log_{10} N$.
log	logarithm to the base 10.
LP	low pressure.
m	meter.
mep	mean effective pressure.
MeV	million electron volts.
MFP	mean free paths.
mph	miles per hour.
N	newton.
NBS	National Bureau of Standards.
OD	outside diameter.
Pa	pascal.
pmole	pound mole.
psf	pounds per square foot.
psi	pounds per square inch.
psia	pounds per square inch absolute.
psig	pounds per square inch gage.
rpm	revolutions per minute.
rps	revolutions per second.
s	second
SAE	Society of Automotive Engineers.
SI	spark ignition; international system of units.
TDC	top dead center.
USASI	U.S.A. Standards Institute (formerly Am. Standards Asso., ASA).
v	vapor.
wg	water gage.

PROBLEMS ON THERMODYNAMICS

1

BASIC PRINCIPLES, CONCEPTS, AND DEFINITIONS

Note: Unless otherwise stated, atmospheric pressure should be taken as 14.696 psia or 101.325 kPaa and local gravity acceleration as 32.174 fps² or 9.806 mps².

PROPERTIES, STATES AND UNITS

1. A 105.3-ℓ system contains 3 kg of water vapor at 100 bar, 813 K. List the values of three intensive properties, one extensive property, and one specific property.

2. Plot these two state points on a pressure (ordinate)–volume (abscissa) plane: at state 1, $p_1 = 60$ bar, $V_1 = 100 \ \ell$; at state 2, $p_2 = 10$ bar, $V_2 = 700 \ \ell$. Now join them with a single straight line. (**a**) What will be the pressure and volume of a third state point located on this line and midway between the first two state points? (**b**) Form a right triangle using the straight line as the hypotenuse. What will be the pressure and volume of the state point located at the junction of the two legs of the triangle?

3. For a given system, two of its independent intensive properties are x and y. State (show proof) which of the following expressions have characteristics of a property (are point functions): (**a**) $y^2 \, dx + 2xy \, dy$, (**b**) $5y \, dx$, (**c**) $x \, dx$, (**d**) $x^2 + y^2$, (**e**) $15x^3 + 4xy^2$, (**f**) $(x^2 + y^2) \, dx + 2xy \, dy$.

Ans. (**a**) has property characteristics, (**b**) does not have property characteristics.

4. The following three terms are being studied: pressure defined as force per unit area, density defined as mass per unit volume, and Young's modulus defined as unit stress per unit strain. (**a**) Using the F-L-τ-m nomenclature, write the dimensions for each defined term. (**b**)

On the basis of each of these three systems of units, fps, cgs, and SI, write the units for each defined term.

FORCE, MASS, AND WEIGHT

5. Express your height, mass and weight ($g = 9.75$ m/s²) in terms of SI units.

6. Five masses in a region where $g = 30.5$ fps² are as follows: m_1 is 500 gm of mass; m_2 weighs 800 gm$_f$; m_3 weighs 15 poundals; m_4 weighs 3 lb$_f$; m_5 is 0.1 slug of mass. What is the total mass expressed (**a**) in grams, (**b**) in pounds, (**c**) in slugs.

Ans. (**a**) 4461 gm, (**b**) 9.84 lb, (**c**) 0.3057 slug.

7. A mass weighing 25 N is suspended from a cord which can be moved vertically, up or down. What are your conclusions regarding the directions and magnitude of acceleration and velocity of the mass when the cord tension is (**a**) 25 N, (**b**) 15 N, (**c**) 35 N?

8. For a ballistics study, a 1.9-gm bullet is fired into soft wood. The bullet strikes the wood surface with a velocity of 380 m/s and penetrates 0.15 m. Find (**a**) the constant retarding force in N, (**b**) the time required to stop the bullet, (**c**) the deceleration in m/s.²

9. If 50 kg of mass are placed on the pan of a spring balance located on a freight elevator and if local gravity acceleration is 9.70 m/s², then (**a**) when the elevator is moving with an upward acceleration of 2.5 m/s^2, what will the balance read? (**b**) if the elevator is stopped, what will the balance read? (**c**) if the supporting cable breaks (elevator falls freely), what will the balance read? (**d**) if the balance reads 350 N, what are the circumstances?

10. Compute the gravitational force between a proton ($m = 1.66 \times 10^{-27}$ kg) and an electron ($m = 9.11 \times 10^{-31}$ kg) in an atom whose radius of electron orbit is 5.29×10^{-11} m. Report answers in units of N and dynes.

11. A mass of 0.1 slug in space is subjected to an external vertical force of 4 lb. If the local gravity acceleration is $g = 30.5$ fps^2 and if frictional effects are neglected, determine the acceleration of the mass if the external vertical force is acting (**a**) upward, (**b**) downward.
Ans. (**a**) 9.5 fps^2.

12. A system has a mass of 30 lb. What total force is necessary to accelerate it 15 fps^2: (**a**) if it is moving on a horizontal frictionless plane; (**b**) if it is moving vertically upward at a point where local gravity is $g = 31.50$ fps^2?

13. Note that the gravity acceleration at equatorial sea level is $g = 32.088$ fps^2 and that its variation is -0.003 fps^2/1000 ft ascent. Find the height in miles above this point for which (**a**) the gravity acceleration becomes $g = 30.504$ fps^2, (**b**) the weight of a given man is decreased by 5%. (**c**) What is the weight of a 180 lb$_m$ man atop the 29,131-ft Mt. Everest in Tibet, relative to this point?
Ans. (**a**) 100 mi, (**b**) 101.2 mi, (**c**) 179.1 lb$_f$.

14. An astronaut located on the surface of the moon ($g = 5.36$ fps^2) places a crater sample on a spring scale (previously calibrated on earth at g_0); a reading of 7.5 lb is noted: (**a**) What is the sample mass? (**b**) If the scale had been of the balance type, what reading would have been noted?

15. The mass of a given airplane at sea level ($g = 32.10$ fps^2) is 10 tons. Find its mass in lb$_m$, slugs, and kg and its (gravitational) weight in lb$_f$ and N when it is travelling at a 50,000-ft elevation. The acceleration of gravity g decreases by 3.33×10^{-6} fps^2 for each foot of elevation. *Ans.* 9070 kg, 19,850 lb$_f$.

16. A girl weighing 470 N hangs suspended on the end of a rope 8 m long. If a friend pushes her laterally to one side until the rope makes an angle of 35° with the vertical, what lateral force is required at this point? What is the tension in the rope? If local $g =$

970 cm/sec^2, what is her mass in kg? In lb$_m$?

17. What is the mass in kilograms and weight in Newtons ($g = 9.65$ m/s^2) of (**a**) a 4000-lb$_m$ automobile, (**b**) a 235-lb$_m$ fullback? Find the mass in grams and the weight in dynes of (**c**) 77 grains of moisture, (**d**) 12 oz of salt.

18. Calculate the magnitude of the gravity acceleration on the surface of the moon and again at a point 1000 km above the surface of the moon; ignore the gravity effects of the earth. The moon has a mean radius of 1740 km and a mass of 7.4×10^{22} kg.
Ans. (surface) $g = 1.63$ m/s^2.

19. How far from the earth must a body be along a line toward the sun so that the gravitational pull of the sun balances that of the earth? Earth-to-sun distance is 9.3×10^7 mi; mass of sun is 3.24×10^5 times mass of earth.
Ans. 1.63×10^5 mi from earth.

DENSITY AND SPECIFIC WEIGHT

20. Two liquids of different densities ($\rho_1 = 1500$ kg/m^3, $\rho_2 = 500$ kg/m^3) are poured together into a 100-ℓ tank, filling it. If the resulting density of the mixture is 800 kg/m^3, find the respective amounts of liquids used. Also, find the weight of the mixture; local $g = 9.675$ m/s^2. *Ans.* $m_1 = 45$ kg.

21. A cylindrical drum (2-ft diameter, 3-ft height) is filled with a fluid whose density is 40 lb/ft^3. Determine (**a**) the total volume of fluid, (**b**) its total mass in pounds and slugs, (**c**) its specific volume, (**d**) its specific weight where $g = 31.90$ fps^2. (**e**) Specify which of the foregoing properties are extensive and which intensive.
Ans. (**a**) 9.43 ft^3, (**b**) 11.72 slugs, (**c**) 0.025 ft^3/lb, (**d**) 39.7 lb/ft^3.

22. The mass of a fluid system is 0.311 slug; its density is 30 lb/ft^3 and $g = 31.90$ fps^2. Find (**a**) the specific volume, (**b**) the specific weight, (**c**) the total volume.

23. If a pump discharges 75 gpm of water whose specific weight is 61.5 lb/ft^3 ($g = 31.95$ fps^2), find (**a**) the mass flow rate, lb/min, and (**b**) the total time required to fill a vertical cylindrical tank 10 ft in diameter and 10 ft high. *Ans.* (**a**) 620 lb/min, (**b**) 78.3 min.

24. It is estimated that the mass of the earth is 5.98×10^{24} kg; its mean radius is 6.38×10^6 m. Find its density in gm/cm^3 and lb$_m$/ft^3. Compare this value to the density of water (62.4 lb$_m$/ft^3). *Ans.* $5.50 \times$ density of water.

PRESSURE

25. By sketching a set of horizontal lines, illustrate the relative magnitude of the following pressures: (**a**) absolute zero, (**b**) atmospheric, (**c**) gage, (**d**) vacuum. Can a pressure ever be less than absolute zero? Explain.

26. Given the barometric pressure of 14.7 psia (29.92 in. Hg abs), make these conversions: (**a**) 80 psig to psia and to atm, (**b**) 20 in. Hg vac to in. Hg abs and to psia, (**c**) 10 psia to psi vac and to Pa, (**d**) 15 in. Hg gage to psia, to torrs, and to Pa.

27. Due to the unavailability of mercury, a barometer was constructed using water in the closed column with a certain amount of oil on top to prevent the boiling of the water. For standard atmospheric pressure, what height of oil will be required and how high will the column of water be if the minimum pressure at the water-oil interface is to be 1 psia? Water density is 62.4 lb_m/ft^3; specific gravity of oil is 0.8.

28. As illustrated, a mercury manometer is attached to the side of a nearly full water tank.

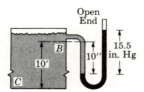

Open
End

15.5
in. Hg

B

10″

10′

C

Problem 28

The reading of the mercury column is 15.5 in. Hg gage. Although air on the water maintains the pressure, the other 10-in. leg of the manometer is full of water; for H_2O, $\rho = 62.3$ lb/ft^3; for Hg, $\rho = 846$ lb/ft^3. If the location is at standard gravity and the temperature of both the water and mercury is 60°F, what is the pressure (psia) in the tank at the level where the manometer is attached? If the tank extends 10 ft below this level, what is the pressure at this depth?   *Ans.* 21.94, 26.27 psia.

29. A 30-m vertical column of fluid (density 1878 kg/m³) is located where $g = 9.65$ mps². Find the pressure at the base of the column.   *Ans.* 543.7 kPa.

30. A weatherman carried an aneroid barometer from the ground floor to his office atop the Sears Tower in Chicago. On the ground level, the barometer read 30.150 in.

Hg abs; topside it read 28.607 in. Hg abs. Assume that the average atmospheric air density was 0.075 lb/ft³ and estimate the height of the building.
      Ans. 1451 ft (approx.).

31. Given the two-compartment vessel shown in the figure. Gage *A* reads 85 psig; gage *B* inside compartment *X* reads 25 psig. If the barometer reads 30.61 in. Hg, determine the reading of gage *C* and convert this reading to an absolute value.   *Ans.* 75 psia.

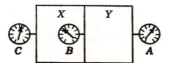

X   *Y*

C   *B*   *A*

Problems 31, 32, 33

32. The same as problem 31 except that the gage readings are: *A* = 15 in. Hg vac., and *B* = 5.4 psig.

33. (**a**) If gage *C* (see figure) reads 350 psig and *B* reads 125 psig, what will gage *A* read? (**b**) If *A* reads 0 psig, what is the maximum reading that *B* can have? State conditions.

34. A vertical composite fluid column whose upper end is open to the atmosphere is composed of 18 in. of mercury (specific gravity is 13.45), 26 in. of water (density is 62 lb/ft³), and 32 in. of oil (specific gravity is 0.825). Determine the pressure (**a**) at the base of the column, (**b**) at the oil-water interface, and (**c**) at the water-mercury interface. The specific gravities are relative to 62.4 lb/ft³ water.
      Ans. (**a**) 25.33 psia, (**b**) 15.65 psia, (**c**) 16.58 psia.

35. A simple mercury manometer connected into a flow line gives readings as shown in the figure. Local gravity is standard and the mercury density is 0.488 lb/in.³. Find the pressure at points *X* and *Y* when the flow line and

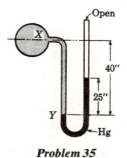

Open

X

40″

25″

Y

Hg

Problem 35

left leg contain (**a**) air whose density is 0.072 lb/ft³, (**b**) water whose density is 62.1 lb/ft³. (**c**) Answer (**a**) and (**b**) if the local gravity is $g = 30$ fps².

Ans. (**a**) 26.90, 26.90, (**b**) 25.46, 26.90, (**c**) 26.10 psia.

36. A manometer containing water (density = 62.1 lb/ft³) and mercury (specific gravity = 13.55) connects two pressure regions A and B as shown in the figure. The local gravity acceleration is $g = 32.00$ fps². If $p_B = 50$ psig, find p_A.   *Ans.* 57.07 psig.

37. The same as 36 except that, in lieu of the mercury, the fluid is a special compound with a specific gravity of 2.00.

Ans. 48.75 psig.

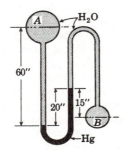

Problems 36, 37

38. A solid frictionless piston P whose mass is 80 lb is pulled up the inside of a 6-in. vertical pipe that has its lower end in a pool of water (density = 62.4 lb/ft³) and its upper end open to the 15 psia atmosphere. See figure. The water rises in contact with the piston to a height of 20 ft above the surface of the pool. If the local gravity acceleration is $g = 31$ fps², find (**a**) the pull F on the piston required at the 20 ft height, (**b**) the pressure exerted by the water on the piston at this point.

Ans. (**a**) 313.2 lb, (**b**) 6.65 psia.

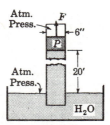

Problems 38, 39

39. If the vapor pressure of the water under the conditions stated in problem 38 is 0.5 psia (point at which the water boils and produces vapor), to what maximum height may the piston be raised and still maintain contact with the liquid water (no evaporation)? What will be the pull on the piston at this point?

40. The composite piston P has a total mass of 40 lb and is supported by the pressure p_C of the flowing methane gas. See figure. If the pressure p_A is 100 psia and the pressure $p_B = 20$ psia, find p_C; local gravity $g = g_0 = 32.174$ fps².

Ans. 34.81 psia.

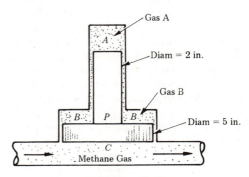

Problems 40, 41

41. The same as problem 40 except that $p_A = 40$, $p_B = 18$, $p_C = 25$ psia and the total mass of the composite piston is unknown; find the mass of the piston.

TEMPERATURE

42. Convert (**a**) 122°F to °C and to K, (**b**) −40°C to °F and to °R, (**c**) 942°R to °C and to K, (**d**) 373 K to °F and to °R.

43. If two thermometers, one reading °C and the other K, are inserted in the same system, under what circumstance will they both have the same numerical reading? What will be the system's temperature when the absolute thermometer reads twice the numerical reading of the Celsius thermometer?

44. A Fahrenheit and a Celsius thermometer are both immersed in a fluid. (**a**) If the two numerical readings are identical, what is the temperature of the fluid expressed as °R? As K? (**b**) What is the fluid temperature if the Fahrenheit reading is numerically twice that of the Celsius reading?   *Ans.* (**b**) 780°R, 433 K.

45. (a) Define a new temperature scale, say °N, in which the boiling and freezing points of water are 1000°N and 100°N, respectively, and correlate this scale with the Fahrenheit and Celsius scales. (b) The °N reading on this scale is a certain number of degrees on a corresponding absolute temperature scale. What is this absolute temperature at 0°N?
Ans. (a) $t_N = 9t_C + 100$, (b) 2360°N abs, approx.

46. For a particular thermocouple, if one junction is maintained at 0°C (cold junction) and the other junction is used as a probe to measure the desired Celsius temperature t, the voltage ε generated in the circuit is related to the temperature t as

$$\varepsilon = t(a + bt)$$

Further, for this thermocouple, when ε is in millivolts mV the two constants are $a = 0.25$, $b = -5.5 \times 10^{-4}$. (a) What are the units of a, b? (b) Determine the value of ε for each of the measured temperatures $-100°C$, 100°C, 200°C, 300°C, 400°C, and plot an εt-curve.
Ans. (b) $\varepsilon = 19.5$ mV for 100°C.

47. For the thermocouple in problem 46, find the rate of change of ε per °C at each of the temperatures shown -100 to 400°C.
Ans. 0.14 mV/°C for 100°C.

48. In problem 46 let the generated voltage ε arbitrarily describe a temperature t in the following linear manner

$$t = c\varepsilon + d$$

where c and d are constants. Arbitrarily let $t_f = 0°$ for the freezing point of water and $t_b = 100°$ for its boiling point. (a) What are the units and numerical values for c and d? (b) Plot an εt-curve for a temperature range -100 to 400°.
Ans. (a) $c = 5.13°/\text{mV}$, $d = 0°$.

CONSERVATION OF MASS

49. A fluid moves in a steady flow manner between two sections in a flow line. At section 1: $A_1 = 1$ sq ft, $v_1 = 1000$ fpm, $v_1 = 4$ ft^3/lb. At section 2: $A_2 = 2$ ft^2, $\rho_2 = 0.20$ lb/ft^3. Calculate (a) the flow (lb/hr) and (b) the velocity (fps) at section 2.
Ans. (a) 15,000 lb/hr, (b) 10.42 fps.

50. Two gaseous streams enter a combining tube and leave as a single mixture, These data apply at the entrance sections: For one gas, $A_1 = 75$ in.^{2}, $v_1 = 500$ fps, $v_1 = 10$ ft^3/lb; for the other gas, $A_2 = 50$ in.^{2}, $\dot{m}_2 = 60,000$ lb/hr, $\rho_2 = 0.12$ lb/ft^3. At exit, $v_3 = 350$ fps, $v_3 = 7$ ft^3/lb. Find (a) the velocity v_2 at section 2, (b) the flow and area at the exit section.
Ans. (a) 400 fps, (b) 123 in.^{2}

51. A 10-ft diameter by 15-ft height vertical tank is receiving water ($\rho = 61.1$ lb/ft^3) at the rate of 300 gpm and is discharging through a 6-in. ID line with a constant velocity of 5 fps. At a given instant, the tank is half full. Find the water level and the mass change in the tank 15 min later.
Ans. 3.90 ft, 17,550 lb.

52. If a pump discharges 284 ℓpm of water whose density is 985 kg/m^3, find (a) the mass flow rate in kg/min, and (b) the total time required to fill a vertical cylindrical tank 3.05 m in diameter and 3.05 m high.

COMPUTER PROGRAMS

53. Write this program. It is desired to plot the curve weight (gravitational) versus height (miles above sea level). At equatorial sea level, $g = 32.088$ fps^2; its variation is -0.003 fps^2/1000 ft ascent. Select a given mass, say 100 lb$_m$, and determine its weight variation as it rises from sea level to a height of 1000 mi.

54. The conversion of temperature readings from °F to the several scales °C, °R, and K is sought. Write a computer program that will permit this operation.

55–60. Several numbers, which the teacher may use for his favorite problems, are left vacant at the end of each chapter.

2

ENERGY CONCEPTS

Note: In all applications of the law of conservation of energy, sketch an energy diagram indicating the magnitude of each energy quantity. Be especially mindful of units.

MASS AND ENERGY

61. Use dimensional analysis and show that the expression $e = mc^2$ has units of energy.

62. In the light of Einstein's theory of relativity, view a system whose mass is 1 gm. (**a**) How much energy may be derived from this system if all of the mass could be converted into energy? (**b**) What will be its mass when it moves at one-half light speed ($c = 186,000$ mps)?

63. An electron has a rest mass of 9.11×10^{-28} gm. What is its mass when moving with a speed of $0.90c$?

64. Scientists have recently developed a powerful pulse laser for research in materials. Find its energy output in watts for each of the following pulse conditions: (**a**) 20 J in 10 psec, (**b**) 200 J in 35 nsec, (**c**) 800 J in 1 msec. (**d**) At its peak pulse, it will produce 10 terawatts (TW) for a period of 10 psec. Find its discharge in joules.
Ans. (**a**) 20 TW, (**b**) 5.72 GW, (**c**) 800 kw, (**d**) 100 J.

65. A cryogenic picovoltmeter using liquid helium reads 4 picovolts (pV) when used in a circuit upon which 80 mamp have been impressed. Find the resistance of the circuit and the resulting power.
Ans. 50 pohms, 320 fW.

66. It is estimated that the United States consumes annually about 1.75×10^{15} Whr of electrical energy. In accordance with Einstein's theory, how many kilograms of matter would have to be destroyed to yield this energy?

POTENTIAL AND KINETIC ENERGIES

67. A 50-lb mass has a potential energy of -4 Btu with respect to a given datum within the earth's standard gravitational field. (**a**) Find its height relative to the datum. (**b**) If the gravitational field is suddenly disturbed such that the local gravity becomes 25 fps², what will be the effect on the potential energy of the mass? *Ans.* (**a**) -62.24 ft, (**b**) -2420 ft-lb.

68. The 600-kg hammer of a pile driver is lifted 2 m above a piling head. What is the change of potential energy? If the hammer is released, what will be its velocity at the instant it strikes the piling? Local $g = 9.65$ m/s².
Ans. 11.58 kJ, 6.21 m/s.

69. Much like Newton's universal law of gravity (see §1.9, *Text*), Coulomb's Law states that the force between two electrical charges varies as the product of the charges and inversely as the square of the distance between them: $F = kq_1q_2/r^2$ where F is in Newtons, q in coulombs, r in meters, and $k = 9.0 \times 10^9$ Nm²/C². Given two small electrical charges q_1 and q_2 positioned on the x-axis as follows: $q_1 = 4\,\mu C$ at $x_1 = -3$ m; $q_2 = +1\,\mu C$ at $x_2 = +2$ m. Find the position on the x-axis of a third electrical charge q_3 that experiences no net force from these two.

70. A triangle ABC has these dimensions: $AB = 4$ m, $BC = 5$ m, $AC = 3$ m. Electrical charges are located at the vertices as follows: $+30\ \mu$C at A, $-160\ \mu$C at B, and $+90\ \mu$C at C. Find the magnitude and direction of the net force on charge A. Review problem 69.
Ans. $2.7\sqrt{2}$ N, 45° below AB.

71. A girl weighing 470 N holds suspended on the end of a rope 8 m long. What will be her gain in potential energy when a friend swings her to one side so that the rope makes an angle of 35° with the vertical? If local $g = 9.70$ m/sec², what is her mass in kg? In lb_m?
Ans. $\Delta P = 679.5$ N-m.

72. There are 400 kg/min of water being handled by a pump. The lift is from a 20-m deep well and the delivery velocity is 15 m/s. Find **(a)** the change in potential energy, **(b)** the kinetic energy, **(c)** the required power of the pumping unit; $g = 9.75$ m/s².

73. When an automobile is travelling at 60 km/hr, its engine is developing 25 hp. **(a)** Find the total resisting force in N. **(b)** Assuming that the resisting force is directly proportional to the speed, what horsepower must the engine develop to drive the automobile at 100 km/hr?
Ans. **(a)** 1118.3 N, **(b)** 69 hp.

74. A 2000-kg elevator accelerates upward uniformly at 1 m/s² from a stopped position. **(a)** What is the tension in the lifting cable? **(b)** At the end of 4 s of operation, what will be the kinetic energy and the change in potential energy? Local gravity acceleration is 9.70 m/s².

75. Compute the mass of the earth knowing that at its surface, 6370 km from the center, a 1-lb mass will be attracted by it with a force of 1 lb.
Ans. 13.1×10^{24} lb.

76. A system is composed of a 10,000-lb elevator moving downward with $v = 5$ fps, a 6000-lb counterweight moving upward with $v = 5$ fps, and a braking pulley with connecting cables. Assume the kinetic energy of the cable and rotating parts to be negligible and determine the frictional energy absorbed by the brake when the elevator is uniformly stopped in 4 ft.
Ans. 22,220 ft-lb.

77. **(a)** A 64,400-lb_m airplane is traveling at 1000 fps (682 mph). How much is its kinetic energy in hp-hr? **(b)** If it suddenly noses vertically upward at this speed, with power off and in the absence of atmospheric resistance,

through what vertical distance will it move? Let the average gravity acceleration be $g = 32$ fps².

78. There are required 33.76 kJ of gravitational work to elevate a mass 76.22 m in the earth's gravitational field where the local gravity is 9.75 m/s². **(a)** Find the mass. **(b)** If the initial potential energy of the mass was 10,551 N-m with respect to the earth's surface, determine its final elevation above this surface.
Ans. **(a)** 45.4 kg, **(b)** 100.1 m.

79. An experimental nose cone whose mass is 100 lb is projected 200 mi above the earth's surface. What gravitational work was required assuming that the gravity acceleration varies in accordance with $g = A - Bh$, where $A = 32.174$ fps² and $B = 3.31 \times 10^{-6}$ for the height h in feet.
Ans. 99.85×10^6 ft-lb.

80. From Newton's law of universal gravitation $F = Gm_1m_2/r^2$, it can be deduced that the force acting on a space vehicle whose mass is m slugs in the vicinity of the moon is

$$F = \frac{mg_m r_m^2}{r^2} = \frac{1185m}{r^2}\ \text{lb}$$

where g_m mps² is the gravity acceleration at the surface of the moon, where $r_m = 1000$ mi (approximately) is the moon's radius, and r mi is the distance of the vehicle from the moon's center; all other gravitational fields are negligible. If by some means the vehicle were brought to rest relative to the moon and 9000 mi from its surface, and then allowed to proceed by gravitational influence of the moon only, with what speed will it strike the moon?

81. Every 6 hr a small satellite orbits the earth; the apogee is triple the perigee. Assume plane motion and no effect of other heavenly bodies. The radius of the earth is approximately 20.91×10^6 ft; let $g = 32.17$ fps² and remain constant. For the satellite find **(a)** its minimum altitude and **(b)** its minimum velocity. *Hint:* Review Kepler's three laws of planetary motion in your mechanics text.
Ans. **(a)** 1249 mi, **(b)** 6300 mph.

MOVING BOUNDARY WORK

82. If 6 ℓ of a gas at a pressure of 100 kPaa are compressed reversibly according to $pV^2 = C$ until the volume becomes 2 ℓ, find the final pressure and the work.
Ans. 900 kPaa, 1200 J.

83. Evaluate the nonflow work in terms of p_1, V_1, p_2, V_2 of a fluid undergoing a reversible state change in accordance with each of the following defining relations: (**a**) $p = C$, (**b**) $V = C$, (**c**) $pV = C$, (**d**) $pV^3 = C$, (**e**) $pV(\ln V) = C$, (**f**) $p = 200/V^2 + 2$ psia.

84. Determine the atmospheric work done as a 2-in. cube of ice melts in a region of 1 atm. At 32°F these densities obtain for water: liquid, 62.42 lb/ft³; solid, 57.15 lb/ft³.

85. During the execution of a reversible nonflow process the work is -156.2 kJ. If $V_1 = 0.845$ m³ and the pressure varies as $p = -730 + 690$ kPaa, where V is in m³, find V_2.

86. Determine the work done by a 1-lb fluid system as it expands slowly within a piston-cylinder arrangement from an initial pressure and volume of 80 psia and 1 ft³, respectively, to a final volume of 4 ft³ in accordance with the following defining relations: (**a**) $p = C$, (**b**) $pV = C$, (**c**) $pV^{1.4} = C$, (**d**) $p = -20V + 100$ psia for V ft³, (**e**) $pV^2 = C$.

Ans. (**a**) 44.5, (**b**) 20.56, (**c**) 15.7, (**d**) $+27.8$, (**e**) 11.1 Btu.

87. Work is done by a substance in a reversible nonflow manner in accordance with $V = (700/p)$ m³, where p is in kPaa. Evaluate the work done on or by the substance as the pressure increases from 70 kPaa to 700 kPaa.

88. A reversible nonflow process occurs from which the work is 9.4 Btu. If the pressure varies as $p = -V^2 + 100/V$ psia (where V is in ft³), and $p_1 = 46$ psia, find p_2 and V_2.

Ans. $p_2 = 9$ psia.

OTHER FORMS OF WORK

89. A force F measured in the x direction is given as $F = a/x^2$ where the constant $a = 9$ N-m². Find the work in joules as F moves from $x_1 = 1$ m to $x_2 = 3$ m.

90. The force in Newtons required to stretch a spring beyond its free length is given by $F = 200x$ where x is in meters. Find the force and work required to stretch the spring 0.1 m; 0.5 m; 1 m.

91. The scale K of a tension spring is variable and is related to its length y such that $K = cy^n$ where c is a constant and n an exponent. Find the work required to stretch the spring from y_1 to y_2.

92. There are required 124 ft-lb of work to compress a spring from its free length y_1 to that

of $y_2 = 2.5$ in.; the constant scale is $K = 100$ lb$_f$/in. Find the free length.

Ans. $y_1 = 7.96$ in.

93. Demonstrate that the work required to stretch a wire within the elastic region is $W = -0.5AEl(\varepsilon)^2$ where, for the wire, l is the initial length, A its cross-sectional area, E is Young's modulus of the material, and ε is the unit strain.

94. In problem 93 let the wire be steel ($E = 30 \times 10^6$ psi) with $A = 0.01$ in.², $l = 10$ ft, and a force be gradually applied until its pulling effect on the wire is 1200 lb$_f$. Find the work using the results in problem 93. Check your solution by solving for work as simply the product of average force and distance.

Ans. $W = -288$ in.-lb$_f$.

95. An areal soap film with surface tension σ is formed by wetting a wire frame (initially closed) and then moving the slide wire S away from leg b by means of a constant force F. See sketch. (**a**) Show that the work done against the resisting surface tension is $W = \sigma \cdot l \cdot b = \sigma \cdot A$. (**b**) Find the work done when $b = 10$ cm, $l = 6$ cm, and $\sigma = 25$ dyne/cm.

Ans. (**b**) 1500 dyne-cm or 1.107×10^{-4} ft-lb.

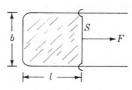

Problem 95

96. Heat is transferred to an elastic sphere containing a gas at 105 kPaa; the diameter of the sphere is 2 m. Because of heating the sphere diameter increases to 2.2 m and the gas pressure increases in direct proportion to the sphere diameter. Find the work of the gas during this heating process.

97. Let an areal surface film be formed on a circular wire frame of radius r_1. (**a**) Show that the work done to form this area against the resisting surface tension σ is $W = \pi r_1^2 \sigma = \sigma A$. (**b**) If $\sigma = 50$ dyne/cm, and the work input of 3300 dyne-cm is required to increase the radius (hence the area) from $r_1 = 2$ in. to r_2, find r_2.

98. A spherical soap bubble of radius r is formed by means of blowing through a small soapy blow pipe. If $r = 15.25$ cm and $\sigma =$

15 dyne/cm, find the work input in overcoming the surface tension in the bubble.

Ans. W = 43,840 dyne-cm.

99. Each second an electric current of 15 amp flows continuously into a resistor of 30 ohms. Compute the power input in kilowatts and horsepower.

Ans. 6.75 kW or 9.05 hp.

100. A 12-V automobile battery is receiving a constant charge from a generator. The voltage across the terminals is 12.5 V; the current is 10 amp. Determine the power input in watts and horsepower.

101. A constant force moves an 18-in. electrical conductor with a velocity of 25 fps orthogonally across a magnetic field whose flux density is 2 weber/m^2; note that 1 weber is equivalent to 1 N-s-m/C. The conductor carries a current of 20 amp. Find the force and the rate of work produced.

Ans. 18.30 N, 139.4 W.

102. A rectangular piston-cylinder arrangement impounds a specific amount of water initially at height y_1, length x_1, and of fixed width Z (perpendicular to the page). The upper water surface is exposed to atmospheric pressure; the water density is ρ. Determine the work done by force F necessary to move the frictionless rectangular piston to a point where the surface of the water is equal to the height y_2 of the piston.

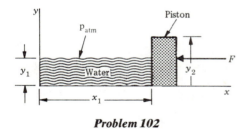

Problem 102

FLOW ENERGY

103. The flow energy of 142 ℓ/min of a fluid passing a boundary to a system is 108.5 kJ/min. Determine the pressure at this point. *Ans.* 764.1 kPaa.

104. A centrifugal air compressor compresses 200 cfm from 12 psia to 90 psia. The initial specific volume is 12.6 ft^3/lb and the final specific volume is 3.25 ft^3/lb. If the inlet suction line is 4-in. ID and the discharge line is 2.5-in. ID, determine (a) the change in flow energy between the boundaries, ft-lb/min, (b) the mass rate of flow, lb/min, and (c) the change in velocity.

Ans. (a) 324,000, (b) 15.88, (c) −12.9 fps.

105. Steam at 50 bar, 900°C has a density of 9.3 kg/m^3. Calculate the flow energy required to move 5 kg/s of this steam.

HEAT AND SPECIFIC HEATS

106. Provide 4 kg of a gaseous substance with 300 kJ of heat at constant volume so that it undergoes a temperature change of 80 K. (a) Find the average specific heat c_v of the substance during this process. (b) If $k = 1.55$ for this gas, find c_p and R.

Ans. (a) 0.9375 kJ/kg-K, (b) $c_p = 1.4531$ kJ/kg K.

107. For a constant pressure system whose mass is 80 lb, 1 hp-min is required to raise its temperature 1°F Determine the specific heat for the system, Btu/lb-°F.

108. If 6 lb of argon undergo a constant pressure heating process from 80°F to 230°F, determine (a) the heat and (b) the change in internal energy. *Ans.* (a) 112 Btu.

109. A 1-kg gaseous system enclosed in a piston-and-cylinder arrangement receives heat while its pressure remains constant at 345 kPaa. The internal energy increases 211 kJ and the temperature increases 70 K. If the work done is 105 kJ, find (a) c_p, (b) the change in volume, (c) c_v, R, and k.

110. The ratio of specific heats is $k = c_p/c_v$ and, for an ideal gas, their difference is $c_p - c_v = R$, a constant. Combine these two expressions and show that $c_v = R/(k - 1)$ and $c_p = kR/(k - 1)$.

111. The following expressions relate to a particular gaseous mass: $pv = 95T$, $h = 120 + 0.6T$ where these units obtain: p in psf, v in ft^3/lb, T in °R and h in Btu/lb. If the specific heats are temperature-dependent only, find c_p and c_v. *Ans.* 0.6, 0.478 Btu/lb$_m$-°R.

112. Compare values of the specific heat c_p for air at 3000°R as obtained from each of three sources: Item B1, Table I, and Fig. 2/9, *Text*. Do the variations justify the use of the last two sources at this elevated temperature?

113. Assume 3 lb of a gas undergo a temperature increase by heating from $t_1 = 40$°F to $t_2 = 1540$°F, with the pressure remaining constant. Using values from Table I, determine the heat transferred if the gas is (a) air, (b) nitrogen, (c) methane.

Ans. (a) 1154.6, (b) 1193 Btu.

CONSERVATION OF ENERGY

114. A system receives 75 kJ of heat while it does 45 kJ of work. How much energy is stored in the system as a result of these actions? What do we call this stored energy increment?

115. These three energy quantities are received by a system: 35 kJ, 55 kJ, and 70 kJ. Of the four energy quantities leaving the system, these three are known: 15 kJ, 25 kJ, 40 kJ. During these energy changes, the system gives up 22 kJ of its stored internal energy. What is the quantity of the fourth energy leaving the system?

116. Steam flows through an adiabatic turbine at the rate of 100 lb/min with $\Delta K = 0$ and $Q = 0$. At entry, its pressure is 175 psia, its volume is 3.16 ft^3/lb and its internal energy is 1166.7 Btu/lb. At exit, its pressure is 0.813 psia, its volume is 328 ft^3/lb and its internal energy is 854.6 Btu/lb. (a) What horsepower is developed? (b) The same as (a) except that the turbine is not adiabatic and the heat loss from it is 10 Btu/lb of steam.

Ans. (a) 861 hp, (b) 838 hp.

117. A 12-V battery receives a quick 20-min charge during which time it receives a steady current supply of 50 amp. In this period it experiences a heat loss of 127 kJ. Find the change of internal energy in the battery during this period.

118. There are removed 11 kJ of heat from a completely enclosed system while it is delivering 32 kJ of work. The system is then restored to its initial state by adding 19 kJ of heat and having a work interaction. What is the magnitude and direction of this work-restoring interaction?

119. Heat is leaking through imperfect insulation into a controlled cold region at the rate of 3000 Btu/hr. A thermoelectric system maintains the region at a steady state temperature and operates on a current of 40 amp with a voltage of 24. Find the heat rejected by the thermoelectric system. *Ans.* 6275 Btu/hr.

120. A family of five persons is occupying a closed living room when power fails on its air conditioning system. Each person gives up 425 Btu/hr under these inactive conditions. Considering no losses from the room, find (a) the increase in internal energy of the room air at the end of 10 min following the power failure and (b) the increase in internal energy of the room system including the air and the people.

PERPETUAL MOTION

121. A thermally insulated storage battery connected to an electric motor constitutes a system which can raise a weight and have no other interaction with its atmosphere. By definition this should constitute a perpetual motion device of the first kind. Explain.

122. An inventor lays claim to a closed system that operates continuously and produces these energy effects during each complete cycle of events: $Q = 2$ Btu, $W = 1600$ ft-lb, $\Delta U = 0$. Prove or refute the validity of his claim.

COMPUTER PROGRAMS

123. A 1-lb fluid system initially at $p_1 = 100$ psia, $v_1 = 1$ ft^3, executes a reversible expansion in a frictionless piston-cylinder arrangement in accordance with $pV^n = c$. Let the final pressure p_2 range from 100 to 10 psia while the final volume is $v_2 = 5$ ft^3 in all cases. Under these constraints write a computer program that will select values of the final pressure, then solve for the respective values of the exponent n and the corresponding work W, and finally will plot a curve of W versus n.

124–130. These numbers may be used for other problems.

3

THE PURE SUBSTANCE

Note: Sketch all state points on the *pV* or *Ts* or both planes; always include the liquid-vapor line. When extracting data from the *hs* or *ph* plane, sketch that plane indicating the method of data selection. In numerous steam problems the data are so chosen that interpolation is reduced to a minimum if the tables in the appendix are used.

PROPERTIES OF THE PURE SUBSTANCE

131. Assume 1 kg of water is at 10^6 Paa (10 bar), 300°C. Use Item B 16(SI) and find its volume, enthalpy, and entropy. Determine its internal energy. Show *hs*-sketch.
Ans. $U = 2796$ kJ/kg.

132. There are 500 ℓ helium in a container at 1.01325 MPaa (10 atm), 180 K. For the helium (use Item B 30) find the total enthalpy and entropy; show *Ts*-sketch.

133. Use several data points selected from Item B 14 and plot the saturated liquid-vapor curve for water on the *pV*-plane. The results will afford the viewer a perspective of the true shape of this curve.

134. The same as problem 133 except that the data points are to be selected from Item B 13 and the saturated liquid-vapor curve is to be plotted for water on the *Ts*-plane.

135. If 1 lb of saturated water vapor is at 100 psia, find its temperature, volume, enthalpy, entropy, and internal energy. Also, find the change in these properties from saturated liquid to saturated vapor at 100 psia. Sketch the *pV* and *Ts* diagrams.

136. A 10-ft³ drum contains saturated vapor at 100°F. What are the pressure and mass of vapor in the drum if the substance is (a) H_2O, (b) NH_3, (c) Freon 12?
Ans. (a) 0.94924 psia, 0.02854 lb$_m$.

137. Complete the following table for water; see Items B 13, B 14, and B 15.

State	(a)	(b)	(c)	(d)	(e)
Pressure, psia	120		50		1200
Temperature, °F		500		900	
Volume, ft³/lb	4.361				
Volume, ft³					
Mass, lb		2	1	3	1.5	4
Quality, %			70		
Moisture, %					20
Enthalpy, Btu	1245.1				
Entropy, Btu/°R				2.1450	

138. (a) What volume is occupied by 5 lb of steam at 2000 psia and 60% quality? (b) What volume is occupied by 5 lb of steam at 20 psia and 60% quality? (c) Is it permissible to omit the volume of the liquid in either of the foregoing cases? Use Item B 14 for data.

139. (a) Sulfur dioxide is at 180°F, 0.40 Btu/°R-lb. Locate this state point on Item B 36 and find the pressure and enthalpy. (b) Consider 2 lb of mercury at 200 psia that have a total enthalpy of 280 Btu. From Item B 34

11

describe its state; include the temperature, entropy, and quality or degrees of superheat.

140. A 500-ℓ drum contains a gaseous substance at 10 atm, 140 K. Find the mass if the substance is (**a**) oxygen (Item B 27), (**b**) nitrogen (Item B 29), or (**c**) helium (Item B 30).

141. The specific heats c_v, c_p (see §§ 2.18, 2.19, *Text*) are desired for steam in the general region of 90 psia, 800°F. To calculate c_p, use the two state points 90 psia, 700°F and 90 psia, 900°F. To calculate c_v, use points 85 psia, 700°F and 100 psia, 900°F; note the volume constancy for these points. Compare these values with those found in Item B 1 given for low pressure water vapor.

142. A 3-ft³ drum contains saturated water and water vapor at 700°F. (**a**) Find the mass of each if their volumes are equal. (**b**) Find the volume occupied by each if their masses are equal.

Ans. 40.95 lb liquid, 19.95 lb vapor.

143. (**a**) Ammonia is at 240°F, 1.42 Btu/°R-lb. Locate this state point on Item B 33 and find the pressure and enthalpy. (**b**) Consider 2 lb of mercury at 100 psia that have a total enthalpy of 320 Btu. From Item B 34, describe its state—include the temperature, entropy, and quality or degrees of superheat.

144. (**a**) If 10 lb of carbon dioxide occupy 4 ft³ at 150 psia, find the enthalpy, temperature, quality or degrees of superheat. Use Item B 31. (**b**) If 5 lb of Freon 12 are at 100 psia, 250°F, locate this state on Item B 35 and find the volume, enthalpy, and entropy.

145. On each of the four charts, Item B 31 (CO_2), Item B 33 (NH^3), Item B 35 (F12), Item B 36 (SO_2), locate the saturated vapor state at 50°F. Now follow the constant entropy line from this saturated vapor state to the full extent of the right side of the chart. For 1 lb of each of the four substances and between the two state point locations, give the changes in pressure, temperature, enthalpy, and volume as read from the charts.

146. (**a**) Compute the specific values for the Helmholtz and Gibbs functions for saturated water vapor at 100 psia. (**b**) Now let the water be saturated liquid at 100 psia and compute these functions. Compare.

147. Evaluate the constants A and B in the relation $h = A + Bpv$ for steam in the vicinity of 10 bar, 350°C; say, 10 bar, 300°C and 10 bar, 400°C. Then check the validity of the resulting relation for 20 bar, 350°C. Compute

the percentage deviation from steam table value of h.

148. Dühring's rule states that if the saturation temperature of one fluid is plotted (rectangular coordinates) versus that of another fluid for the same pressures, a straight line (approximately) will result. Using water and ammonia, check this statement for the pressure range 10 psia to 100 psia, and write an equation for the resulting curve.

149. Assume 1 mole (kg) of water is at 20 bar, 400°C (see Item B 16-SI). Calculate the Gibbs property $G = H - TS$ and the internal energy U.

Ans. $G = -27,936$ kJ, $U = 53,028$ kJ.

150. Calculate the value of c_p for water vapor in the region of 30 bar, 450°C; use Item B 16(SI) and finite differences. Suggest use these two points: 30 bar, 440°C and 30 bar, 460°C for the finite differences of T and h. Remember—$c_p = (\partial h / \partial T)p$.

151. A 100-ℓ rigid tank with adiabatic walls is divided into equal parts A and B by a partition. On one side is steam at 1 bar, 200°C; on the other side is steam at 20 bar, 400°C. The partition is removed and thorough mixing occurs. Determine the equilibrium state (p, t) and ΔS. See Item B 16 (SI) for property values.

152. According to Gibbs' phase rule, see equation (a) § 3.8, *Text*, how many degrees of freedom does a system consisting of a pure substance have if that substance is a superheated vapor or gas? If it is a mixture of vapor and liquid? It is is at the triple point (§ 3.4, *Text*)?

PHASE CHANGES

153. Liquid air undergoes a phase change at constant pressure of 20 atm until it is saturated vapor. Find the change in enthalpy and entropy for a mass of 10 kg of air. Use Item B 26; show sketch.

154. If 1 lb of saturated water vapor is at 100 psia, find its temperature, volume, enthalpy, entropy, and internal energy. Also, find the change in these properties from saturated liquid to saturated vapor at 100 psia. Show pV and TS diagrams. See Item B 14.

155. A cooling process takes place at constant $p = 4$ atm for 0.32 kg oxygen initially at $T_1 = 190$ K; the final entropy is $s_2 = 135$ J/gmol-K. Use Item B 27, show

sketch thereof, and find (**a**) final temperature T_2, K, (**b**) total ΔS_{12}, J/K, (**c**) total ΔV_{12}, ℓ, (**d**) total ΔH_{12}, J; (**e**) calculate the total ΔU_{12}, J.
Ans. (**b**) -450 J/K, (**d**) $-54,450$ J.

156. Assume 5 kg of nitrogen are heated at constant volume from 95 K to 250 K; the specific volume is $v = 0.1$ cm^3/gm. Use Item B 29 (show sketch thereof) and determine (**a**) density ρ, gm/cm^3, (**b**) total ΔS_{12}, J/K, (**c**) total ΔH_{12}, J, (**d**) p_1 and p_2, atm; (**e**) total ΔU_{12}, J.
Ans. (**b**) 82.5 kJ/K, (**c**) 1.450 MJ.

157. Consider 2 kg of saturated liquid air at 3.03975 MPaa (30 atm) that undergo a constant pressure process until the temperature becomes 293 K. From Item B 26, determine the total change of enthalpy and entropy. What was the initial temperature? Show Ts-sketch of process. *Ans.* 597 kJ, 3.643 kJ/K.

158. Initially 10 gm of hydrogen are at 5 atm, 105 K. The state is changed until $p_2 = 1$ atm, $s_2 = 7$ cal/gm-K. Find ΔS and ΔH. What is the final temperature? Show Ts diagram.

GAS TABLES

159. Air at 100°F undergoes a temperature change to 1500°F while its pressure remains relatively low. Use Item B 2 and for $m = 10$ lb air find ΔH_{12}, ΔU_{12} and $\Delta \phi_{12}$. What are the ratios p_{r2}/p_{r1} and v_{r1}/v_{r2}?
Ans. $\Delta H_{12} = 3598$ Btu, $p_{r2}/p_{r1} = 102$.

160. A gaseous fluid with properties similar to those given in Item B 8 is at 260°F. It is compressed until $p_{r2}/p_{r1} = 10$. For 2 pmoles find (**a**) final temperature T_2, (**c**) ΔH_{12}, (**c**) ΔU_{12}, (**d**) $\Delta \phi_{12}$, (**e**) ratio v_{r1}/v_{r2}.

161. For each of the gases listed in Item B 2-10, compare the respective values of enthalpy $\bar{h}$ at 1000°R and based upon 1 pmole of the gas. Which has the large $\bar{h}$? Which the smaller? Which two are closest in $\bar{h}$-values?

162. Assume 1 kg-mole of a gas at a relatively low pressure is at 300 K. For each of the gases, Item B 2 through B 10, find values for these quantities: (**a**) H, (**b**) p_r, (**c**) U, (**d**) v_r, (**e**) ϕ.
Ans. Air (Item B 2): (**a**) 8253 (129.06) Btu, (**b**) 1.3860, (**c**) 5885 (92.04) Btu, (**d**) 9229 (144.32), (**e**) 38 (0.60078) Btu/°R.

163. Carbon dioxide at 5000°R and relatively low pressure has its v_{r1} increased 10,000-fold; find T_2. Also find ΔH_{12}, ΔU_{12}, $\Delta \phi_{12}$ for 4 lb CO_2. Use Item B 3.

COMPRESSED LIQUID

164. Liquid water leaves a pump at 3000 psia, 300°F. For this compressed state, use Table II and find its volume v, enthalpy h, and entropy s. From Item B 13 find these values for saturated liquid water at 300°F and compare.

165. The water you drink from a fountain at 50°F is in a compressed (subcooled) state. At 50°F its saturation pressure is 0.17796 psia, yet it leaves the fountain at 14.7 psia. Does this compressed condition have much effect on its volume or enthalpy?

166. Assume 10 lb of water are at 3000 psia, 200°F. (**a**) Find the total enthalpy and entropy. Use Table II. (**b**) What volume will this mass occupy? (**c**) Compare the values found in (**a**) and (**b**) with those for saturated liquid water at 200°F. (**d**) Now compute the enthalpy h_B for the compressed liquid state using equation (3-3), *Text* and compare with value noted in (**a**).
Ans. (**a**) 1748.8 Btu, 2.904 Btu/°R, (**b**) 0.1648 ft^3, (**c**) 1680.9 Btu, 2.940 Btu/°R, 0.16637 ft^3.

THE MOLLIER DIAGRAM

167. Steam undergoes an isenthalpic process ($h = c$) from 15 bar, 350°C to 100 bar. Use Item B 16(SI) and find final temperature t_2, Δv_{12}, Δs_{12}.

168. Saturated steam vapor at 250°C moves along its isotherm until the pressure becomes 1 bar. Locate the end state points on the Mollier chart (Item B 16 SI) and for each pound of steam processed find (**a**) p_1, (**b**) Δh_{12}, (**c**) Δs_{12}, (**d**) Δv_{12}.

169. Assume 5 lb/min of steam are expanded from 400 psia, 700°F, to 6 psia with the entropy remaining constant. Locate the two end points on the Mollier Chart (Item B 16) and find ΔH, the quality for the final state, and Δt. What is the entropy at either state point? Show the hs-diagram.
Ans. 1730 Btu/min, 88%, 530°F, 8.20 Btu/min-°R.

170. Consider 1 kg-mole of water that is heated at constant pressure ($p = 5$ bar) from a wet state ($x_1 = 85\%$) to 400°C. Use Item B 16(SI) and find the changes of volume, enthalpy, and entropy. Show hs-sketch.

171. Cool 1500 ℓ of water at constant volume from 40 bar, 612°C, to 400°C. Use Item B 16(SI), show sketch of process, and find (**a**) mass of water processed, (**b**) change of enthalpy, (**c**) change of entropy, (**d**) change of internal energy.

172. If 10 lb/sec of steam undergo a constant entropy process from 250 psia, 700°F, to atmospheric pressure, sketch this process on the Mollier chart (Item B 16) and find t_2, s_2, percentage moisture, ΔH_{12}.

Ans. 212°F 17.00 Btu/°R-sec, 4%, −2600 Btu/sec.

THE *ph*-CHART

173. Freon 12 undergoes a change of state from saturated liquid at 200 psia to superheated vapor at 200 psia, 240°F; see Item B 35. For each pound of Freon 12, find (**a**) h_{fg}, (**b**) Δh_{12}, (**c**) final entropy s_2 and volume v_2. Show *ph* sketch.

174. Assume 10 lb/sec of ammonia (see Item B 33) are compressed isentropically from 10 psia, 20°F to 100 psia. Make a *ph* sketch of this process and find (**a**) ΔH, (**b**) volume handled at each state point, cfs, (**c**) temperature at the final state.

175. Sulfur dioxide (Item B 36) is being used as a refrigerant. During a constant entropy compression process, the SO_2 changes state from 13 psia, 20°F to 300 psia. (**a**) Make a *ph* sketch and find the final temperature and Δh. (**b**) If the SO_2 vapor at point 2 is now cooled at the constant pressure of 300 psia until it liquefies, find the temperature of the liquid and the Δh for this condensing process.

Ans. (**a**) 440°F, 63 Btu/lb, (**b**) 187°F, −171 Btu/lb.

COMPUTER PROGRAM

176. The variations of c_v, c_p, and $k = c_p/c_v$ with pressure and temperature are being studied for superheated steam. Let the pressure range be 15–100 psia and the temperature range be 250–900°F. See §§ 2.18, 2.19 *Text*, for discussion of the specific heats. Write a computer program that will produce the respective values throughout the p and t ranges described. Assume that the steam table data are stored in the memory of the computer.

177–180. These numbers may be used for other problems.

4

THE FIRST LAW, ENERGY

Note: Sketch a mass-energy diagram for each problem and be careful of the signs (+ and −) on all energies, especially work and heat.

FIRST LAW

181. During a certain cyclic process a system receives 100 kJ of heat from a reservoir while it is discharging 60 kJ of heat to a sink. Two work quantities are noted during this process. One is an input work of 15 kJ. Find the other work quantity. Also find the net work and state if this is done on or by the system.

182. A system is capable of executing a cyclic process as indicated in the pV sketch; it may be executed either clockwise *abca* or counterclockwise *adca*. (a) When going clockwise to state c, 80 kJ of heat flow to the system and 35 kJ of work are done by it. Returning to state a from c, 60 kJ of heat flow from the system. Find the work along the path ca. (b)

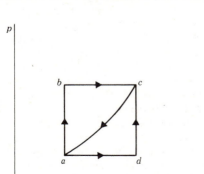

Problems 182, 189

When going counterclockwise to state c, 70 kJ of heat flow to the system. Find the work during the process *adc*.

Ans. (a) $W_{ca} = -15$ kJ, (b) $W_{adc} = 25$ kJ.

183. For a certain system executing a cyclic process 250 J of heat are absorbed by the system and 100 J of heat are rejected. The system also receives 30 W-s of electrical power while it moves a 3 kg mass vertically by means of a pulley arrangement. How far does the mass move? Up or down? Local $g = 9.65$ m/s^2.

INTERNAL ENERGY

184. Show that as a consequence of the first law, internal energy E exists and is a property.

185. There are 2 kg of fluid mass in a closed container at rest on a given datum; local gravity is $g = 9.65$ m/sec^2. The container is now raised vertically 1000 m and the fluid mass given a swirling velocity of 50 m/sec. Initially the internal energy of the fluid was $E_1 = U_1 = 20$ kJ. Find E_2.

186. The internal energy of a certain closed system is given by $U = A + BpV$. Show that if it undergoes a reversible nonflow process with $Q = 0$, the relation between p and V is $pV^k = C$, where C is some constant and $k = (B+1)/B$.

187. The internal energy E of a given system is a function of temperature $(t, °C)$ only and is given as $E = 30 + 0.3t$ IT cal. During the execution of a given process, the work done per degree temperature change is $dW/dt = 0.11$ kg-m/°C. Find the heat Q as the temperature changes from 200°C to 400°C. Also, find E_1 and E_2.

Ans. $Q = 467$ J, $E_1 = 377$ J, $E_2 = 628$ J.

188. The work and the heat per degree change of temperature for a system executing a nonflow process are given by $dW/dt = 80$ W-sec/°F and $dQ/dt = 15$ IT cal/°F, respectively. Determine the change of internal energy for the system as its temperature increases from 150°F to 250°F. *Ans.* −1721 J.

189. Reconsider the system in problem 182 executing the cyclic process(es) as described. When executing the clockwise change of state, what will be the change of internal energy when state c is reached? When executing the counterclockwise change of state, what will be the change of internal energy when state c is reached? What is the net change of internal energy for the system executing either cyclic process?

190. A liquid, contained by a rigid adiabatic shell, is stirred by internal paddles; a rise in temperature is noted. For the process, evaluate each of the following integrals with respect to zero? $\int dQ, \int dW,$ and $\int dE$.

191. Assume 3 kg/s of fluid are moving through an insulated pipe under these conditions: $u_1 = 30$ J/kg and $v_1 = 5$ m/s. (a) Find E_1. (b) If the fluid flows through an upward bend of the pipe until $u_2 = 35$ J/kg and $v_2 = 2$ m/s, through what vertical height did the fluid travel? Local $g = 9.75$ m/s^2.

Ans. (a) 127.5 J, (b) 0.564 m.

ENTHALPY

192. A fluid changes state from $p_1 = 15$ psia, $V_1 = 20$ ft^3 to $p_2 = 100$ psia, $V_2 = 2$ ft^3; the internal energy U is the same in both states. Find ΔH. *Ans.* $\Delta H = -18.51$ Btu.

193. If 1 kg of steam at 100 bar, 700°C, occupies 0.04354 m^3, its internal energy is 3432 kJ. Calculate its enthalpy and compare answer with the value extracted from Item B 16(SI).

194. Conveniently, enthalpy brings together internal energy and either pV-work

for a closed system or flow energy (equivalent to the pV-product) for an open system for which the fluid is flowing. What happens when a closed system undergoes a constant volume process in which there is neither boundary work nor flow? Does enthalpy disappear? Is it equivalent to the internal energy?

CLOSED SYSTEMS

195. A closed system executes a series of processes for which two of the three quantities W, Q and ΔU are given for each process. Find the value of the unknown quantity in each case.
(a) $W = +10$ hp, $Q = +500$ Btu/min, $\Delta U = ?$
(b) $W = +65$ Btu, $Q = ?$, $\Delta U = -25$ Btu.
(c) $W = ?$, $Q = +25$ kW, $\Delta U = 0$.
(d) $W = -389$ ft lb, $Q = -1.5$ Btu, $\Delta U = ?$
(e) $W = +2 \times 10^8$ gm-cm, $Q = +5000$ gm-cal, $\Delta U = ?$ *Ans.* (a) $\Delta U = +76$ Btu/min.

196. A closed gaseous system undergoes a reversible process during which 25 Btu are rejected, the volume changes from 5 ft^3 to 2 ft^3, and the pressure remains constant at 50 psia. Find the change of internal energy.

Ans. 2.8 Btu.

197. There are received 15 Btu of heat by a rigid $(V = C)$ closed system. (a) Find W and ΔU. (b) If the system had received this energy through paddle work and without heat flow, find W and ΔU. (c) Evaluate $\int p\, dV$ in both cases and discuss.

198. A closed system executes a series of processes for which two of the three quantities, W, Q, and ΔE are given for each process. Find the value of the unknown quantity in each case.
(a) $W = -35$ kJ, $Q = ?$, $\Delta E = -35$ kJ.
(b) $W = +1.2$ MJ, $Q = +645$ kJ, $\Delta E = ?$
(c) $W = ?$, $Q = 5$ Btu, $\Delta E = 4.22$ kJ.

199. During a reversible process executed by a nonflow system, the pressure increases from 344.74 kPaa to 1378.96 kPaa in accordance with $pV = C$, and the internal energy increases 22,577 J; the initial volume is $V_1 = 85$ ℓ. Find the heat. *Ans.* −18,045 J.

200. During the execution of a nonflow process by a system, the work per degree temperature increase is $dW/dt = 70$ ft-lb/°F and the internal energy may be expressed as $U = 20 + 0.5t$ ft-lb, a function of the temperature t°F. Determine the heat if the temperature changes from 50°F to 100°F. *Ans.* 4.54 Btu.

201. A closed system executes a reversible process wherein the pressure and volume vary in accordance with $pV^n = C$; $Q = 16.247$ kJ, $\Delta U = 47.475$ kJ. If $p_1 = 138$ kPaa, $V_1 = 141.6$ ℓ, and $p_2 = 827.4$ kPaa, find n and V_2.

202. During a reversible process executed by a nonflow system, the pressure increases from 50 psia to 200 psia in accordance with $pV = C$, and the internal energy increases 21.4 Btu; the initial volume is $V_1 = 3$ ft³. Find the heat. *Ans.* -17 Btu.

203. A closed system consists of 1 gm (1 cm³) of water. When vaporized at 1 atm, it occupies 1671 cm³; the heat of vaporization is 539 cal/gm. Find the external work and the increase in enthalpy during vaporization.

204. In a certain process, a closed system receives 211 kJ of heat while its boundaries move outward against a constant external pressure of 689.48 kPaa; there is no change of internal energy. Find ΔV and ΔH.

OPEN SYSTEMS, STEADY FLOW-STEADY STATE

205. An internally reversible process occurs in a system during which $Q = -12$ kJ, $\Delta U = -79$ kJ, and $\Delta H = -111$ kJ. (a) Find the work if the system is nonflow. (b) Determine the shaft work and the change of flow energy if the system is steady-state, steady-flow with $\Delta K = 4$ kJ. (c) Using the conditions stated in (b), evaluate $\int p \, dV$ and $-\int V \, dp$ in kJ.
Ans. (a) 67 kJ, (b) 95 kJ, -32 kJ, (c) 76 kJ, 99 kJ.

206. A steady-flow, steady-state thermodynamic system receives 100 lb/min of a fluid at 30 psia and 200°F and discharges it from a point 80 ft above the entrance section at 150 psia and 600°F. The fluid enters with a velocity of 7200 fpm and leaves with a velocity of 2400 fpm. During this process, there are supplied 25,000 Btu/hr of heat from an external source, and the increase in enthalpy is 2.0 Btu/lb. Determine the work done in horsepower. *Ans.* 5.48 hp.

207. Steam enters an adiabatic turbine at 50 bar, 500°C and, after a steady-flow, steady-state process, exhausts at 0.1 bar, quality, $x = 95\%$. Neglect the ΔP and ΔK changes for the steam between inlet and exit points of the turbine. (a) For a flow of 1 kg/sec, find the

work. (b) What must be the mass flow rate of steam if the turbine produces 500 kW?

208. A gaseous substance whose properties are unknown, except as specified, undergoes an internally reversible process during which

$$V = (-0.1p + 300)\text{ft}^3$$

when p is in psfa. (a) For this process, find $-\int V \, dp$ and $\int p \, dV$, both in Btu, if the pressure changes from 1000 psfa to 100 psfa. (b) Sketch the process (realistically) on the pV-plane and compute the area "back" of the curve (no integration). (c) If the process is steady-state, steady-flow with the kinetic energy increasing 25 Btu, $\Delta P = 0$, and the enthalpy decreasing 300 Btu, determine the work and the heat. (d) If the process is nonflow, what is the work and the change of internal energy?
Ans. (a) 283, 63.7; (c) 258, -17; (d) 63.7, -80.7 Btu.

209. Assume 5 lb/sec of fluid enter a steady-state, steady-flow system with $p_1 = 100$ psia, $\rho_1 = 0.2$ lb/ft³, $v_1 = 100$ fps, $u_1 = 800$ Btu/lb, and leave with $p_2 = 20$ psia, $\rho_2 = 0.05$ lb/ft³, $v_2 = 500$ fps, and $u_2 = 780$ Btu/lb. During passage through the open system, each pound rejects 10 Btu of heat. Find the work in horsepower. *Ans.* 168 hp.

210. (a) In a steam nozzle (Fig. 4/9, § 4.11, *Text*), no work is done and the heat is zero. Apply the steady-state, steady-flow energy equation, and find the expression for the final velocity: (1) if the initial velocity is not negligible and (2) if the initial velocity is negligible. Show the energy diagram for 1 lb of steam. (b) There are supplied to a nozzle 2400 lb/hr of steam at an absolute pressure of 200 psia. At the entrance, $v_1 = 6000$ fpm, $v_1 = 2.29$ ft³/lb, and $u_1 = 1113.7$ Btu/lb. At exit, $p_2 = 14.7$ psia, $v_2 = 26.77$ ft³/lb, and $u_2 = 1077.5$ Btu/lb. Calculate the exit velocity.

211. A steady-state, steady-flow compressor draws in 500 cfm of air whose density is 0.079 lb/ft³ and discharges it with a density of 0.304 lb/ft³. At the suction, $p_1 = 15$ psia; at discharge, $p_2 = 80$ psia. The increase in specific internal energy is 33.8 Btu/lb, and the heat from the air by cooling is 13 Btu/lb. Neglecting changes of potential and kinetic energy, determine the work done on the air in Btu/min and in hp. *Ans.* -2385 Btu/min.

212. A constant enthalpy (isoenthalpic) steady-flow, steady-state turbine receives

1 kJ/s steam at 70 bar, 540°C and exhausts at 7 bar; across the turbine, $\Delta P = 0$ and $\Delta K = 0$. Find Q and W. See Item B 16(SI) for properties.

PROPERTY RELATIONS

213. Begin with the definition of enthalpy, $h = u + pv$, and show that for a reversible process, $-v\,dp = dQ - dh$.

214. Develop the expression $-v\,dp = dK + dP + dW$ stating all restrictions.

215. Show that for a steady flow process, $\int p\,dv = \Delta(pv) + \Delta K + \Delta P + W_{sf}$.

216. Apply each of the integrals, $\int p\,dv$ and $-\int v\,dp$, to a process wherein the pressure and the volume vary between two state points in accordance with $pv^n = c$ and find that one integral is n times the other. Here n is an exponent and c a constant.

217. An analysis of the flow of a compressible fluid through a frictionless nozzle will result in the expression $dK = -v\,dp$. Often this analysis is based upon the nozzle as being adiabatic. Show that this expression obtains for a frictionless nozzle, independent of heat consideration. State all restrictions involved.

218. A closed system consists of a vertical cylinder with a frictionless piston of mass m. Show that if the piston is displaced, its change in potential energy will be $\Delta P = p\,\Delta V$ where p is the pressure it imposes on the fluid within the cylinder.

OPEN SYSTEMS, TRANSIENT FLOW

219. An insulated, evacuated, hollow sphere rests in atmospheric air at 1 bar, 37°C. Suddenly a pinhole appears in the shell of the sphere permitting an inflow of air. What will be the temperature of the air within the sphere at the moment inflow ceases?

220. An adiabatic vessel contains steam at 1025 psia, 750°F. A valve is opened slowly permitting an outflow of steam; it is closed quickly when the steam remaining in the vessel becomes saturated vapor. What fractional part of the original steam remains? Assume that this part underwent a reversible adiabatic expansion.   *Ans.* 30.3%.

221. A 10-in. diameter, adiabatic cylinder C (see figure) is fitted with a frctionless, leak-

proof piston P that has an attached unstressed spring S whose scale is $k = 1000$ lb/in. The cylinder is connected by a closed valve A to line L in which steam flows at 500 psia, 700°F; the spring side of the cylinder is evacuated. Valve A is now opened slowly permitting steam to move the piston through distance x, thus compressing the spring. At this point valve A is closed, trapping steam in the cylinder at 150 psia. Find the temperature and the mass of steam in the cylinder.

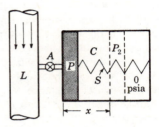

Problem 221

222. An evacuated adiabatic cylinder has a volume of 0.535 ft³ and is connected by a closed valve to a line in which steam flows at 500 psia, 700°F. The valve is slowly opened, permitting an inflow of steam, and quickly closed when the cylinder pressure becomes 150 psia. Determine the temperature and mass of steam in the cylinder.

223. Steam at 15 bar, 300°C is contained in a 1-m³ rigid sphere. A valve is opened to allow steam to escape slowly while heat is added to the steam in the sphere at a rate to maintain its temperature constant. What heat has been supplied when the pressure in the sphere reaches 1 bar? *Hint:* Plot a curve of enthalpy versus mass flow out and approximate the integral $\int h\,dm$.

224. A perfectly insulated system consists of a rigid tank containing 2 lb steam at 350 psia, 800°F, connected through a closed valve and piping to the base of a vertical cylinder containing a frictionless piston whose topside is subjected to atmospheric pressure (14.7 psia). Initially the piston rests on the bottom of the cylinder and exerts a pressure of 80 psia. The valve is gradually opened allowing the steam from the tank to enter the cylinder and slowly raise the piston until the pressure on the two sides of the valve are balanced; the steam remaining in the tank is at 400°F. Determine the temperature of the steam within the cylinder.

225. Steam at 70 bar, 650°C, is in a rigid container which is fitted with a closed valve; the container is immersed in a liquid bath which is maintained at a constant temperature of 650°C by an electrical input of I^2R. The valve on the container is slowly opened permitting steam to escape to the atmosphere until the container pressure becomes 7 bar. Find the electrical input per cubic foot of container volume. The only heat interaction is between the bath and the container of steam.

226. A thermodynamic system consists of an adiabatic piston and cylinder arrangement connected to a main through which steam is flowing at 200 psia, 600°F. See figure. Initially valve V is closed, 0.1 lb of O_2 occupies the left side of the cylinder at 15 psia, 220°F, and 0.05 lb steam occupies the right side at 15 psia, 220°F; the intervening piston P is adiabatic and frictionless. Valve V is now slowly opened and then closed when the pressure of 200 psia obtains in the cylinder. Find the new states of the O_2 and steam in the cylinder and the mass of steam that flowed in the steam side.

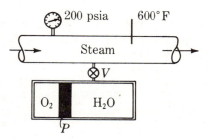

Problems 226, 227

227. The same as problem 226 except that the frictionless piston is nonadiabatic; the cylinder walls remain adiabatic.

228. Steam at 400 psia, 540°F, 200 fps flows in a main to which are connected three systems A, B, and C by valves that are initially closed; see figure. The systems are initially evacuated. Valve to A is opened slowly permitting steam to fill the 1 ft^3 adiabatic rigid cylinder to a pressure of 200 psia and is then closed. Valve to B is opened slowly permitting steam to raise the 1 ft^2 piston 1 ft and is then closed; the piston was initially resting on the valve opening and is weighted so as to impose a pressure of 200 psia on the steam. Valve to C is

opened permitting steam to raise the 1 ft^2 massless piston and is then closed; the massless piston was initially resting on the valve opening and is restrained by an internal negator spring which subjects the steam at all times to a pressure of 200 psia. Find the final temperature and the mass of steam in each system.

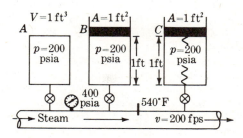

Problem 228

229. Two hundred cubic feet of steam at 400 psia, 800°F are contained in an adiabatic cylinder C; the piston P rests on stops and is capable of exerting a pressure of 400 psia. A turbine is connected to the cylinder; see figure. Valve B, which was initially closed, is slowly opened permitting steam to flow through the turbine and in turn be exhausted to the atmosphere ($p_0 = 14.7$ psia). When the flow of steam finally ceases, find the turbine work and the steam flow through the turbine. Assume adiabatic and frictionless flow.

Ans. 19,950 Btu, 102.13 lb.

230. The same as problem 229 except that prior to opening valve B, the stops are removed from supporting the frictionless piston.

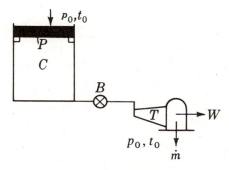

Problems 229, 230

FRICTIONAL ENERGY

231. A 1460-kg automobile is brought to rest in a distance of 122 m from a speed of 113 km/hr. The kinetic energy of rotation of the wheel is negligible. (a) How much frictional energy is absorbed by the brakes? (b) If we imagine the stopping being brought about by a constant collinear force resisting the motion, how much is this force? Use only energy principles.   *Ans.* (a) 719 kJ, (b) 5893 N.

232. The feasibility of fusion welding is being studied. This action utilizes the energy destroyed by friction. For this study, these data are available. Kinetic energy is stored in a 322-lb flywheel, where moment of inertia is $I = 5$ slug-ft^2, rotating at $\omega = 30$ rad/sec. Two 0.5-in. diameter steel rods are to be butt-welded (end-to-end) with one turning with the flywheel, the other stationary. The rods are pressed together with appropriate force and friction between the ends brings the flywheel to rest. Will the molecular energy of the rod ends be increased sufficiently to cause the steel to fuse? Steel has a density of 0.286 lb/in.^{3}, a melting point of 2600°F, and a specific heat of 0.12 Btu/lb-°R. The active length of each rod affected by friction is $\frac{1}{16}$ in. and no significant energy leaves the rod as heat. Find the temperature rise. Do you judge this idea feasible?

233. An automotive engine delivering 100 hp is supplied with combustion air at 90°F and fuel with chemical energy (heating value) of 20,400 Btu/lb. There are 13.5 lb air/lb fuel. The exhaust gases leave at 1250°F with a specific heat of $c_p = 0.275$ Btu/lb-°F. The engine uses fuel at the rate of 0.55 lb fuel/hp-hr delivered. If all frictional losses and heat transfer effects are represented by E_f, determine its amount, assuming negligible kinetic energy changes. The datum for the enthalpy and chemical energy is 0°F.
                    Ans. 10,140 Btu/min.

234. A portion of an inclined 8-in. (ID) pipe containing flowing water ($\rho = 1.90$ slugs/ft^3) has two pressure gages attached 2000 ft apart. The upstream gage reads 21.1 psig and is 50 ft above the datum; the downstream gage is 38 ft above the datum. The flow rate is 1.55 cfs, and it is estimated that the friction head for the pipe is 1.1 ft of H$_2$O per 100 ft of pipe length; $Q = 0$. Using the energy equation, estimate the reading on the downstream gage.   *Ans.* 16.86 psig.

INCOMPRESSIBLE FLUID FLOW

235. Apply the steady flow equation (energy balance) to liquid water flowing without friction in a pipe and obtain the classical Bernoulli equation which states that the sum of these three head-differences is zero: pressure head, velocity head, and gravitational head.

236. A small blower handles 1530 cfm of air whose density is $\rho = 0.073$ lb/ft^3. The static and velocity heads are 6.45 and 0.48 in. wg (at 60°F), respectively. Local gravity acceleration is $g = 31.95$ fps^2. (a) Find the power input to the air from the blower. (b) If the initial velocity is negligible, find the final velocity.
                    Ans. (a) 1.66 hp, (b) 2800 fpm.

237. Air is removed from a large space and given a velocity of 63 fps by a fan. The air density is $\rho = 0.075$ lb/ft^3 and the work done on the air is 0.0155 hp-min/lb air. Find static head on the fan, in. wg (at 100°F).

238. A large forced-draft fan is handling air at 14.7 psia, 110°F under a total head of 10.5 in. wg (at 110°F). The power input to the fan is 300 hp and the fan is 75% efficient. Compute the volume of air handled each minute. Local gravity acceleration is $g = 31.85$ fps^2.   *Ans.* 138,000 cfm.

239. Water flows steadily through the pipe system shown in the figure. These data apply: $D_1 = 1$ ft, $D_2 = D_3 = 0.5$ ft; $p_1 = 12$ psig, $v_1 = 10$ fps; propeller input energy $W_p = 3.91$ hp. Assume that the internal energy u and the density $\rho = 62.4$ lb/ft^3 remain constant. Solve for (a) v_2, (b) p_2, and (c) p_3.
                    Ans. (a) 40 fps, (b) 1.9 psig, (c) 3.8 psig.

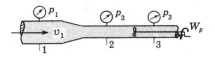

Problem 239

240. An injector (Fig. f/7, Foreword, *Text*) draws in cold water at 72°F, with an enthalpy of $h_w = 40$ Btu/lb, from a level of 6 ft below the center line of the injector. Entering steam (pumping fluid) at 155 psia has an enthalpy of $h_s = 1194$ Btu/lb and a velocity of 175 fps. The liquid mixture leaves the injector at 140 psia and 166°F with an enthalpy of $h_m = 134.3$ Btu/lb and a velocity of 100 fps. There are 4.05 lb/min of steam and

44.8 lb/min of water entering. Sketch an energy diagram and determine the heat in Btu/min.   *Ans.* −67 Btu/min.

241. A hydraulic pump is handling 5 cfs of 60°F water through an 8-in. (ID) suction line and a 6-in (ID) discharge line. The suction gage is on the pump centerline and reads 10 in. Hg vac; the discharge gage is 20 ft above the cen-terline. If the energy input to the water is 100 hp, find the reading of the discharge gage.

242. What would be the pump horsepower input to the water in problem 241 if the dis-charge pressure gage read 100 psig, the other data remaining the same?

243–250. These numbers may be used for other problems.

5

THE SECOND LAW, ENTROPY

Note: A *Ts* diagram should be very helpful for solving the problems in this chapter. Be ever mindful of the statements of the second law given in § 5.2, *Text*. Finally, always bear in mind that entropy is a property.

CARNOT CYCLE

251. There are supplied 3.60 MJ of heat to a Carnot power cycle operating between 900 K and 300 K. Sketch the *Ts* diagram and find (**a**) total change of entropy during the heating or cooling process, (**b**) heat rejected from the cycle, (**c**) evaluation of $\oint dQ$, (**d**) total change of entropy during any one cycle.

Ans. (**a**) 4 kJ/K, (**b**) 1.20 MJ, (**c**) 2.40 MJ.

252. A Carnot engine receives 100 J of heat from its high-temperature (400 K) reservoir and rejects 80 J to its sink. Find the temperature of the sink.

253. Two heat reservoirs (500 K and 300 K) operate a Carnot engine between them. (**a**) If the engine receives 1000 J from the 500 K reservoir, what heat is rejected to the 300 K reservoir? (**b**) If the engine were operated in reverse as a refrigerator and received 1000 J from the 300 K reservoir, what heat is delivered to the 500 K reservoir? (**c**) What is the heat equivalent of the mechanical work required to operate the refrigerator in (b)?

CLAUSIUS INEQUALITY

254. The Clausius Inequality $\oint dQ/T \leqq 0$ holds true for all cyclic processes. The principle of increasing entropy states that $\Delta S \geqq 0$ for all

isolated systems. Are these conflicting statements? Explain.

255. Demonstrate that the expression $\Delta S \geqq 0$ results from the application of Clausius' inequality to an isolated system.

256. Demonstrate that if the Clausius statement of the second law, § 5.2, *Text*, were suddenly discovered invalid, a consequence would be the violation of the Kelvin–Planck statement.

257. A Carnot power cycle 1–2–3–4 has superimposed an actual cycle 1–2′–3–4′ (actual adiabatic expansion 1–2′ and actual adiabatic compression 3–4′). See figure. Demonstrate the validity of the Clausius inequality $\oint dQ/T \leqq 0$ by applying it first to the Carnot cycle and noting that $\oint dQ/T = 0$ and then to the actual cycle and noting that $\oint dQ/T < 0$.

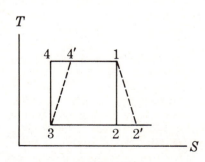

Problem 257

258. An inventor claims that not only has he developed a truly reversible adiabatic refrigerant compressor, but also has invented a throttling valve that will cause the state of the fluid to move along a path of diminishing entropy. As a consequence, the capacity (refrigeration) of a refrigerating system is increased. Refute the claims of this inventor, especially the one relevant to the throttling action, by applying the Clausius inequality to a reversed cycle employing these claims.

ENTROPY PRODUCTION

259. An industrial space heater (air blown over an electrical grid) uses 30 kW-hr of electrical energy to heat the incoming atmospheric air from 10°C to 48.9°C. Calculate the entropy production of the air system and of the universe.

260. Steam with $h = 2442.6$ kJ/kg flows at the rate of 22.7 kg/s into a water-steam condenser at the constant temperature of 48.9°C. The condensed steam leaves with $h = 181.4$ kJ/kg. The cooling water ($c_p = 4.187$ kJ/kg-K) enters at 24.4°C and leaves at 37.8°C. Consider the condenser an adiabatic steady flow system with $\Delta P = 0$ and $\Delta K = 0$. Compute the entropy production for the system; $t_0 = 21.1$°C.

Ans. $\Delta S_p = 9.3$ kJ/K-s.

261. There are transferred 500 kJ of heat from reservoir A (at 1000 K) to reservoir B (at 500 K); in each case the reservoirs remain at constant temperature (see § 1.23, *Text*). According to the second law, what is the net change of entropy of the two reservoirs?

262. A liquid system whose mass is m kg at temperature T was formed by bringing together adiabatically two equal masses of the liquid; initially, one mass was at T_1 and the other at T_2. Show that the entropy production for the system (and of the universe) is $\Delta S_p = mc_p(T_1 + T_2)/2(T_1 T_2)^{1/2}$ where the specific heat of the liquid is c_p. Also, prove that ΔS_p must be positive.

263. An electric current of 15 amp flows continuously through a 30-ohm resistor being maintained at a constant temperature of 28°C by moving cool air (initially at 15°C) across it. For each minute find the entropy production (a) in the resistor, (b) in the air if its temperature rise is $\Delta t = 10°C$, and (c) of the universe.

264. During a reversible process, a closed system does 50 kJ of work while it receives 50 kJ of heat. State if the entropy change is positive, negative, or zero. Show tangible proof.

265. A 50-gal insulated water heater undergoes a recovery cycle from 90°F to 170°F in 30 min; the mass of water involved is 415 lb. Find the entropy production of the universe (a) if the heating is done by electricity, (b) if the heating is done by a constant temperature source at 840°F with all heat being received by the water ($c_p = 1.0$ Btu/lb-°F).

Ans. (a) 1.873 Btu/°R-min, (b) 1.012 Btu/°R-min.

266. Assume 1 lb of helium undergoes a cycle as follows: heat added 1–2 isobarically from 140°F to 440°F, irreversible adiabatic expansion 2–3 to 80°F during which $\Delta S = 0.01$ Btu/lb-°R, heat rejection 3–4 isothermally at 80°F until $S_4 = S_1$; then the cycle is completed with an isentropic process 4–1. Determine (a) $\oint dQ/T$, (b) the internal entropy growth and ΔS for the cycle, (c) the entropy production for the universe if the source and sink temperatures are each constant and are 440°F, 80°F, respectively.

Ans. (a) -0.01 Btu/lb-°R, (b) 0.01, 0 Btu/lb-°R, (c) 0.231 Btu/cycle-°R.

267. From a constant temperature reservoir (in the surroundings) at 3000°F, there are transferred 2000 Btu of heat to a Carnot-type engine. The engine receives the heat at 440°F and discharges at the sink temperature of 80°F. (a) Are the heat transfers reversible? Compute the change of entropy of the engine system accompanying the heat added process and the heat rejection process. (b) What is the net change of entropy of the universe in one cycle? of the engine in one cycle? (c) When all the Carnot work produced has been used, what is ΔS_p for the universe? (d) If the input to the engine is 2000 Btu of paddle work (other events remaining as first described), what is ΔS_p for the universe?

Ans. (a) 2.222, -2.222 Btu/°R, (b) 1.644 Btu/°R, 0, (c) 3.124, (d) 2.222 Btu/°R.

268. A gaseous system of 2 lb of CO_2 receives 100 Btu of energy, first half by isothermal heating and last half by paddle work with the temperature kept constant. Initially, $p_1 = 200$ psia, $t_1 = 340$°F; the sink temperature is $t_0 = 60$°F. The energy source remains at a constant temperature of 540°F. (a) Find ΔS of the system through heating; through paddle work. **(b)** Compute the entropy production of the universe and the final pressure of the system.

269. A source of heat at constant temperature of 1000°R supplies 63.5 Btu/sec to a cyclic system that receives the heat while at constant pressure. The working substance expands isentropically to the sink temperature of 500°R, rejects heat isothermally and reversibly to the sink, then returns isentropically to its initial state. Sketch the events on the *TS* plane. The cyclic work is 12 Btu/sec. For 1 sec, determine **(a)** $\oint dQ/T$ and ΔS for the cycle, **(b)** the entropy production of the universe. **(c)** If the energy input to the system is paddle work instead of heat what is the entropy production of the universe?

Ans. **(a)** 0, **(b)** 0.0395, **(c)** 0.103 Btu/°R-sec.

AVAILABILITY, CLOSED SYSTEM

270. Find the availability of a 1-kg mass of water in a closed container at a pressure of 13.79 bar and in the following state: **(a)** its temperature is 427°C; **(b)** it is saturated vapor; **(c)** it is saturated liquid ($h = 827$ kJ/kg, $v = 0.00115$ m^3/kg, $s = 2.2772$ kJ/kg-K). In all cases, the surrounding atmosphere is at $p_0 = 1$ atm, $t_0 = 26.7$°C ($h_0 = 111.75$ kJ/kg, $v_0 = 0.001$ m^3/kg, $S_0 = 0.3903$ kJ/kg-K). See Item B 16(SI) for other steam properties.

Ans. **(a)** 818 kJ.

271. Find the ratio of the availabilities of hydrogen to air, each pound of gas in a closed system at $p_1 = p_0$, T_1; the environment is at p_0, T_0.

Ans. 14.24 to 1.0.

272. During a constant pressure nonflow process 787 kJ of heat are abstracted from 2.27 kg of nitrogen initially at 1378.96 kPaa, 427°C; the environmental conditions are $p_0 = 101.325$ kPa, $t_0 = 15.6$°C. Find **(a)** the change in availability, **(b)** the maximum work the system could do either initially or finally, **(c)** the entropy production for the universe.

273. Assume 2 mole of oxygen are confined in a container at 100 psia, 500°F; the surroundings are at $p_0 = 14.7$, $t_0 = 80$°F. Find the availability of the oxygen. Use Item B 7.

Ans. 2466 Btu.

274. Consider 1 lb of air at 120°F that receives energy at constant volume, nonflow, with a pressure increase from $p_1 = 20$ psia to

$p_2 = 75$ psia. If the environmental conditions are $p_0 = 15$ psia and $t_0 = 60$°F, determine the resulting change of availability of the air if the energy is **(a)** heat, **(b)** paddle-wheel work, and **(c)** electrical energy. **(d)** Find the entropy production of the universe in each case; heat source is at minimum temperature.

Ans. **(a)** 160 Btu.

AVAILABILITY, STEADY FLOW SYSTEM

275. Assume 1 kg/s of steam at 50 bar flows at 50 m/s and is in the following state: **(a)** its temperature is 500°C; **(b)** it is saturated vapor; **(c)** it is saturated liquid ($h = 1154.4$ kJ/kg, $v = 0.0013$ m^3/kg, $s = 2.921$ kJ/kg-K). In all cases the surrounding atmosphere is at $p_0 = 1$ bar, $t_0 = 27$°C ($h_0 = 113.2$ kJ/kg, $v_0 = 0.001$ m^3/kg, $s_0 = 0.3951$ kJ/kg-K). Use Item B 16(SI) for required properties not given. Find the availability for each state.

276. Air leaves a nozzle at 14.7 psia, 740°F, 2000 fps in an environment where $p_0 = 14.7$ psia, $t_0 = 80$°F. For each 1 lb/sec, what is the maximum work that this jet is capable of producing; $\Delta P = 0$. Use Item B 2.

Ans. 137 Btu/sec.

277. Find the availability of a 1-lb mass of water that is flowing at 10 fps, is subjected to a pressure of 200 psia, and is in the following state: **(a)** its temperature is 800°F; **(b)** it is saturated vapor; **(c)** it is saturated liquid. In all cases, the surrounding atmosphere is at $p_0 = 14.7$ psia, $t_0 = 80$°F.   *Ans.* **(a)** 474.0 Btu/lb.

278. A system consisting of 2 lb of oxygen receives heat at constant pressure of 20 psia, the state changing from 20 psia and 150°F to 640°F in an environment where $p_0 = 15$ psia and $t_0 = 40$°F. **(a)** For both nonflow and steady flow processes ($\Delta P = 0$, $\Delta K = 0$) to the dead state, determine the availability of the oxygen before and after heating. **(b)** What is the change of availability? Solve by gas tables.

Ans. (Steady flow) **(a)** 22.5, 113 Btu, **(b)** 90.5 Btu.

279. Saturated steam vapor at 90°F enters the shell side of surface type condenser and leaves as saturated liquid at 90°F. Cooling water flows through the condenser tubes entering at 60°F and in the mass ratio of 57.9 lb water/1 lb steam. Find **(a)** exit temperature of water, **(b)** change in availability of the steam,

(c) change in availability of the water, (d) entropy production of the universe per pound of steam. For the surroundings, $p_0 = 14.7$ psia, $t_0 = 50°F$.

280. Gases at the rate of 20 lb/sec depart a gas turbine with small kinetic energy at a temperature of 2000°R where the environment is at 500°R; the exhaust pressure and the environment are both 15 psia. The gases are products for 400% stoichiometric air ($M_p = 28.9$ lb/mole). See Item B 8. Determine (a) the work that the exhaust gases could do if there were some way to bring them to the dead state reversibly, (b) the entropy production of the universe.

281. Determine the availability of a 5-kg air system at 5 bar, 250°C which is immersed in an environment of $p_0 = 1$ bar, $t_0 = 37°C$ (a) when nonflow conditions obtain, (b) when steady flow obtains with $\Delta P = 0$, $\Delta K = 0$. Solve this problem using Item B 1.

282. An economizer (gas-to-water, steady flow heat exchanger, Fig. f/2, Foreword *Text*) receives 405,800 lb/hr of water ($c_p = 1.0$) and 536,000 lb/hr of gas ($c_p = 0.24$). The water is heated from 263°F to 384°F while the gas cools from 767°F to 386°F in an internally reversible manner. If the kinetic energy changes are negligible and if $p_0 = 15$ psia and $t_0 = 60°F$, compute the change of availability of the water, of the gas, and of the system.

IRREVERSIBILITY

283. Develop the relation between heat and entropy that occurs during an irreversible process, namely, $\int_{irr} ds > \int_{irr} dQ/T$.

284. Find the irreversibility in each of the following situations:

(a) 200 kJ of heat are transferred to the atmosphere directly from a constant-temperature reservoir that is at $p_A = p_0$ and 400 K.

(b) 200 kJ of heat are transferred directly from the atmosphere to a constant-temperature reservoir that is at $p_B = p_0$ and 200 K.

(c) 200 kJ of heat are transferred directly from reservoir A to reservoir B.

In all cases, the atmosphere is at $p_0 = 1$ atm, 300 K.

285. A frictionless piston-cylinder arrangement contains 1 lb of water initially at 100 psia, 400°F; the surrounding atmosphere is $p_0 = 14.7$ psia, $t_0 = 80°F$. Find the change in

availability, the entropy production of the universe, and the irreversibility in each of the following cases: (a) the system receives heat isothermally until its volume doubles; the heat source is at the minimum possible temperature; (b) the system receives heat at constant pressure until its volume doubles; the heat source is at the minimum possible temperature; (c) the same as (b) except that the process occurs because of internal stirring rather than a heat interaction.

286. Assume 1 kg of wet steam initially at 15 bar, quality $x = 80\%$, is contained in a frictionless piston-cylinder arrangement; $p_0 = 1$ bar, $t_0 = 20°C$ ($h_0 = 84$ kJ/kg, $v_0 = 0.001$ m³/kg, $s_0 = 0.2964$ kJ/kg-K). Heat is received ($p = c$) until the steam becomes dry vapor at 400°C; the heat reservoir is at the lowest possible constant temperature. (a) For the process find the change in availability of the steam, the irreversibility, and the available portion of the heat transferred. (b) If the energy input had been by means of internal paddle work instead of heat, find the change of availability and the irreversibility.

287. For each of the following described processes, a steady flow of water vapor at 120 psia, 500°F enters the device at low velocity and leaves at 35 psia; $p_0 = 14.7$ psia, $t_0 = 40°F$. For each case find the change of availability, the entropy production of the universe, and the irreversibility; (a) it expands reversibly and adiabatically in a turbine and leaves with a low velocity; (b) it expands reversibly and adiabatically in a nozzle; (c) it expands adiabatically through a porous membrane and leaves with a low velocity.

288. Gaseous carbon dioxide is compressed adiabatically from 15 psia, 600°R to 60 psia, 900°R; the surroundings are at $p_0 = 15$ psia, $T_0 = 500°R$. For both nonflow and steady flow of 1 mole/sec, find (a) the entropy production of the universe, (b) the irreversibility. Use Item B 3.

Ans. (a) 1.278 Btu/°R-sec, (b) 639 Btu/sec.

289. A system of 1 lb of steam at 200 psia, 400°F is confined in a frictionless and adiabatic piston-cylinder arrangement. Stirring (paddle) work is accomplished until the initial volume is doubled with the pressure remaining constant; $p_0 = 14.7$, $t_0 = 80°F$. For the steam, $h_1 = 1210.8$ Btu/lb, $v_1 = 2.36$ ft³/lb, $s_1 = 1.5599$ Btu/lb-°R; $t_2 = 1134°F$, $h_2 = 1597.2$ Btu/lb, $s_2 = 1.8862$ Btu/lb-°R, $v_2 = 4.72$ ft³/lb. Find

(a) the change in availability, (b) the entropy production of the universe, (c) the irreversibility. (d) If the volume increase had been accomplished by heating only with the source at the least constant temperature possible, find the entropy production of the universe and the irreversibility.

Ans. (a) 129.3 Btu/lb, (b) 0.3263 Btu/°R-lb, (c) 176.2 Btu/lb, (d) 0.0838 Btu/°R-lb, 45.2 Btu/lb.

290.   Steam at 456°F with a specific heat of $c_p = 0.6$ Btu/°R-lb is heated to 708°F in a heat exchanger by heat from hot gas whose $c_p = 0.24$ and whose initial temperature is 1500°F. The steady rate of flow is gas 52.5 lb/sec, steam 25 lb/sec. Compute (a) the final gas temperature; (b) the entropy growth; (c) the change of availability and the irreversibility for the process if $p_0 = 14.7$ psia, $t_0 = 70$°F.

Ans. (a) 1185°F, (b) 1.63 Btu/°R-sec, (c) $I = 864$ Btu/sec.

291.   Assume 1 mole/sec of an ideal gas is throttled in a steady flow adiabatic manner from 150 psia to 30 psia; $p_0 = 15$ psia, $t_0 = 60$°F. Find (a) the entropy production of the universe, (b) the change in availability, (c) the irreversibility.

292.   A jet engine on test stand receives air at the rate of 10 lb/sec at 14 psia and 520°R, compresses it adiabatically with $\Delta K \approx 0$ to 98 psia, with a compressor efficiency of 83%. The available sink is at 510°R. Determine (a) the actual work of compression, (b) the change of availability of the air, (c) the change of availability of the immediate surroundings (control volume = internal surfaces of the compressor and inlet and exit sections), (d) the irreversibility of the compression. (e) If the compression is isentropic, what is the change of availability of the process, of the surroundings, and the irreversibility?

Ans. (a) 1117 Btu/sec, (b) 1070 kW, (c) 1178 kW, (d) 103 Btu/sec.

293.   An isothermal source consists of condensing steam at 500°F (also at constant pressure). This source heats the working fluid helium 1–2 (a steady flow system) from 140°F to 440°F with $p = C$. The helium then expands adiabatically 2–3 to 80°F with $\Delta s = 0.1$ Btu/lb-°R, rejects heat isothermally 3–4 until an isentropic process 4–1 returns it to state 1. For a flow rate of 1 lb/sec, compute (a) the change of availability accompanying the exchange with the source, (b) the irreversibility of the adiabatic expansion, (c) $\oint dQ$ and $\oint dQ/T$ for the cycle, (d) the irreversibility for a whole number of cycles per second.

Ans. (a) −57.8, (b) 50, (c) 46.7 Btu/sec, −0.1 Btu/sec-°R, (d) 131.85 Btu/sec.

294.   Assume 200 kW are received by a gear box that delivers 190 kW while operating in a steady state at 60°C; the environment is at $T_0 = 278$ K. Find the entropy production of the universe and the irreversibility.

AVAILABLE HEAT

295.   During the execution of a cycle, 2 kg of air receive heat at constant pressure while the temperature increases from 482°C to 649°C in an internally reversible manner. The natural sink temperature is 35°C. Determine the amount of heat that can be converted into work.

296.   The temperature of 5 lb of air is raised from 100°F to 400°F at constant pressure with an electrical coil. (a) How much energy is required? Is this input reversible? (b) If the environmental temperature is $t_0 = 40$°F, what part of the above energy was available before it entered the gaseous system? After it entered? (c) Find ΔS of the gaseous system; of the surroundings. (d) What is the entropy production?

Ans. (a) 360, (b) 360, 103.5 Btu, (c) $\Delta S_g = 0.513$, (d) 0.513 Btu/°R.

297.   A thermodynamic cyclic system operates on 2 lb/sec of gas ($R = 60$, $c_p = 0.2315$, $k = 1.50$) as follows: 1–2, isentropic compression ($p_1 = 20$ psia, $t_1 = 120$°F, $p_2 = 224$ psia, $r_k = 5$); 2–3, isothermal expansion ($Q = +482$ Btu/sec, $T_3 = 1297$°R, $V_3 = 54$ cfs); 3–1, constant pressure ($Q = -332$ Btu/sec). The system receives its heat from a constant pressure source of 3 lb/sec of nitrogen originally at 2500°R; the system rejects its heat to a sink whose temperature is 60°F. Determine the amount of available energy as heat (a) that enters the system, (b) that leaves the system; compute (c) the available part of Q_A before it leaves the source, (d) the net ΔS of the universe, (e) the efficiency of the system.

Ans. (Item B 1): (a) 289, (b) 139, (c) 365.5 Btu/sec, (d) +0.415 Btu/sec-°R, (e) 31.1%.

298.   There are handled 50 lb/min of argon by a system in the following cyclic manner:

1–2, constant pressure ($p_1 = 15$ psia, $t_1 = 400°F$, $V_1 = 770$ cfm, $T_2 = 640°R$, $Q = -1375$ Btu/min); 2–3, polytropic, compression with $n = 2$ ($c_n = 0.02484$, $Q = +2740$ Btu/min, $V_3 = 128$ cfm, $p_3 = 298$ psia, $T_3 = 2845°R$); 3–1, isentropic expansion. An external constant pressure source consisting of 10 lb/min of oxygen initially at $4500°R$ supplies heat to the system; the system rejects heat to a sink at $100°F$. Determine (a) the available part of Q_A before it leaves the source, (b) the amount of available energy as the heat enters the system, (c) the amount of available energy just as the heat leaves the system, (d) the efficiency of the system, (e) the net ΔS of the universe.

Ans. (Item B 1): (a) 2340, (b) 1705, (c) 340 Btu/min, (d) 49.8%, (e) 1.756 Btu/min-°R.

299. Consider 2 lb of gaseous CO_2 at 15 psia, $140°F$, that receive 100 Btu of heat in the following reversible nonflow manner: 50 Btu with $p = C$, 1–2, followed by 50 Btu with $T = C$, 2–3. The sink temperature is $T_0 = 500°R$. Find (a) T_2, (b) the portion of the heat that is available, (c) the entropy production of the universe if the source is at minimum constant temperature.

300. Air is compressed in an internally reversible steady flow process from 14.7 psia, $80°F$ to $330°F$ at 50 lb/min ($\Delta P = 0$, $\Delta K = 0$). Circulating water enters the cooling jacket at $70°F$ and leaves at $80°F$ with a steady rate of 50 lb/min, receiving heat only from the air during compression. Compute (a) the compressor work, (b) ΔS for the air and for the water, (c) the available portion of the heat as it leaves the air ($T_0 = 520°R$), (d) the change in availability of the air, (e) the change in availability of the circulating water, (f) the irreversibility of the simultaneous events of compression and the heating of the water.

HELMHOLTZ AND GIBBS FUNCTIONS

301. There are added 50 Btu of heat to 2 lb of oxygen at constant temperature. Determine the change in (a) the Helmholtz function, (b) the Gibbs function. (c) Does either of the above answers signify anything? (d) If the constant temperature is $600°R$ and the sink temperature is $500°R$, what portion of the heat is available? Is unavailable?

302. Assume 2 lb/sec of carbon monoxide at 120 psia, $100°F$ expand to a state of 15 psia, $100°F$; $t_0 = 100°F$, $\Delta P = 0$, $\Delta K = 0$. (a) Find the maximum work possible for any process between these state points. (b) What is the heat if the process is a reversible isothermal?

Ans. (a) 165, (b) 165 Btu/sec.

303. When 3 lb of air are at 100 psia, $1000°R$, use Item B 2 to determine (a) the Helmholtz function, (b) the Gibbs function. (c) If the air expands to 20 psia and $1000°R$, what maximum work can be expected and what will be the total entropy of the air?

Ans. (a) −4340, (b) −4134, (c) 331 Btu, 5.188 Btu/°R.

304. A system consisting of a stoichiometric mixture of 1 mole of CH_4 and 2 mole of O_2 at 1 atm and $77°F$ reacts to produce a products-mixture of 1 mol of CO_2 and 2 mole of H_2O vapor also at 1 atm and $77°F$. Using Item B 11, determine ΔS and the maximum amount of work per mole of CH_4 that can be developed from this reaction.

Ans. 344,504 Btu/mole CH_4, −1.235 Btu/mole CH_4-°R.

305. Assume 2 mole of carbon monoxide react with 1 mole of oxygen in a system to produce 2 mole of carbon dioxide, all at 1 atm and $77°F$. For the reaction, find the maximum work possible, the change of entropy and the irreversibility. See Item B 11.

Ans. 219,266 Btu, −45.092 Btu/°R, 219,266 Btu.

306. System A undergoes a reversible chemical reaction in an electrolytic cell. System B, exactly like A, undergoes an irreversible reaction. For both systems, the pressure remains constant at 30 psia, and each evolves 3.5 ft^3 of gas. During the reversible process A, 260 Btu of electrical energy are delivered and the temperature remains constant at $400°F$. During the irreversible process B, 100 Btu of electrical energy are delivered, 180 Btu of heat absorbed, and the process starts and ends at $400°F$. For each system, determine (a) the work done on the surroundings, (b) the change of internal energy (note that t_2 is the same in each system), (c) the heat, (d) ΔS, (e) ΔA, (f) ΔG.

Ans. (a) 19.4, (b) 60.6, (c) 340 Btu (A), (d) 0.395 Btu/°R, (e) −279.4, (f) −260 Btu.

307. Demonstrate (prove) that lines of constant pressure in the wet region of a two-phase fluid are also lines of constant Gibbs function when depicted on the *TS* plane.

EQUILIBRIUM

308.   The *Text*, § 5.26, gives as one criterion of equilibrium for an isolated system of constant mass, $\Delta S)_{E,m} \leqq 0$. Under these same conditions, another criterion must also obtain, $\Delta E)_{S,m} \geqq 0$. This simply states that if a system of constant mass is in stable equilibrium, the energy of the system must increase, or remain constant, for all possible adiabatic spontaneous variations. Demonstrate that these two criteria are equivalent.

309.   Apply the criterion $\Delta E)_{S,m} \geqq 0$ to a system composed of a marble resting on the bottom of a bowl and demonstrate that the system is in a state of static equilibrium.

310.   In problem 309 let the system be the same except invert the bowl bottom-side-up, balance the marble on the spherical bowl surface, and demonstrate that this system is not in a state of stable equilibrium. Use the criterion $\Delta E)_{S,m} \geqq 0$.

311.   Differentiate the Gibbs function $G = H - TS$ and note that if the temperature remains unchanged, there results $(\partial p / \partial G)_T = 1/v = \rho$, density. This states that for a given fluid, the slope of its isotherm on the *pG* plane is solely a function of its density. Apply this idea to a liquid-vapor water system in equilibrium at 1 atm, 212°F, and discuss the merits of the criterion $\Delta G)_{p,T} \geqq 0$. Note that at 1 atm, 212°F, the density of the liquid water is 1600 times that of the water vapor.

312.   A heat engine operating in differential size reversible cycles interacts with two identical masses of finite constant heat capacities which serve as reservoirs to the engine. The masses undergo no phase change and remain at constant pressure. Show that the masses will tend toward a final equilibrium temperature of $T = (T_1 T_2)^{1/2}$ where T_1 and T_2 are the respective initial temperatures of the masses. Also show that the total work produced is $W = mc_p(T_1 + T_2 - 2T)$ where c_p is the specific heat of the masses.

PROBABILITY

313.   Five cards each have a single number written thereon: 1, 2, 3, 4, and 5. Let two cards be withdrawn in succession. What is the probability that the sum of the two card numbers will be odd? How many microstates are represented by the problem statement?
          Ans. 3 to 5, 12 microstates.

314.   The same as problem 313 except let the probability relate to the sum being even.

315.   A system is comprised of two dice, *A* and *B*. The pair of dice is now rolled. What is the probability of rolling an 8 (combined sum of the numbers on the two upper faces)? How many microstates are represented by this statement?   *Ans.* 5 to 36, 5 microstates.

316.   The same as problem 315 except let the probability relate to the number (sum) 5.

PERPETUAL MOTION, SECOND KIND

317.   Your automobile battery produces work and exchanges heat with only one reservoir (the atmosphere). Is this not in violation of the second law?

318.   All reversible heat engines have identical efficiencies when operating within the same temperature limits. Demonstrate that if this were not so, a perpetual motion machine of the second kind would result. Accomplish this by selecting two reversible engines, assign different efficiencies to them, and let the engine with the higher efficiency drive the one with the lower as a heat pump.

319.   It is possible for a reversible adiabatic path to cross an isotherm at three different points on a *pv* plane; however the middle point of intersection must represent two different states, rather than a single state. What must be true about the two areas formed between the two end intersections?

320.   A heat engine operates between two temperature limits and is known to have an efficiency less than that of a reversible engine operating between these same limits. Prove that the known engine must be an irreversible one.

321.   The ordinary household refrigerator is a system that receives work (electrical energy) and exchanges heat with a single reservoir (the kitchen, say). Why does this not refute the Kelvin-Planck statement of the second law as given in § 5.2(B), *Text*? Explain.

322.   An inventor proposes a heat engine that receives heat, 160 kJ/min at 800 K. For a sink temperature of 500 K, he claims that 65 kJ/min of work are delivered. Do you think that this claim is justifiable? Is any thermodynamic principle violated? Explain.

COMPUTER PROGRAMS

323. The entropy production of a gaseous system interacting with a constant temperature (T_s) heat source is being studied. Three gases $(H_2, N_2, \text{ and } CO_2)$ are used; see Table I. Let the source temperature be 2778 K and let each gaseous system interact independently and be heated at constant pressure from 300 K to 2222 K. First account for the variation of specific heats and find the entropy production of the gas/source system. Second, use the constant specific heats found in Item B 1 and find the entropy production. Compare results. Write a program for the foregoing problem.

324. Write a computer program for this problem. Air (p_1, T_1) is energized adiabatically by a stirring action until its final state (p_2, T_2) is reached; environmental conditions are p_0, T_0. Find the irreversibility of the process by using temperature increments between T_1 and T_2 and summing the irreversibilities found for the increments. First account for the specific heat variation (Table I) and then assume a constant specific heat (Item B 1). Compare results.

325–330. These numbers may be used for other problems.

6

THE IDEAL GAS

Note: Review the contents of Item B 1 for data on a group of selected gases. In the solutions of problems, be mindful of units.

BOYLE'S LAW

331. For an ideal gas expanding according to Boyle's law, integrate the expressions (**a**) $\int p\,dV$ and (**b**) $-\int V\,dp$. (**c**) Sketch the process on the pV plane and shade the areas which represent these integrals. Discuss their significance.

332. The temperature of an ideal gas remains constant while the absolute pressure changes from 103.4 kPaa to 827.2 kPaa. (**a**) If the initial volume is 80 ℓ, what is the final volume? (**b**) For 160 gm of the gas, determine the change of density expressed as a percentage of the initial density.

Ans. (**a**) 10 ℓ, (**b**) 700% increase.

333. The atmospheric pressure at the base of a mountain is 730 mm Hg and at its top is 365 mm Hg. The atmospheric temperature is 15.55°C, constant from base to top. Local gravity is $g = 9.75$ m/s². Find the height of the mountain.

334. The temperature of an ideal gas remains constant while the pressure changes from 15 psia to 150 psia. (**a**) If the initial volume is 2.8 ft³, what is the final volume? (**b**) For 0.35 lb of gas, determine the change of density as a percentage of the initial density.

Ans. (**a**) 0.28 ft³, (**b**) +900%.

335. Prove that the trace of an isothermal process on the pV-plane for an ideal gas must

be negative in slope with a curvature that is concave upwards.

336. An empty tin can with height of 6 in. and a diameter of 3 in. is open at one end and closed at the other end. If the vertical can, with the open end down, be slowly immersed in water (density of 62.4 lb/ft³), how far will the water rise inside the can, (**a**) when the closed end is at the water surface and (**b**) when the closed end is 10 ft beneath the water surface? Thermal equilibrium obtains at all times; $T = C$; neglect any vapor pressure.

337. The density of an ideal gas is doubled while its temperature remains constant. (**a**) Determine the ratio p_1/p_2. (**b**) If $p_1 = 20$ in. Hg vacuum, find p_2 and express in psia and in psig.

Ans. (**a**) 0.5, (**b**) 9.74 psia.

338. The pressure on 142 ℓ/min of air is boosted reversibly from 2068.44 kPaa to 6205.32 kPaa while the temperature remains constant at 24°C; $\Delta U = 0$. (**a**) Find $\int p\,dV$ and $-\int V\,dp$. (**b**) For a nonflow process, find W, Q, ΔH, and ΔS. (**c**) For a steady flow process during which $\Delta K = 5$ kJ/min and $\Delta P = 0$, find $\int p\,dv$, $-\int V\,dp$, W, ΔE_f, ΔH, Q, and ΔS.

Ans. (**b**) $W = -322.6$ kJ/min, $\Delta S = -1.086$ kJ/K-min.

CHARLES' LAW

339. Sketch lines of constant specific volume on the pV and Ts planes and prove that all constant volume lines on a given plane have the same slope at a specified temperature T and constant specific heat c_v.

340. Sulfur dioxide at a temperature of 204°C occupies a volume of 0.3 m³. (**a**) If the volume is increased to 0.9 m³ while the pressure is maintained constant (ideal gas behavior), what is the final temperature in K? In °C? (**b**) If the initial volume is maintained constant and the pressure tripled, what is the final temperature in K? In °C?

341. The temperature of 4.82 lb of oxygen occcupying 8 ft³ is changed from 110°F to 200°F while the pressure remains constant at 115 psia. Determine (**a**) the final volume and (**b**) the change in density expressed as a percentage of the initial density. (**c**) Now with the pressure varying, but with the volume constant, determine the final pressure if the absolute temperature is quadrupled.

Ans. (**a**) 9.26 ft³, (**b**) −13.61%, (**c**) 460 psia.

342. An automobile tire contains a certain volume of air at 30 psig and 70°F. The barometric pressure is 29.50 in. Hg. If, due to running conditions, the temperature of the air in the tire rises to 160°F, what will be the gage pressure? Assume that the air is an ideal gas and that the tire does not stretch.

Ans. 37.5 psig.

343. Let the tire in problem 342 initially contain 0.25 lb of air and have an automatic valve that releases air whenever the pressure exceeds 34 psig. Under certain running conditions, the steady-state temperature becomes 180°F. (**a**) What mass of air escapes? (**b**) What is the tire pressure when the remaining air has returned to 70°F?

344. At atmospheric pressure and 62°F, the approximate density of hydrogen is determined as $\rho = 0.00529$ lb/ft³; at $t = 32°F$, $\rho = 0.00562$ lb/ft³. From these data compute the approximate absolute zero point on the Fahrenheit scale.

345. At atmospheric pressure and 62°F, the approximate density of helium is measured as $\rho = 0.0105$ lb/ft³; at 32°F, $\rho = 0.01112$ lb/ft³. Compute the approximate absolute zero point from these data on the Fahrenheit scale.

346. Assume 10 ft³/min ($\dot{m} = 0.988$ lb/min) of hydrogen initially at $p_1 = 400$ psia, $t_1 = 300°F$ are cooled at constant volume to 120°F in an internally reversible manner. (**a**) Evaluate the integrals $\int p \, dV$ and $-\int V \, dp$. (**b**) For a nonflow process, find p_2, ΔU, ΔH, Q, and

ΔS. (**c**) Solve part (**b**) if the process is steady flow with $\Delta P = 0$, $\Delta K = 0$.

Ans. (**a**) 0, +176 Btu/min, (**b**) $p_2 = 305$ psia, $Q = -434$ Btu/min, $\Delta S = -0.649$ Btu/min-°R, (**c**) $W = 176$ Btu/min.

347. The same as problem 346 except that the process occurs at constant pressure to 120°F.

AVOGADRO'S LAW

348. Using Avogadro's principle, compare the relative densities of gases, each at the same pressure and temperature: oxygen to methane; helium to hydrogen; xenon to propane.

349. At 2068.44 kPaa, 37.8°C, 0.142 m³ of methane have a total mass of 1.82 kg. Using Avogadro's principle find the mass of carbon dioxide contained in a 0.85-m³ tank at 2068.44 kPaa, 37.8°C. *Ans.* 30 kg.

350. Which is the heavier—dry air (per properties in Item B1) or wet air (mixture of dry air and water vapor—as atmospheric air)? *Suggestion*: Compare the density of dry air with that of water vapor (considered to act as an ideal gas) at the same pressure and temperature.

351. (**a**) Assuming that all gases at 1 atm, 32°F occupy the standard mole volume of 359 ft³, find the densities of these gases at 1 atm, 32°F: mercury; hydrogen; neon; ozone; air. (**b**) For this state, compare each of the densities of the first four gases to that of the last one, air.

352. At 300 psia, 100°F, 5 ft³ of methane have a total mass of 4.01 lb. Using Avogadro's principle, find the mass of carbon dioxide contained in a 30-ft³ tank at 300 psia, 100°F.

Ans. 66.09 lb.

EQUATION OF STATE, IDEAL GAS

353. Express the ideal gas equation $pv - RT$ in each of the following differential forms:

$$dp/p + dv/v = dT/T$$

$$dp/p - d\rho/\rho = dT/T$$

354. For an ideal gas, show the difference in the specific heats c_p and c_v is simply the gas constant R, that is, $c_p - c_v = R$.

355. (**a**) What is the specific volume of a gas at 180 psia and 90°F when its density is

0.0446 lb/ft^3 at 14.7 psia and 32°F? (a) Calculate its gas constant and approximate molecular weight.   *Ans.* (a) 2.05 ft^3/lb, (b) 95.5, 16.

356. A certain gas at 15 in. Hg abs and 90°F occupies 10 ft^3. (a) If the state is changed until the volume is 30 ft^3 and the temperature is 540°F, determine the final pressure. (b) If the state is changed until the initial pressure is trebled and the temperature increased to 400°F, determine the final volume.
    Ans. (a) 0.446 psia, (b) 5.21 ft^3.

357. A steel company plans on using 17 m^3 of O$_2$ in processing 1 metric ton of steel. If this volume is measured at 101.325 kPaa and 21°C, what mass of O$_2$ is needed for a 20,000 metric ton/month furnace?

358. It is planned to lift and move logs from almost inaccessible forest areas by means of balloons. Helium at atmospheric pressure (101.325 kPaa) and temperature (21.1°C) is to be used in the balloons. What minimum balloon diameter (assume spherical shape) will be required for a gross lifting force of 20 metric tons?   *Ans.* 33.3 m.

359. A drum 6 in. in diameter and 40 in. long contained acetylene at 250 psia and 80°F. After some of the acetylene was used, the pressure was 100 psia and the temperature was 70°F. (a) What proportion of the acetylene was used? (b) What volume would the used acetylene occupy at 14.7 psia and 60°F?
    Ans. (a) 59.2%, (b) 6.34 ft^3.

360. (a) A sphere, 6 ft in diameter, contains oxygen at 300 psia and 80°F. How many drums 6 in. in diameter and 2 ft long, which are initially devoid of any gas, can be filled to a pressure of 50 psia and 65°F? Assume that the temperature of the oxygen left in the sphere remains at 80°F. (b) The same as (a) except that the drums initially contain O$_2$ at 20 psia and 65°F.   *Ans.* (a) 1400, (b) 2337.

361. Air is pumped into a 20-ft^3 tank until the pressure is 135 psig. When the pump is stopped, the temperature is 200°F. (a) What mass is in the tank? What is its density? (b) If the air is allowed to cool to 70°F, what is the pressure of the cooled air? The density?
    Ans. (a) 12.26 lb, 0.613 lb/ft^3, (b) 120.2 psia.

362. The height of a cylindrical tank, containing 15 lb of gas at 70 psia and 115°F, is triple its diameter; the gas constant is $R = 45$ ft lb/lb-°R. Find the tank dimensions in feet.
    Ans. Height = 7.605 ft.

363. A 60-ft^3 tank containing helium at 250°F is evacuated from atmospheric pressure until the vacuum is 28.9 in. Hg. (a) What mass of 250°F air is left in the tank? (b) What mass was pumped out? (c) If the air left in the tank is cooled to a temperature of 36°F, what is the pressure in psia and in in. Hg?
    Ans. (a) 0.0158 lb, (b) 0.4477 lb, (c) 0.3505 psia.

364. A 12-ft^3 tank contained hydrogen sulfide gas at 150 psia and 60°F after 5 lb of the gas had been drawn out. Before any gas left the tank the temperature was 70°F. What mass of gas was in the tank originally and what was its pressure?

365. A balloon, considered spherical, is 30 ft in diameter. The surrounding air is at 60°F and the barometer reads 29.60 in. Hg. What gross load may the balloon lift if it is filled with (a) hydrogen at 70°F and atmospheric pressure, (b) helium at 70°F and atmospheric pressure? (c) Helium is nearly twice as heavy as hydrogen. Does it have half the lifting force of hydrogen?   *Ans.* (a) 997.1 lb, (b) 925.2 lb.

366. A 50-ft^3 tank is being filled with oxygen. At a particular instant the temperature is 240°F, the pressure is 200 psia and each is increasing at rates of 50°F/sec and 20 psi/sec, respectively. Find the flow rate of oxygen into the tank at this instant.

367. There are withdrawn 200 ft^3 of air measured at 15 psia and 90°F from a 50-ft^3 tank containing air initially at 100 psia and 140°F. What is the pressure of the air remaining in the tank if its temperature is 130°F?

368. Two spheres, each 6 ft in diameter, are connected by a pipe in which there is a valve. Each sphere contains helium at a temperature of 80°F. With the valve closed, one sphere contains 3.75 lb and the other 1.25 lb of helium. After the valve has been open long enough for equilibrium to obtain, what is the common pressure in the spheres if there is no loss or gain of energy?   *Ans.* 32 psia.

369. The same as problem 368 except that the spheres contain hydrogen.

370. A closed vessel A contains 3 ft^3 (V_A) of air at $p_A = 500$ psia and a temperature of $t_A = 120$°F. This vessel connects with vessel B, which contains an unknown volume of air V_B at 15 psia and 50°F. After the valve separating the two vessels is opened, the resulting pressure and temperature are $p_m = 200$ psia and

$t_m = 70°F$, respectively. What is the volume V_B? *Ans.* 4.17 ft³.

371. A system consists of two vessels A and B with a connecting valve. The vessel A contains 15 ft³ of nitrogen at 220 psia and 110°F. Vessel B contains 2 lb of nitrogen at 80 psia and 60°F. After the valve separating the two vessels is opened, the resulting equilibrium temperature becomes 90°F. What is the final pressure p_m? *Ans.* 180.5 psia.

372. The figure is a diagrammatic representation of air springs for an automobile. System A represents four springs, one at each wheel, with a total volume of 1070 in.³, and where for the normal load of F, the pressure is maintained at $p_A = 100$ psig. The system B represents a storage tank, whose volume is 820 in.³, which is normally maintained at a pressure of 250 psig, any bled air being replenished by the compressor when the pressure in B falls below the control point. It is desired to ascertain events during the designing of the whole system. (a) Let A and B be in thermal equilibrium with the environment at 80°F; then the temperature of the surroundings drops to 60°F. If A and B remain in thermal equilibrium with t_0 and if the pressure in A is kept constant by action of the automatic valve D, compute the final pressure in the tank (compressor not acting) and the amount of air taken from the tank. (b) Let A and B remain in thermal equilibrium with the environment while the temperature changes from 80°F to 100°F, and as before, the pressure in the air spring remains at 100 psig in order to maintain normal ride height. With the compressor not operating, the provision is to allow air to escape to the atmosphere through valve G to maintain constant p_A. Determine the amount of air to escape and the final pressure in the tank B. (Courtesy *General Motors Engineering Journal*).

Ans. (a) 235 psig, 0.0137 lb, (b) 0.0127 lb, 260 psig.

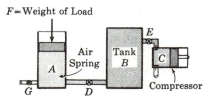

F = Weight of Load

Problem 372

ENERGY RELATIONS, IDEAL GAS

373. A 283-ℓ tank A contains air at 689.48 kPaa and 37.8°C. Another 283-ℓ tank B contains air at 6894.8 kPaa and 37.8°C. Which system is capable of producing more work? Does the product pV represent energy stored in the tank? Explain.

374. The decrease in internal energy of 3 lb of an ideal gas is −325 Btu when the pressure decreases from 100 psia to 20 psia and the volume increases from 1.5 ft³ to 4.5 ft³; $c_v = 0.25$. Determine (a) the change of enthalpy and (b) t_1 and t_2. *Ans.* (a) −336.2 Btu, (b) $t_1 = 623°F$, $t_2 = 190°F$.

375. The increase of enthalpy of an ideal gas is 141.7 kJ when the pressure increases from 103.4 kPaa to 1034 kPaa and the volume decreases from 477 ℓ to 74.5 ℓ. Determine (a) the change of internal energy, (b) the final temperature of the gas if the initial temperature is 28.3°C. *Ans.* (a) 114 kJ, (b) 198°C.

376. Assume 10 lb of an ideal gas with $R = 50.8$ ft-lb/lb-°R and $k = 1.18$ are heated from 75°F to 200°F. What is (a) the change of internal energy, (b) the change of enthalpy, (c) the change in the value of pV, (d) C_p in Btu/mole-°R? *Ans.* (a) 453.3, (b) 535, (c) 81.7 Btu, (d) 13.02 Btu/mole-°R.

377. Consider 4 lb of a certain gas with $R = 80$ ft-lb/lb-°R that undergo a process and results in these changes: $\Delta U = 1382$, $\Delta H = 2075$ Btu. Find (a) k, c_v, c_p; (b) the temperature change. (c) If the process had been internally reversible with $p = c$, find $Q, W, \int p\, dV, -\int V\, dp$ for both nonflow and steady flow ($\Delta P = 0$, $\Delta K = 0$).

378. For a certain ideal gas, $R = 77.8$ ft-lb/lb-°R and $c_p = 0.2 + 0.0002T$ Btu/lb-°R. It is heated from 40°F to 140°F. For 1 lb, find (a) the change of internal energy, (b) the change of enthalpy, (c) the change of entropy if the heating is at constant volume, (d) the change of entropy if the heating is at constant pressure, and (e) the value of k at 140°F. *Ans.* (a) 21 Btu/lb, (d) 0.0565 Btu/lb-°R, (e) 1.455.

379. Two vessels A and B of different sizes are connected by a pipe with a valve (similar to Joule's set-up). Vessel A contains 142 ℓ of air at 2767.92 kPaa, 93.33°C. Vessel B, of unknown volume, contains air at 68.95 kPaa, 4.44°C. The valve is opened and, when the properties have been determined, it is found that $p_m = 1378.96$ kPaa, $t_m = 43.33$°C. (a) What is the volume of vessel B? (b) Compute the heat and entropy change. (c) What work is delivered?

GAS CONSTANTS AND SPECIFIC HEATS

380. The internal energy of a certain ideal gas is related to its temperature as $u = RT/2$. Determine the specific heat ratio $k = c_p/c_v$ for this gas.

381. Calculate the values of c_p, k, and the molar specific heats C_v and C_p of certain gases having values of R ft-lb/lb-°R and c_v Btu/lb-°R, given as follows: (a) $R = 60$ ft-lb/lb-°R, $c_v = 0.2$, (b) $R = 400$ ft-lb/lb-°R, $c_v = 0.76$, (c) $R = 250$ ft-lb/lb-°R, $c_v = 0.42$.

Ans. (a) c_p: 0.277 Btu/lb-°R, 7.13 Btu/mole-°R; $k = 1.385$.

382. For a certain ideal gas, $R = 0.277$ kJ/kg-K and $k = 1.384$. (a) What are the values of c_p and c_v? (b) What mass of this gas would occupy a volume of 0.425 m³ at 517.11 kPaa and 26.7°C? (c) If 31.65 kJ are transferred to this gas at constant volume in (b), what are the resulting temperature and pressure?

Ans. (a) $c_p = 0.9984$ kJ/kg-K, (b) 2.647 kg, (c) 43.27°C, 545.7 kPaa.

383. The constant pressure specific heat of Freon 22 ($CHClF_2$) at 1 atm is $c_p = 0.1403 + 0.000141t$ Btu/lb-°F, where t is °F; its molecular weight is $M = 86.48$. For a temperature of $t = 200$°F, determine the various values needed to fill in Item B 1.

384. A gas initially at $p_1 = 15$ psia and $V_1 = 2$ ft³ undergoes a process to $p_2 = 90$ psia and $V_2 = 0.6$ ft³, during which the enthalpy increases 15.45 Btu; $c_v = 2.4354$ Btu/lb-°R. Determine (a) c_p, (b) R, and (c) ΔU.

385. An unknown gas at $p_1 = 95$ psia and $V_1 = 4$ ft³ undergoes a process to $p_2 = 15$ psia and $V_2 = 16.56$ ft³, during which the enthalpy decreases 83 Btu; $c_v = 0.1573$ Btu/lb-°R. Determine (a) c_p, (b) R, and (c) ΔU.

Ans. (a) 0.223 Btu/lb-°R, (b) 51.1, (c) −58.6 Btu.

386. A gas initially at $p_1 = 120$ psia and $V_1 = 9.87$ ft³ changes state to a point where $p_2 = 40$ psia and $V_2 = 23.4$ ft³, during which the internal energy decreases 116.6 Btu; $c_p = 0.24$ Btu/lb-°R. Determine (a) c_v, (b) R, (c) ΔH.

387. For a certain ideal gas, $R = 51.4$ ft-lb/lb-°R and $k = 1.384$. (a) What are the values of c_p and c_v? (b) What mass of this gas would occupy a volume of 15 ft³ at 75 psia and 80°F? (c) If 30 Btu are transferred to this gas at constant volume in (b) what are the resulting temperature and pressure?

Ans. (a) $c_p = 0.238$, (b) 5.84 lb, (c) 109.9°F, 79.1 psia.

388. For a certain ideal gas $R = 320$ J/kg-K and $c_v = 0.84$ kJ/kg-K. (a) Find c_p and k. (b) If 5 kg of this gas undergo a reversible nonflow constant pressure process from $V_1 = 1.133$ m³, $p_1 = 690$ kPaa to a state where $t_2 = 555$°C, find ΔU, ΔH, Q, and W. (c) If the process in (b) had been a reversible steady flow type with $\Delta P = 0$ and $\Delta K \approx 0$, find W.

DALTON'S LAW

389. The partial pressures of a four-component gaseous mixture (CO, CH_4, N_2, Ar) at 33°C are respectively: 7, 21, 14, 28 kPaa. For the mixture find its pressure and volumetric analysis.

390. A mixture is formed at 689.48 kPaa, 37.8°C by bringing together these gases—each volume before mixing measured at 689.48 kPaa, 37.8°C: 3 mole CO_2, 2 mole N_2, 4.5 mole O_2. Find the partial pressures of the components after mixing.

Ans. $p_{CO_2} = 217.7$ kPaa.

391. In a multicomponent gaseous mixture, two of the constituents (neon and xenon) are included volumetrically as 12% and 25%, respectively. If the neon exerts a partial pressure of 331 kPaa, find the mixture pressure and the partial pressure of the xenon.

392. An air mass of 0.454 kg and an unknown mass of CO_2 occupy a 85-ℓ tank at 2068.44 kPaa. If the partial pressure of the CO_2 is 344.74 kPaa (ideal gas), determine its mass. *Ans.* 0.138 kg.

THROTTLING PROCESS

393. Show that the Joule–Thomson coefficient, $\mu = (dT/dp)_h$, must be zero when applied to an ideal gas.

394. Air undergoes an adiabatic throttling process from 538.99 kPaa to 103.42 kPaa. What is the change of specific entropy? (Air is an ideal gas). *Ans.* $\Delta s = 0.497$ kJ/kg-K.

395. Under given conditions, a certain gas with a Joule-Thomson coefficient of $\mu = 0.025$ K/kPa undergoes a pressure decrease of 1500 kPa when processed slowly through an adiabatic porous plug. What is its temperature change?

396. Assume 2 lb of a certain gas, for which $c_v = 0.1751$ and $c_p = 0.202$ Btu/lb-°R, are throttled adiabatically from an initial volume of 4 ft³ until its entropy increase is 0.189 Btu/°R. What is the final volume?
Ans. $V_2 = 134.2$ ft³.

397. The entropy increase of 1 kg of hydrogen is 0.5234 kJ/K when it is throttled adiabatically from 1379 kPaa. What is the final pressure? *Ans.* 1215 kPaa.

ENTROPY

398. After a series of state changes, the pressure and volume of 5 kg of nitrogen are each doubled. What is ΔS?
Ans. +6.1845 kJ/K.

399. Consider 10 lb of hydrogen initially at 80°F and occupying 6 ft³ that undergo a state change to 150°F; an entropy increase of 8.02 Btu/°R is observed. Find the total volume.

400. Helium changes its state from 85 psia, 272°R and 6.86 ft³ to 1372 psia, 0.425 ft³. For 0.2 pmole, find the entropy change and the final absolute entropy. See Table III.
Ans. $-1.10, 3.552$ Btu/°R.

401. The pressure and absolute temperature of 1 kg argon are each doubled from 1 atm, 25°C. What is the final absolute entropy? Use Table III.

402. (a) If 1 lb of air at 80°F, occupying 6 ft³, changes state until the temperature is 150°F and the volume is 10 ft³, determine ΔS. (b) If 10 ft³ of air at 60°F and 25 psia change state until $p_2 = 100$ psia and $V_2 = 8$ ft³, determine ΔS. (c) If 10 ft³ of air at 150 psig and 40°F undergo a series of state changes until $t_2 = 140$°F and $p_2 = 300$ psig, determine ΔS.
Ans. (a) 0.0557, (b) 0.266, (c) -0.00522 Btu/°R.

403. For two or more separated ideal gases at the same temperature and pressure diffusing to a uniform mixture, show that the net entropy change is $\Delta S = -\bar{R} \sum_i \eta_i \ln x_i$, where x_i is the mole fraction of the ith component in the mixture; η_i, moles of i.

404. (a) Derive the following equation from the change of entropy between any two states of an ideal gas with constant specific heats:

$$\Delta s = c_p \ln \frac{v_2}{v_1} + c_v \ln \frac{p_2}{p_1}$$

(b) Helium changes its state from 586.06 kPaa and 194 ℓ to 9,459.67 kPaa and 28.3 ℓ. What is ΔS for 0.2 kg-mole? *Ans.* -1.0624 kJ/K.

405. After a series of state changes, the pressure and volume of 2.268 kg of nitrogen are each doubled. What is ΔS?
Ans. +2.805 kJ/K.

406. A certain system may execute a process in two different ways. First, it can do so reversibly such that the heat to the system is given by $dQ/dT = 0.95$ kJ/K. Secondly, it can change between the same end states as observed in the first process except the temperature rise is accomplished by a combination of stirring and a heat addition of only half that of the first. Find ΔS if in both cases the temperature rise is from 277 K to 333 K.

407. When a certain gas ($c_p = 1.25$ kJ/kg-K) expands reversibly and adiabatically from $v_1 = 28$ ℓ/kg and $T_1 = 555$ K to $v_2 = 84$ ℓ/kg, its temperature drops by 165 K. When it expands adiabatically from the same initial state into a vacuum to $v_2 = 84$ ℓ/kg, its temperature drops by only 28 K. Find ΔS per kg in each instance.

GAS TABLES

408. Consider 2 lb of air that undergo a state change from 1 atm, 560°R to 960°R in a frictionless manner and without a change of entropy. Use Item B 2 and find (a) ΔU, (b) ΔH, (c) the final pressure, (d) the volume ratio V_1/V_2.

409. There are expanded 1.5 pmole of CO from 60 psia, 800°R to 15 psia, 800°R. Use Item B 4 and find the change of entropy. Are the values of p_r and v_r relevant in this problem? Why? *Ans.* 4.13 Btu/°R.

410. There are compressed 60 lb/sec of N_2 from 140°F without entropy change; the volume ratio is $V_1/V_2 = 5$. If the process is a reversible steady flow wherein $\Delta K = 0$, $\Delta P = 0$, use Item B 6 and find (a) T_2, (b) the ratio p_2/p_1, (c) ΔpV, (d) the work.

© ΔpV

$H_1 = U_1 + p_1 V$

$H_2 = U_2 + p_2 V_2$

$\Delta H = \Delta U + \Delta pV$

$\Delta H - \Delta U = \Delta pV$

Ans. (a) 1128°R, (b) 9.41, (c) 2160 Btu/sec, (d) −7910 Btu/sec.

411. Assume 3 mole of O_2 undergo a cooling process from 1 atm, 1700°R to 1 atm, 800°R. (a) Find ΔS. (b) If the system is of the closed type, find Q and W. Use Item B 7.

412. For comparison of specific heat values found in Item B 1 versus those obtained from the respective gas tables, note that for air, $c_p = 0.24$ and is assumed to be constant according to Item B 1. From values of enthalpy found in Item B 2, compute c_p using first these two temperatures, 500°R and 1500°R; then repeat using 2000°R and 6000°R. Compare.

Ans. 0.24, 0.2497, 0.2994 Btu/lb-°R.

413. A gas turbine compresses 100 lb/sec of air from 1 atm, 40°F through a pressure range of $p_2/p_1 = 10$; the steady flow process is frictionless and without entropy change. Use Item B 2 and find (a) T_2, (b) ΔH, (c) ΔU, (d) the change in flow energy, (e) W where $\Delta P = 0$, $\Delta K = 0$.

Ans. (a) 960°R, (b) 11,158, (c) 8006, (d) 3152, (e) −11,158 Btu/sec.

COMPUTER PROBLEMS

414. It is desired to compare the lifting characteristics of the several gases given in Item B 1 when each has been placed in a balloon that is subject to a normal atmosphere. It is known that all data given in this table have been stored in the memory of the computer. Write the program.

415. Write a computer program for the following problem. The change of entropy ΔS for an ideal gas may be written in terms of c_p, T, R, and p. Select one of the gases from Table I, let its temperature change from T_1 to T_2, account for the variation of c_p with temperature and find the change of entropy for any one pressure $p_1 = p_2 = p$ (or range of pressures $p_1 \neq p_2$). Also find ΔS using a c_p based upon the average of the temperatures T_1 and T_2 and given pressure (or range of pressures). Compare results.

416. Program this problem. The data shown in the gas tables (Items B 2 through B 10) have been stored in the memory of the computer. Given an initial state point (p_1, T_1, v_1) for one of these gases, find the temperature T_2 after it has undergone a specific isentropic pressure change p_1 to p_2, (or sets of pressure ratio p_2/p_1 changes). For this process the relationship $p_2/p_1 = p_{r2}/p_{r1}$ is noted.

417–420. These numbers may be used for other problems.

7

PROCESSES OF FLUIDS

Note: State units of each answer, indicate clearly whether work is done on or by the system, whether heat passes in or out, and whether the internal energy, enthalpy and/or entropy increases or decreases. A sketch of the process on the pV and TS planes should be included in all solutions. Where appropriate include also sketches on the hs and ph planes. Use the Items B 2 through B 10 as appropriate.

ISOMETRIC PROCESS

421. A thermodynamic system consists of a fluid mass within an insulated (adiabatic) rigid container having a set of internal paddles. The mass is stirred by rotating the paddles with external work W_p. For the system, evaluate each of the following expressions stating whether its value is equal to, less than, or greater than zero: (**a**) net work, (**b**) ΔU, (**c**) ΔH, (**d**) ΔS, (**d**) $\int dQ/T$, (**f**) ΔpV, (**g**) $\int p\,dV$, (**h**) $-\int V\,dp$.

422. There are 1.36 kg of air at 137.9 kPaa stirred with internal paddles in an insulated rigid container, whose volume is 0.142 m³, until the pressure becomes 689.5 kPaa. Determine: (**a**) the work input, (**b**) $\Delta(pV)$, (**c**) ΔE_f, and (**d**) Q *Ans.* (**a**) 196.2, (**b**) 78.3 kJ.

423. A certain quantity of 30°C saturated water ($v_f = 0.001$ m³, $h_f = 125.7$ kJ/kg, $p_{sat} = 0.04$ bar) is injected into a 0.3 m³ evacuated drum and then heated until the pressure and temperature become 20 bar and 300°C, respectively. Determine (**a**) the mass of water used and (**b**) the heat required.

424. A reversible, nonflow, constant volume process decreases the internal energy by 316.5 kJ for 2.268 kg of a gas for which

$R = 430$ J/kg-K and $k = 1.35$. For the process, determine (**a**) the work, (**b**) the heat, and (**c**) the change of entropy if the initial temperature is 204.4°C.
    Ans. (**b**) -316.5 kJ, (**c**) -0.7572 kJ/K.

425. The internal energy of a perfectly insulated and rigid 283-ℓ gaseous nitrogen system is increased 2930 kJ by means of internal stirrers (paddles). If the initial pressure is $p_1 = 1379$ kPaa, find p_2 and ΔS per kg mass.

426. A vessel having a volume of 100 ft³ contains 1 ft³ of saturated liquid water and 99 ft³ of saturated water vapor at 15 psia. Heat is transferred until the vessel is filled with saturated vapor. Determine the heat transfer for this process.

427. During a cryogenic experiment, 2 gm-mole of oxygen are placed in closed 1-ℓ Dewar flask at 120 K. After some time, the temperature is noted to be 215 K. Use Item B 27 and find (**a**) the increase in pressure, (**b**) Q, (**c**) the irreversibility; $T_0 = 300$ K.

428. There are 1.36 kg of gas, for which $R = 377$ J/kg-K and $k = 1.25$, that undergo a nonflow constant volume process from $p_1 = 551.6$ kPaa and $t_1 = 60$°C to $p_2 = 1655$ kPaa. During the process the gas is internally stirred, and there are also added 105.5 kJ of heat.

Determine (**a**) t_2, (**b**) the work input, (**c**) Q, (**d**) ΔU, and (**e**) ΔS.

Ans. (**a**) 999 K, (**b**) −1260.5 kJ, (**e**) 2.253 kJ/K.

429. A closed rigid vessel contains a saturated mixture of water and steam at atmospheric pressure. When this particular mixture is heated, the state point will eventually reach the critical point. What are the original volumetric proportions of liquid and vapor? How much heat must be supplied if the container has a volume of 4 in.³?

430. There are 2 lb of a liquid-vapor mixture ($x_1 = 50\%$) of CO_2 contained in a rigid vessel at 90 psia. Heat is absorbed by the CO_2 until its temperature becomes 400°F; the environment is at $p_0 = 14.7$ psia, $t_0 = 80°F$. Use Item B 31 and determine (**a**) the final pressure p_2 and volume, (**b**) Q and that portion of Q which is available ($s_1 = 0.150$ Btu/°R-lb), (**c**) the irreversibility if the heat source is at the minimum constant temperature.

431. If 4 lb of NH_3 at 200 psia and 360°F are cooled at constant volume to $t_2 = 100°F$, find (**a**) p_2, (**b**) ΔU, (**c**) Q and (**d**) W.

Ans. (**a**) 130 psia, approximately, (**b**) −470.4 Btu.

432. A 2-ft³ rigid tank with adiabatic walls is divided into equal parts A and B by a partition. On one side is steam at 100 psia, 340°F; on the other side is steam at 600 psia, 600°F. The partition is removed and thorough mixing occurs. Determine the equilibrium state (p, t) and ΔS.

433. Assume 5 lb of saturated Freon F12 vapor at 20°F are in a closed rigid, adiabatic vessel and are supplied with paddle work until the temperature rises to 240°F; the sink temperature is $t_0 = 70°F$. For the process determine (**a**) the available energy that enters the system, (**b**) the available energy lost, (**c**) the entropy change of the surroundings, (**d**) the entropy production.

434. A pressure vessel contains 2.5 lb of saturated steam at 70 psia. Determine the amount of heat which must be rejected in order to reduce the quality to 60%. What will be the pressure and temperature of the steam at this new state? *Ans.* $Q = -875$ Btu.

435. Consider 1 lb of saturated steam that is contained in a constant-volume rigid container initially at 100 psia; heat is removed until the pressure is halved. The heat sink is at the maximum possible constant temperature;

environmental conditions are $p_0 = 14.7$ psia, $T_0 = 500°R$. Find (**a**) the change in availability, (**b**) the irreversibility.

436. A gas whose composition is not known has 42.2 kJ of paddle work input at constant volume of 566 ℓ. Initially, $p_1 = 138$ kPaa, $t_1 = 26.7°C$; finally, $t_2 = 82.2°C$. What are ΔU and Q if $k = c_p/c_v = 1.21$?

Ans. 68.9, 26.7 kJ.

ISOBARIC PROCESS

437. For a constant pressure system whose mass is 80 lb, 1 hp-min is required to raise its temperature 1°F. Determine the specific heat for the system, Btu/lb-°F.

438. A vertical, frictionless piston-and-cylinder arrangement contains 1 kg of steam at 25 bar, 260°C. Heating occurs at constant pressure causing the piston to move upward until the initial volume is doubled; local $g = 9.145$ m/s². Find (**a**) the change in potential energy of the piston, (**b**) the heat. (**c**) If the process had occurred because of an input of paddle work only (no heat), find the net work of the system.

Ans. (**a**) 224, (**b**) 1018, (**c**) −794 kJ.

439. There are expanded 0.90 kg/s of steam at constant pressure from 30 bar and 70% quality to a final state. If the process is nonflow for which $W = 121.3$ kJ/s, find (**a**) the final temperature, (**b**) Q, (**c**) the available part of Q for a sink temperature of $t_0 = 27°C$.

Ans. (**a**) 282°C, (**b**) 966, (**c**) 414 kJ/s.

440. Assume 2 lb of hydrogen simultaneously reject heat and receive paddle-work input in a nonflow change of state at constant pressure from an initial temperature of 250°F to a final temperature of 90°F. See figure. If the heat rejected is thrice the paddle work, determine (**a**) ΔU, ΔH, and ΔS for the system, (**b**) Q, (**c**) W_{net}.

Ans. (Item B 5) (**a**) −786, −1102 Btu, −1.762 Btu/°R, (**b**) −1653, (**c**) −867 Btu.

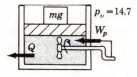

Problem 440

441. A vertical, frictionless piston-and-cylinder arrangement contains 2 lb of steam at

400 psia, 500°F. Heating occurs at constant pressure causing the piston to move upward until the initial volume is doubled; local $g = 30$ fps^2. Find (a) the change in potential energy of the piston, (b) the heat. (c) If the process had occurred because of an input of paddle work only (no heat), find the net work of the system.

Ans. (a) 183, (b) 860.6, (c) −677.6 Btu.

442. Ammonia vapor saturated at 10 psia undergoes a constant pressure non-flow process until the temperature is 320°F. For 1 lb, find (a) Δh, (b) Δv, (c) Δs, (d) Q, (e) W, and (f) Δu. (g) The same as before except that the process is steady flow with $\Delta P = 0$, $\Delta K = -2$ Btu/lb. See Item B 33.

443. A piston-cylinder system with internal paddles, contains 4 lb of steam at 650 psia and 550°F. There is an input of paddle work of 200 Btu and of heat of 196.4 Btu. Determine (a) t_2, (b) the net work of the system, (c) ΔS for the steam, (d) ΔS of the universe if the heat comes from a constant temperature system at 1000°F, (e) the change of potential (gravitational) energy of the piston if the pressure of the surroundings is 14 psia.

Ans. (a) 700°F, (b) −109.7 Btu, (c) 0.3668, (d) 0.2323 Btu/°R, (e) 88.5 Btu.

444. Carbon dioxide is being considered as a possible coolant for an unmanned orbiting space platform. Saturated vapor enters a constant pressure steady flow heat absorber and leaves at 30 psia, 450°F. Find Q and ΔS for each 1-lb/sec. Use Item B 31.

445. If 2 kg of steam at 18 bar and 288°C undergo a constant pressure process until the quality becomes 50% ($h_2 = 2220$ kJ/kg, $v_2 = 0.075$ m^3/kg, $s_2 = 5.18$ kJ/kg-K), find W, ΔH, Q, ΔU, and ΔS: (a) if the process is nonflow, (b) if the process is steady flow with $\Delta K = 0$. See Item B 16 (SI).

Ans. (a) $W = -220.7$ kJ, $Q = -1566$ kJ, $\Delta S = -3.20$ kJ/K.

446. Consider that 1 lb of air has a decrease of internal energy of 20.58 Btu while its Fahrenheit temperature is reduced to one third of the initial temperature during a reversible nonflow constant pressure process. Determine (a) the initial and final temperatures, (b) Q, (c) W, and (d) ΔS. Use Item B 1.

Ans. (a) $t_1 = 180$°F, $t_2 = 60$°F.

447. Oxygen at the rate of 3 lb/min undergoes a reversible isobaric process during which its entropy changes −0.35 Btu/lb-°R; $V_1 = 17.75$ ft^3 and $t_1 = 400$°F. For both nonflow and steady flow ($\Delta P = 0$, $\Delta K = 0$) processes, compute (a) ΔU and ΔH, (b) W, (c) Q.

Ans. (Item B 1) (a) −324, −451.6, (b) −127.6, (c) −451.6 Btu/min.

448. Air at 690 kPaa in a frictionless piston-cylinder arrangement remains at constant pressure while its temperature changes from 27°C to 94°C; a heat loss of 14 kJ/kg is experienced and the input energy is in the form of paddle work. The environmental pressure is 1 bar. For unit mass of 1 kg and constant specific heats compute (a) the property changes Δh, Δu, Δs, (b) the boundary work, (c) the paddle work, (d) the work in displacing the surrounding, (e) the net work.

449. Assume 5 lb of an ideal gas with $R = 38.7$ ft-lb/lb-°R and $k = 1.668$ have 300 Btu of heat added during a reversible constant pressure change of state. The initial temperature is 80°F. Determine (a) the final temperature, (b) ΔU, ΔH and ΔS, (c) W.

Ans. (a) 564°F, (b) 180, 300 Btu, 0.397 Btu/°R, (c) 120 Btu, 0.

450. There are expanded 2 lb/sec of steam at constant pressure from 400 psia and 50% quality to a final state. If the process is nonflow for which $W = 115$ Btu/sec, find (a) the final temperature, (b) Q, (c) the available part of Q for a sink temperature of $t_0 = 60$°F.

Ans. (a) 540°F, (b) 915.8, (c) 392.3 Btu/sec.

451. Consider that 5 lb/sec of Freon 12 are evaporated at constant pressure, $p = 20$ psia, from saturated liquid to a state where $t_2 = 60$°F; for the initial state, $t_1 = -8.1$°F, $s_{fl} = 0.01551$ Btu/°R-lb, $v_{fl} = 0.01345$ ft^3/lb. For nonflow reversible conditions find (a) Δs, (b) Q, (c) W. (d) If the process is steady flow with $\Delta P = 0$, $\Delta K = 0$, find Q and W. Use Item B 35.

ISOTHERMAL PROCESS

452. (a) Demonstrate that for a reversible isothermal process (gas or vapor) depicted on the pV-plane, the area beneath the trace is exactly equal to that behind (to the left of) the trace. (b) Prove that this trace must be concave upward and have a negative slope on this plane.

453. There are 2.27 kg/min of steam undergoing an isothermal process from 27.6 bar, 316°C to 6.9 bar. Sketch the pV and TS diagrams, and determine (a) ΔS, (b) Q, (c) W for nonflow, (d) W for steady flow with $\Delta P = 0$, $\Delta K = +42$ kJ/min. Use Item B 16 (SI).

Ans. (**a**) 1.6 kJ/K-min, (**b**) 942, (**c**) 846, (**d**) 798 kJ/min.

454. Helium at 100 atm, 165 K expands isothermally to 1 atm. For 2 kg, find (**a**) W for nonflow and for a steady flow process ($\Delta P = 0$, $\Delta K = 0$), (**b**) ΔU, (**c**) Q, and (**d**) ΔS. Use Item B 30.

455. During a reversible process there are abstracted 317 kJ/s from 1.134 kg/s of a certain gas while the temperature remains constant at 26.7°C. For this gas, $c_p = 2.232$ and $c_v = 1.713$ kJ/kg-K. The initial pressure is 586 kPaa. For both nonflow and steady flow ($\Delta P = 0$, $\Delta K \approx 0$) processes, determine (**a**) V_1, V_2, and p_2, (**b**) W and Q, (**c**) ΔS and ΔH.

Ans. (**a**) 302, 50 ℓ/s, 3539 kPaa, (**b**) -317 kJ/s, (**c**) $\Delta S = -1.056$ kJ/K-s.

456. Saturated Freon 12 liquid ($v_1 = 0.0109$ ft³/lb, $s_1 = 0.0144$ Btu/lb-°R) is evaporated at constant temperature in a refrigeration system; it leaves as saturated vapor at 19 psia. For steady flow of 1 lb/sec find Q and W. What is the final entropy? Use Item B 35.

457. Assume 5 lb of wet steam (quality = 33%) are heated at constant temperature to a saturated state. If during the nonflow process the heat transferred in Btu is numerically equal to twice the initial enthalpy, determine (**a**) the initial and final pressure and temperature, (**b**) the heat, (**c**) the work, (**d**) the change of entropy.

458. A two-fluid H_2O/NH_3 system (see figure) is composed of two weighted, frictionless pistons A and B, a conducting rigid partition P, 10 lb of saturated H_2O vapor at 300°F in part S, and 5 lb of saturated NH_3 liquid ($v_f = 0.02597$ ft³/lb, $s_f = 0.2322$ Btu/lb-°R) at 60°F in part N; $p_0 = 14.7$ psia. Heat now flows from the condensing steam through partition P to boil the NH_3. At the instant the last drop of liquid NH_3 is evaporated, find for the

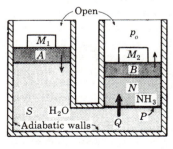

Problem 458

process (**a**) Q, (**b**) the amount of steam condensed, (**c**) ΔS for the H_2O, (**d**) ΔS for the NH_3, (**e**) ΔS for the total system, (**f**) the net work for S and N, (**g**) the available part of Q as it left the H_2O for $t_0 = 60°F$, and after it entered the NH_3, (**h**) the net change of potential energy of the piston-weight systems.

459. Mercury is being considered as a working fluid for a heat engine aboard an orbiting space platform. Radiant heat is absorbed by the mercury initially at 100 psia, $y_1 = 45$ per cent; the final state is 0.5 psia, 900°F. For each pound of mercury being circulated, find (**a**) Δs, Δh, (**b**) Q, (**c**) W where $\Delta P = 0$, $\Delta K = 0$. (**d**) If the constant temperature radiant source is at 10,000 °R, find the entropy production for this heat interaction. Use Item B 34.

460. A closed gaseous system of 14 ℓ of methane at 414 kPaa, 277 K is supplied with paddle work W_p while the frictionless piston moves to a point where $p_2 = 138$ kPaa; the temperature remains constant during this process. (**a**) Estimate the work done on the piston. (**b**) Determine ΔU, ΔH. (**c**) Find the paddle work W_p and the net work of the process. (**d**) Find the work done on the surroundings ($p_0 = 1$ atm) and the work against the resisting force. Show a complete energy diagram.

461. The gain in entropy during an isothermal nonflow process of 5 lb of air at 60°F is 0.462 Btu/°R. What is (**a**) the ratio V_2/V_1, (**b**) the ratio p_2/p_1, (**c**) W, and (**d**) Q?

Ans. (**a**) 3.85, (**b**) 0.2595, (**c**) 240.3 Btu.

462. If 10 kg/min of air are compressed isothermally from $p_1 = 96$ kPaa and $V_1 = 7.65$ m³ to $p_2 = 620$ kPaa, find the work, the change of entropy, and the heat for (**a**) a nonflow process, and (**b**) a steady flow process with $v_1 = 15$ m/s and $v_2 = 60$ m/s ($\Delta P = 0$).

463. There are received 889 Btu/sec of heat by 10 lb/sec of sulfur dioxide (Item B 36) which undergo a steady flow isothermal process from saturated vapor at 300°F; $\Delta P = 0$, $\Delta K = 0$. Find (**a**) Δs, Δp, Δh, (**b**) W, (**c**) the irreversibility of the process if the source is one of constant temperature at 540°F and the sink is $t_0 = 40°F$.

Ans. (**a**) 0.117 Btu/°R-lb, 900 psia, 48 Btu/lb, (**b**) 409 Btu/sec, (**c**) 140.5 Btu/sec.

464. Assume 5 lb of steam initially saturated at 600°F are heated at constant temperature. If during the nonflow process the heat transferred in Btu is numerically equal to half the initial enthalpy, determine (**a**) the initial and final pressure, (**b**) the heat, (**c**) the work (**d**) the change of entropy.

465. There are compressed isothermally 800 cfm of air measured at 80°F and 200 psia; $p_2 = 600$ psia. For both nonflow and steady flow ($v_1 = 75$ fps, $v_2 = 150$ fps, $\Delta P = 0$) processes, compute (**a**) $\int p \, dV$ and $-\int V \, dp$, (**b**) ΔU, ΔH, and ΔS, (**c**) work and heat.

Ans. (**a**) $-32{,}500$ Btu/min, (**b**) $\Delta S = -60.24$ Btu/°R-min   (**c**) $W_n = -32{,}500$, $W_{sf} = -32{,}770$, $Q = -32{,}500$ Btu/min.

ISENTROPIC PROCESS

466. A given gaseous system undergoes an isentropic process, state 1 to state 2. (**a**) Combine the two relations $pv = RT$ and $pv^k = c$ and show that $T_2/T_1 = (p_2/p_1)^{(k-1)/k} = (v_1/v_2)^{k-1}$. (**b**) Integrate the two expressions, using $pv^k = c$, and show that $-\int v \, dp$ is k times $\int p \, dv$ by comparison.

467. The internal energy of a certain ideal gas is given by the expression $u = 850 + 0.529pv$ Btu/lb where p is in psia. Determine the exponent k in $pv^k = C$ for this gas undergoing an isentropic process.

Ans. $\mathbf{k} = 1.35$.

468. The defining equation ($pV^k = C$) for an isentropic process may be developed in the following manner: Sketch an isentropic process 1–2 on the TS-plane; then through point 1, sketch a constant volume process, and through point 2, extend an isothermal process such that these two processes intersect at point 3. By equating the sum of the entropy changes along 1–3–2 to zero, the temperatures may be eliminated from this expression and the desired form obtained. Demonstrate.

469. Steam flows isentropically through a nozzle from 1517 kPaa, 288°C to 965 kPaa. Sketch the TS diagram and for $\dot{m} = 454$ g/s, determine (**a**) Δs, (**b**) t_2, (**c**) W, (**d**) ΔK. (**e**) Assume a nozzle efficiency $e_n = 94\%$ and solve for the preceding parts.

Ans. (**b**) 232°C, (**d**) 48.3 kJ/s.

470. Consider 10 lb/sec of steam at 110 psia, 600°F, that enter a small ideal steady-state, steady-flow turbine and, after isentropic expansion, exhaust at 20 psia; $\Delta P = 0$, $\Delta K = 0$. Sketch the process on the pV and TS planes, use Item B 15, and find (**a**) exhaust temperature t_2, (**b**) W in kW and MJ/hr. (**c**) Now use

the Mollier chart (Item B 16) and check answers in (**a**) and (**b**).

Ans. (**a**) 250°F, (**b**) 1707 kW, 6145 MJ/hr.

471. During an isentropic process of 1.36 kg/s of air, the temperature increases from 4.44°C to 115.6°C. For a nonflow process and for a steady flow process ($\Delta K = 0, \Delta P = 0$), find (**a**) ΔU, (**b**) W, (**c**) ΔH, (**d**) ΔS, and (**e**) Q.

Ans. (**a**) 108.8, (**b**) -108.8, (**c**) 152.2 kJ/s.

472. During an isentropic process of 3 lb/sec of air, the temperature increases from 40°F to 240°F. For a nonflow process and for a steady flow process ($\Delta K = 0$, $\Delta P = 0$), find (**a**) W, (**b**) ΔU, (**c**) ΔH, (**d**) ΔS, and (**e**) Q.

Ans. (Item B 2) (**a**) -103.14, (**b**) 103.14, (**c**) 144.24 Btu/sec.

473. Hydrogen is compressed isentropically from $p_1 = 108$ psia, $\dot{V}_1 = 3$ cfs, and $t_1 = 40$°F to $p_2 = 256$ psia. For both nonflow and steady flow ($\Delta P = 0$, $\Delta K = 0$) processes, find (**a**) t_2 and V_2, (**b**) $\int p \, dV$ and $-\int V \, dp$, (**c**) ΔH, ΔU, and ΔS, (**d**) W and Q.

Ans. (Item B 1) (**a**) 181°F, 1.62 cfs, (**b**) -41.9, -58.8, (**c**) 58.8, 41.9, Btu/sec, 0.

474. Assume 1 ft³/min of air at 160 psia, 260°F is expanded isentropically to 20 psia. What is the work (**a**) for nonflow conditions, (**b**) for steady flow where $\Delta P = 0$, $\Delta K = 0$? Use Item B 2.   *Ans.* (**a**) 33.1, (**b**) 46.4 Btu/min.

475. As an ideal gas, oxygen passes through an adiabatic, frictionless horizontal nozzle in a steady flow manner. The isentropic decrease in temperature from entrance to exit is -40°C. (**a**) If the initial velocity is 30 m/s, find the exit velocity. (**b**) If the entrance state is 345 kPaa, 333 K, find the exit pressure.

476. Consider 10 lb/sec of air that are compressed from 15 psia, 80°F, to 75 psia in an isentropic manner. Find the final temperature, work, and heat if the process is (**a**) nonflow, (**b**) steady flow; $\Delta P = 0$, $\Delta K = 0$.

ADIABATIC PROCESSES, REVERSIBLE AND IRREVERSIBLE

477. Assume 1 lb/sec of an ideal gas undergoes an isentropic process through an engine from 95.3 psig and volume of 0.6 ft³/lb to a final volume of 3.6 ft³/lb. If $c_p = 0.124$ and $c_v = 0.093$ Btu/lb-°F, what are (**a**) t_2, (**b**) nonflow W, (**c**) steady flow W when $\Delta P = 0$ and $\Delta K = -2$ Btu/lb, and (**d**) ΔU? (**e**) The actual steady flow work of an adiabatic expansion from the given state 1 to the same final pressure is 18 Btu/sec, $\Delta P = 0$; $\Delta K = -2$ Btu/lb. What is ΔS?

Ans. (a) $-243°F$, (b) 16.55, (c) 24.05, (d) -16.55 Btu/sec, (e) $+0.0248$ Btu/sec-°R.

478. During an isentropic process of 4 lb/sec of air, the temperature increases from 40°F to 340°F. Compute (a) ΔU, ΔH, Q, and ΔS, (b) $\int p\,dV$ and $-\int V\,dp$, (c) the nonflow work, (d) the steady flow work where $\Delta P = 0$, $\Delta K = -10$ Btu/sec. (e) For an irreversible adiabatic process from the same initial state to the same final pressure, the final temperature is 400°F. Find the works, nonflow and steady flow ($\Delta P = 0$, $\Delta K = -10$ Btu/sec). What is ΔS for this process?

479. Assume 5 lb/sec of NH_3 are compressed adiabatically from 100 psia, 170°F to 220 psia in steady flow; $\Delta K = 0$. The entropy increases 0.1950 Btu/sec-°R because of irreversible effects. Determine (a) $t_{2'}$, (b) W', (c) the extra work needed because of irreversible effects.

Ans. (a) 340°F, (b) 454, (c) -151 Btu/sec.

480. Consider 1 lb/sec of steam that flows isentropically through a nozzle from 220 psia and 550°F to 140 psia. Sketch the *TS* diagram and determine (a) Δs, (b) t_2, (c) W, (d) ΔK. (e) Assume nozzle efficiency $e_n = 94$ percent and solve for the preceding parts.

Ans. (b) 450°F, (d) 45.8 Btu/sec.

481. A throttling process of 2 lb of a certain gas occurs adiabatically causing an entropy increase of 0.189 Btu/°R. For the gas, $c_v = 0.1751$ and $c_p = 0.202$ Btu/lb-°R. If the initial volume is $V_1 = 4$ ft³, find V_2. *Ans.* 136 ft³.

482. An adiabatic expansion of air occurs through a nozzle from 828 kPaa 71°C to 138 kPaa. The initial kinetic energy is negligible. (a) For an isentropic expansion, compute the specific volume, temperature, and speed at the exit section. (b) If the end states are related by $pV^{1.3} = C$ in an irreversible adiabatic process, find v_2, t_2, v_2, and ΔS.

483. A throttling calorimeter is connected to a steam main in which the pressure is 15 bar. In the calorimeter, $p_2 = 1$ bar and $t_2 = 110°C$. Compute the quality and the percentage moisture of the steam sampled. See Item B 16(SI).

Ans. $y = 5.2\%$.

484. A throttling calorimeter is connected to a steam main in which the pressure is 150 psia. In the calorimeter, $p_2 = 15$ psia and $t_2 = 250°F$. Compute the quality and the percen-

tage moisture of the steam sampled, (a) using the superheat tables, (b) using saturated steam tables and the specific heat of steam, and (c) using the Mollier chart, making a sketch to show your solution. *Ans.* $y = 2.94\%$.

485. An electric calorimeter C samples steam from a main M as shown in the figure. Given these data: $p_1 = 300$ psia, $p_2 = 20$ psia, $t_2 = 350°F$, electric power input $= 400$ W, flow rate through the calorimeter, $\dot{m}_s = 0.5$ lb/min, $\Delta K_{1-2} = 0$. Find x_1. *Ans.* 96%.

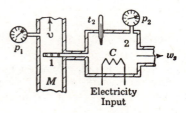

Problems 485, 486

486. For the electric calorimeter shown in the figure, these data apply: $p_1 = 200$ psia, $p_2 = 15$ psia, $t_2 = 300°F$, electric power input $= 70$ W, flow rate $\dot{m}_s = 0.3$ lb/min, $\Delta K_{1-2} = +0.5$ Btu/lb. Find y_1.

487. Steam leaves a boiler at 100 bar, 500°C. Due to frictional losses in the adiabatic pipe and throttling at the turbine, the pressure drops to 80 bar. Determine (a) the temperature of steam entering the turbine, (b) the gain of entropy and the irreversibility for a sink temperature of 305 K. Use Item B 16(SI).

488. Assume 10 lb of steam occupying a volume of 16.525 ft³ at 600°F expand adiabatically to 15 psia. (a) If the process is reversible, find p_1, x_2, ΔH, W (nonflow), W (steady flow with $\Delta K = 35$ Btu). (b) If the process is irreversible with $x_2 = 100\%$, solve all parts asked for in (a).

489. Nitrogen at 90 psia and 110°F undergoes an adiabatic expansion to 15 psia, the rate being 2 lb/sec. (a) For both nonflow and steady flow ($\Delta P = 0$, $\Delta K \approx 0$) isentropic processes, find t_2, ΔH, ΔU, W, and Q. (b) If the efficiency of the expansion (ratio of actual work divided by ideal work) is 80%, determine the items asked for in (a) and also ΔS.

Ans. (Item B 6) (a) $-118°F$, -113.5, -81.3, 81.3, 113.5 Btu/sec, (b) $-72°F$, -90.8, -65, 65, 90.8 Btu/sec, 0.062 Btu/sec-°R.

490. Consider 1 lb/sec of oxygen at 15 psia and 80°F that is compressed during an adiabatic process to 75 psia. For both nonflow and steady flow ($\Delta P = 0$, $\Delta K = 12$ Btu/sec) isentropic processes, determine (**a**) Δh, Δu, and W. (**b**) During the actual irreversible adiabatic, the change of entropy is $+0.0097$ Btu/lb-°R. Determine T_2, Δh, Δu, W, and Q.

Ans. (**a**) (Item B 1) 69.1, 49.5, −49.5, −81.1 Btu/sec. (**b**) (Item B 7) 880°R, 76.3, 54.3, $W_{sf} = -88.3$ Btu/sec.

491. Assume $5\,\text{ft}^3/\text{sec}$ of hydrogen at 15 psia and 80°F are compressed during an irreversible adiabatic process to 90 psia and 522°F. (**a**) For a nonflow compression, determine m in the equation $pV^m = C$, V_2, W, ΔS. (**b**) For steady flow with $\Delta P = 0.5$ Btu/sec. $v_1 = 300$ fps, and $v_2 = 10$ fps, what are W and ΔS?

Ans. (**a**) (Item B 1) 1.50, 1.5125 ft³, −28.05 Btu/sec; (**b**) −39.85 Btu/sec, 0.0072 Btu/°R-sec.

492. Expand adiabatically $6\,\text{lb/sec}$ of helium at 80°F until the initial pressure is halved. For both nonflow and steady flow ($\Delta P = 0$, $\Delta K = -36$ Btu/sec), find W, ΔU, and ΔS: (**a**) if the process is reversible and (**b**) if the process is irreversible with the end states related by $pV^{1.4} = C$.

493. During a refrigerating cycle, 1 lb/sec of saturated Freon 12 vapor is compressed from 19 psia to 200 psia, 170°F. The process is a steady flow irreversible adiabatic ($\Delta P = 0$, $\Delta K = 0$). (**a**) Find W and the compressor efficiency. (**b**) The compressed Freon 12 flows through a long pipe to a condenser, arriving at 180 psia, 160°F; $t_0 = 80$°F. Compute the loss of availability and the irreversibility. Was there any heat interaction during flow in the pipe?

494. Steadily flowing streams of steam A and B meet and mix, then flow in a steady state in a pipe C, all under adiabatic conditions. Stream A is at 800 psia, 700°F and flows at 100 lb/sec; stream B is saturated vapor at 800 psia and flows at 356 lb/sec. (**a**) Determine the state of the mixture C and the irreversibility of the process for a sink temperature of $t_0 = 100$°F; $\Delta P = 0$; $\Delta K = 0$; $\Delta p = 0$. (**b**) If the speed of the fluid in C is 100 fps what is the pipe diameter?

Ans. (**a**) $t_c = 550$°F, 435 Btu/sec, (**b**) 23 in.

POLYTROPIC PROCESS

495. For a compressible fluid undergoing a reversible polytropic process ($pV^n = C$), prove that $-\int V\,dp = n \int p\,dv$.

496. Demonstrate that the equivalent specific heat for a polytropic heating process is $c_n = c_v(k - n)/(1 - n)$.

497. Assume 4 kg of steam at 12 bar, 260°C expand into the wet region to 90°C in a polytropic process where $pV^{1.156} = C$. Find (**a**) y_2, ΔH, ΔU, ΔS, (**b**) $\int p\,dV$, (**c**) $-\int V\,dp$, (**d**) W for nonflow, and (**e**) W for steady flow if $\Delta K = -3$ kJ/kg. What does $-\int V\,dp$ represent in this process? (**f**) Find Q from steady flow and also from nonflow energy equations. Use Item B 16 (SI).

498. The work required to compress a gas reversibly according to $pV^{1.30} = C$ is 67,790 J if there is no flow. Determine ΔU and Q if the gas is (**a**) air, (**b**) methane.

Ans. (**a**) 50.90, −16.99 kJ.

499. Consider 1 lb of steam, initially saturated at 160 psia, that expands nonflow according to $pV^{1.13} = C$ to 15 psia. Determine (**a**) v_2, (**b**) x_2, (**c**) W, (**d**) Δu, and (**e**) Q. (**f**) If the process is steady flow with $\Delta K = +2$ Btu/lb, what is the work?

Ans. (**a**) 23 ft³/lb, (**b**) 87.3%, (**c**) 153.8, (**d**) −147.9, (**e**) 5.9, (**f**) 172 Btu/lb.

500. As part of a refrigeration cycle, 1 lb/s of saturated Freon 12 vapor at −10°F is compressed polytropically to 200 psia, 200°F. (**a**) For nonflow conditions find n in $pV^n = C$, Δs, W, Q; the irreversibility if $t_0 = 40$°F and if all rejected heat is received by the sink. (**b**) For steady flow conditions, $\Delta P = 0$ and $\Delta K = 0$, find W, Q, and the irreversibility. See Item B 35.

501. We have 1 lb of NH_3 that is polytropically compressed from saturated vapor at $p_1 = 25$ psia to $p_2 = 140$ psia and 180°F. Calculate (**a**) n in $pV^n = C$, (**b**) $-\int V\,dp$, (**c**) $\int p\,dV$, (**d**) Δu, (**e**) W and Q for nonflow, (**f**) W and Q for steady flow with $\Delta K = -2$ Btu/lb, $\Delta P = 0$.

Ans. (**a**) 1.24, (**c**) −64,500 ft-lb, (**d**) 69, (**e**) −82.9, −13, (**f**) −99.9 Btu/lb.

502. Assume 5 lb of steam, occupying 10.752 ft³ at 250 psia, expand according to $pV^{1.25} = C$ until $p_2 = 10$ psia. Calculate (**a**) y_2, (**b**) ΔH, (**c**) ΔS, (**d**) ΔU, and (**e**) W and Q for nonflow and for steady flow with $\Delta K = 0$, $\Delta P = 0$.

Ans. (**a**) 26.51%, (**b**) −1903 Btu, (**c**) −1.03 Btu/°R, (**d**) −1666.8, (**e**) 944.7 (nonflow), −722 Btu.

503. Consider 2 lb of air at 90°F that are expanded by a reversible polytropic process with $n = 1.25$ until the pressure is halved. For both nonflow and steady flow ($v_1 = 10$ fps, $v_2 = 400$ fps, $\Delta P = 0$) processes, compute (**a**) ΔU, ΔH, ΔS, (**b**) W, (**c**) Q.

Ans. (Item B 1) (**a**) $\Delta S = 0.02852$ Btu/°R, (**b**) 39.2, 42.6 Btu.

504. Compress 4 kg/s of CO_2 gas polytropically ($pV^{1.2} = C$) from $p_1 = 103.4$ kPaa, $t_1 = 60°C$, to $t_2 = 227°C$. Assuming ideal gas action, find p_2, W, Q, ΔS (**a**) as a nonflow process, (**b**) as a steady flow process where $\Delta P = 0$, $\Delta K = 0$.

505. During a reversible process, p and V of a fluid system at the end of states are related by $pV^2 = C$. If the fluid changes state from $p_1 = 100$ psia, $V_1 = 3$ cfs to $p_2 = 20$ psia, find (**a**) the nonflow work and the steady flow work where $\Delta P = 0$, $\Delta K = 0$. (**b**) Find Q and ΔS if the fluid is nitrogen. *Ans.* (**a**) 30.7, 61.4 Btu.

506. The work required to compress a gas reversibly according to $pV^{1.30} = C$ is 50,000 ft-lb if there is no flow. Determine ΔU and Q if the gas is (**a**) air, (**b**) methane.

Ans. (**a**) 48.2, -16.1 Btu.

507. Helium undergoes a nonflow polytropic process from $V_1 = 2$ cu ft and $p_1 = 14.4$ psia to $p_2 = 100$ psia. Assuming that 9.54 Btu of work are done during the process, determine the value of n in $pV^n = C$, and find Q.

Ans. 1.559, -1.517 Btu.

508. Hydrogen at 2 lb/min undergoes a steady flow polytropic process from $p_1 = 50$ psia, $v_1 = 90$ ft³/lb, $v_1 = 300$ fps, $\Delta P = 0$, until the pressure, volume, and velocity are doubled. Determine (**a**) n in $pV^n = C$, (**b**) T_1 and T_2, (**c**) ΔH, ΔU, and ΔS, (**d**) $\int p\,dV$ and $-\int V\,dp$, (**e**) W and Q.

Ans. (Item B 5) (**a**) -1. (**b**) 846°R, 3384°R, (**c**) 18,710, 13,710 Btu/min, 8.705 Btu/min-°R (**d**) 2500, -2500, (**e**) -2511, 16,210 Btu/min.

509. Assume 2 lb of gas, for which $R = 26$ ft lb/lb-°R and $k = 1.10$, undergo a polytropic process from $p_1 = 15$ psia and $t_1 = 100°F$ to $p_2 = 75$ psia and $V_2 = 3.72$ ft³. For both nonflow and steady flow ($\Delta P = 0$, $\Delta K \approx 0$) processes, determine (**a**) n in $pV^n = C$, (**b**) ΔH, ΔU, and ΔS, (**c**) $\int p\,dV$ and $-\int V\,dp$, (**d**) W and Q.

Ans. (**a**) 1.25, (**b**) 156.5, 142.2 Btu, 0.129 Btu/°R, (**c**) -57, -71.3, (**d**) -57, -71.3, 85.3 Btu.

510. The same as problem 509 except that $c_v = 0.180$ and $R = 56$ ($k \neq 1.10$).

511. During a polytropic process, 10 lb/sec of oxygen expand reversibly from 1500°R to 1000°R, the expansion ratio being $r_e = V_2/V_1 = 4$. For both nonflow and flow ($\Delta P = 0$, $\Delta K = 0$), compute (**a**) the exponent n in $pV^n = C$, (**b**) ΔU, ΔH, and ΔS, (**c**) $\int p\,dV$ and $-\int V\,dp$, (**d**) W and Q. (**e**) If the process is an irreversible adiabatic, find the exponent m in $pV^m = C$ and ΔU, ΔH, ΔS, W.

Ans. (Item B 7) (**a**) 1.2925, (**b**) -917.5, -1228 Btu/sec, $+0.118$ Btu/sec-°R, (**c**) 1060, 1370, (**d**) $W_{nf} = 1060$, $W_{sf} = 1370$, $Q = 142$ Btu/sec.

512. A nonflow process of 1 lb air occurs in a system in such a way that the relation obtains $pv^{1.2} = c$ while the temperature increases from 90°F to 479°R; the pressure ratio is $r_p = p_2/p_1 = 0.5$. If the foregoing process is irreversible with a paddle work input of $W_p = 7.3$ Btu/lb and $Q = 0$, calculate (**a**) Δh, Δu, and Δs; (**b**) the net work of the system. (**c**) If the process is internally reversible ($W_p = 0$), what are Δh, Δu, Q, Δs, and W for the gaseous system? Use Item B 2.

513. Expand 2 kg of steam at 15 bar, 300°C, into the wet region to 100°C in a polytropic process where $pV^{1.21} = C$. Find (**a**) y_2, ΔH, ΔU, ΔS, (**b**) $\int p\,dV$, (**c**) $-\int V\,dp$, (**d**) W for nonflow, and (**e**) W for steady flow if $\Delta K = -7$ kJ/kg. What does $-\int V\,dp$ represent in this process? (**f**) Find Q from steady flow and also from nonflow energy equations.

514. Helium undergoes a steady flow polytropic process from $V_1 = 2$ ft³ and $p_1 = 14.4$ psia to $p_2 = 100$ psia. Assuming that 14.88 Btu of work are done during the process, determine the value of n in $pV^n = C$, and find Q; $\Delta K = 0$, $\Delta P = 0$.

STAGNATION STATE

515. A turbojet plane flies at an altitude of 25,000 ft where the atmospheric conditions are 6.20 psia and $-20°F$. Compute the stagnation temperature and pressure of the layer of air wetting the plane's outer surface if the plane speed is (**a**) 600 mph, (**b**) 1000 mph, (**c**) 3000 mph. Plot a curve of stagnation temperature t_0 and pressure p_0 as a function of the Mach number. Use Item B 2.

Ans. (**a**) 504.6°R, 10.03 psia.

516. A stagnation probe was fabricated using ordinary solder (melting point 183°C). Estimate the limiting air velocity to which probe may be subjected based on normal static conditions of 1 atm, 26.7°C.

517. (a) Determine the stagnation properties pressure, temperature, enthalpy, density, and entropy for air at 10 psia, 60°F and moving with a speed of 8000 fps; also find its Mach number. (b) What is the pressure after stagnation if the diffuser efficiency is 92%?

518. A moving experimental jet plane has an instrument panel that indicates these air stagnation property readings: $t_0 = 1600$°F, $p_0 = 1240$ psia. The environmental barometric pressure is 5 psia. What is the speed of the plane expressed in mph? Expressed as a Mach number? *Ans.* 3100 mph, 4.35.

519. Flowing steam at 55 bar, 425°C, moving at 122 m/s in a line, is suddenly stopped by an instantaneous closing of a valve. Find the pressure and temperature of the steam initially interfaced at the valve surface.

520. A 150-grain (9.72-gm) bullet is fired into the atmosphere (1 bar, 25°C). The velocity of the bullet is 900 m/s. Find the temperature at the leading tip of the bullet.

TRANSIENT PROCESSES

521. A 142-ℓ drum contains oxygen initially at 552 kPaa and 37.8°C. The drum is fitted with an automatic pressure release valve that maintains the maximum pressure constant at 689.5 kPaa. Determine the heat transferred to the oxygen while the temperature of that which remains in the drum increases to 282.2°C. *Ans.* 173 kJ.

522. Compressed air leaves the cylinder of a hand operated tire pump and enters a large tank at 520 kPaa. The plunger (piston) in the cylinder has a 30-cm travel; atmospheric air enters the cylinder at 1 bar, 27°C. Assume the compression process to be isentropic. At what point in the stroke will air enter the tank? What will be its temperature at this point?

523. A 100-ft³ rigid tank T containing air at 1 atm and 60°F is evacuated to zero pressure, theoretically, by a vacuum pump P (see figure). Heat Q_T is added to the air in the tank at a rate to maintain a constant tank temperature; heat Q_p is rejected at the pump so that compression

is isothermal. Find (a) Q_T, (b) the pump work W_p, and (c) Q_p. Solve first by using Item B 1; then by Item B 5.
Ans. (Item B 1) (a) 272, (b) −272, (c) −272 Btu.

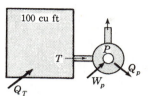

Problem 523

524. The adiabatic system shown in the figure contains a nitrogen-filled tank A, a liquid-filled tank B, connecting line with pressure regulator C, and closed valve D. Initially, the nitrogen is at 600 psia, 140°F. The pressure regulator maintains a constant pressure of 100 psia on the liquid at all times. Valve D is opened permitting the nitrogen to flow from tank A until its pressure becomes $p_A = 100$ psia; 8 ft³ of liquid are forced out of tank B during the process. Find (a) the volume of tank A, and (b) the final gas temperature in the two tanks. (*Hint*: Where required, assume that the nitrogen remaining in tank A undergoes a reversible expansion. Also, neglect vapor pressure effect in tank B after process occurs.)
Ans. (a) 2.24 ft³, (b) 360°R, 495°R.

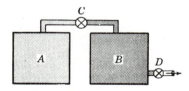

Problem 524

525. A vessel B (see figure) contains air at 100 psia and 140°F. It is connected to an open-end cylinder A on the bottom of which is a frictionless piston whose area is 1 ft². The load L on the piston is 3890 lb. The connecting valve at C is opened a small amount and air flows into A, raising the piston 2 ft, at which point the system $A + B$ is in internal equilibrium. Barometric pressure is 13.5 psia. The whole system is perfectly insulated except that heat-flow through the partition between A and

B occurs freely (helping to keep the temperature the same throughout *A* and *B*). Compute the mass of air involved and the final temperature of the system.

Ans. 0.861 lb, 497°R.

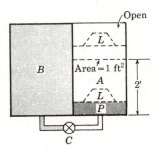

Problem 525

526. A portable oxygen tank *A* for use in a space project has a volume of 0.2 ft³. It is to be charged from a supply line in which the O_2 is flowing steadily at 100 fps, 180 psia and 60°F. When charging started, the tank contained O_2 at 40°F and 1 atm. Charging ceases when the mass m_2 in the tank is six times the original amount. If the tank walls are adiabatic, compute the final temperature and pressure.

Ans. (Item B4) 240°F, 8.38 atm.

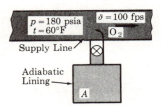

Problem 526

527. A perfectly insulated system consists of a rigid tank containing 2 lb steam at 350 psia, 800°F connected through a closed valve and piping to the base of a vertical cylinder containing a frictionless piston whose topside is subjected to atmospheric pressure (14.7 psia). Initially the piston rests on the bottom of the cylinder and exerts a pressure of 80 psia. The valve is gradually opened allowing the steam from the tank to enter the cylinder and slowly raise the piston until the pressure on the two sides of the valve are balanced; the steam remaining in the tank is at 400°F. Determine the temperature of the steam within the cylinder.

528. Steam at 1000 psia, 1200°F is in a rigid container which is fitted with a closed valve; the container is immersed in a liquid bath which is maintained at a constant temperature of 1200°F by an electrical input of I^2R. The valve on the container is slowly opened permitting steam to escape to the atmosphere until the container pressure becomes 100 psia. Find the electrical input per cubic foot of container volume. The only heat interaction is between the bath and the container of steam.

529. A pellet gun system consists of a 2-in.³ driving air chamber directly connected to a barrel whose length is 20 in. and the bore is 0.1 in.² Find the muzzle velocity of a pellet whose mass is 0.05 lb if the chamber contains air at 500 psig. 70°F; trigger action releases the compressed air which propels the pellet. Assume that no air leaks around the pellet and that the action is frictionless and adiabatic. Atmospheric pressure is 14.7 psia.

Ans. 252 fps.

530. A frictionless cylinder-piston arrangement *C* (see figure) containing 4 ft³ of H_2 at 600 psia and 140°F is connected through a closed valve *A* to a drum *D* that contains 0.767 ft³ of H_2 at 20 psia and 80°F. Valve *A* is opened slightly and hydrogen flows from the cylinder to the drum while the piston *P* with mass *B* moves to maintain a constant pressure in the cylinder. All walls are adiabatic. What is the temperature and mass in the drum *D* when its pressure reaches 100 psia? *Suggestion*: Make a trial solution using Item B 1, and then make a final balance using Item B 5.

Ans. (Item B 1) 758°R, 0.019 lb.

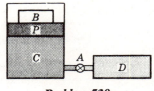

Problem 530

531. Assume 10 ft³ of oxygen at 20 psia and 40°F are contained in a rigid tank having adiabatic walls. The tank is now recharged to 200 psia from a flow line that supplies the oxygen at a constant 200 psia, 80°F. What is the temperature of the O_2 in the recharged tank and how much O_2 was added. See suggestion in problem 530.

Ans. (Item B 1) 717°R, 7.15 lb.

EFFICIENCIES, RATIOS

532. A gas, with properties similar to those in Item B 9, is used in a nuclear reactor/gas turbine system. During its movement in the system the gas enters a compressor at 50 psia, 500°R and leaves it at 1020°R; the pressure ratio is $r_p = 10$. Find the compressor efficiency.
Ans. 84.3%.

533. Freon F-12 is being used in a refrigeration system. A compressor receives saturated F12 vapor at 0°F and discharges it at 400 psia, 240°F. Use Item B 35 and solve for the compression efficiency.

534. Oxygen passes through an adiabatic nozzle in a steady flow manner. At entrance $p_1 = 345$ kPaa, 335 K and negligible kinetic energy; at discharge, $p_2 = 180$ kPaa. For a nozzle efficiency of $\eta_n = 90\%$, find the exit velocity and temperature.

535. A compressor receives sulfur dioxide vapor at 13 psia, 20°F and delivers it at 300 psia. If the compressor efficiency is 85%, find the discharge temperature and the increase in entropy due to the irreversible compression. See Item B 36 for properties.

536. Steam at 30 bar, 400°C enters a small turbine and exhausts at 1 bar; the engine efficiency is $\eta_{eng} = 73.6\%$. Find the enthalpy and temperature of the exhaust steam. Use Item B 16 (SI). *Ans.* 2700 kJ/kg, 112°C.

537. Carbon monoxide is compressed from 500°R to 1000°R in an isentropic manner. What is its pressure ratio? Use Item B 1 and compare results using Item B 4.

COMPUTER PROGRAMS

538. Write a program for this problem. It is desired to study the effect of superheat on the fluid jet from an ideal steam nozzle. Let the initial (entering) steam pressure remain constant at 600 psia and vary its entering temperature from that of saturation (486°F) to 1200°F while the exit (discharge) pressure remains constant at 400 psia. Solve for the discharge velocity and the mass rate if the nozzle discharge area is 1 in². Plot curves of velocity and mass rate versus degree of superheat.

539. The solution to problem 524 involves a trial and error method. Program this problem so that it may be solved on the computer through iteration.

540. The variation of c_v, c_p, and k with pressure and temperature are being studied for superheat steam. Let the pressure range be 250°F to 900°F. Using the definitions of these three quantities $c_v = (\partial u/\partial T)_v$, $c_p = (\partial h/\partial T)_p$, $k = c_p/c_v$, write a program that will produce their respective values throughout the p and t ranges described. Assume that the steam table data are stored in the memory of computer.

541–550. These numbers may be used for other problems.

8

GAS CYCLES

Note: Sketch all cycles on the pV- and TS-planes whether or not the problem calls for a sketch. Number all points and label all processes. Specify units for all answers. Remember the equivalency of $\oint p\,dV$ and $-\oint V\,dp$ for obtaining cycle work.

CYCLES, GENERAL

551. The execution of a cyclic process by a closed system involves the following four heat interactions: $Q_1 = 50$, $Q_2 = -75$, $Q_3 = 125$, $Q_4 = -40$ kcal. Concurrently, four work interactions occur during the cyclic process: $W_1 = 200$, $W_2 = -124$, $W_3 = 100$, $W_4 = ?$ kJ. Find (**a**) the fourth work W_4 and (**b**) the efficiency e. (**c**) What are ΔU and ΔS for this cyclic process?

Ans. (**a**) 75 kJ, (**b**) 34.26%, (**c**) 0.

552. The same as problem 551 except that the four heats are 90, −35, 70, and −50 cal; three of the four works are 75, −60, and 25 W-s.

553. The thermal efficiency of a particular engine operating on an ideal cycle is 30%. Determine (**a**) the heat supplied per 1200 W-hr of work developed, (**b**) the ratio of heat supplied to heat rejected, and (**c**) the ratio of work developed to heat rejected.

Ans. (**a**) 14,399 kJ, (**b**) 1.43, (**c**) 0.428.

554. A thermodynamic cycle with elements as described in Fig. 8/1, *Text*, operates as follows: engine produces 40 hp; hot body supplies 4000 Btu/min; small pump (to circulate working substance) absorbs 2 kW. Sketch the system and calculate (**a**) the net work, (**b**) the heat rejected, and (**c**) the thermal efficiency.

Ans. (**a**) 27.32 hp, (**b**) 2417 Btu/min, (**c**) 39.6%.

555. A cycle is completed as described: heat Q_1 is added isothermally at temperature $T_1 = 3000°R$; after an isentropic process to $T_2 = 2000°R$, additional heat Q_2 is added isothermally; this is followed by an isentropic process to $T_3 = 500°R$, where heat is rejected isothermally to the sink until an isentropic compression returns the working substance to its original state. The heats added are proportional to the temperatures at which they are received. Sketch the cycle on the TS plane and compute its thermal efficiency.

556. Consider a 100,000-kW steam power plant as a system in which the amount of energy supplied (bought) per kW-hr transmitted (sold) is 13,500 Btu when the plant is operating at rated load. See Foreword, *Text*. Determine (**a**) the plant thermal efficiency, (**b**) the heat absorbed by the sink (atmosphere) for each kW-hr transmitted, (**c**) the fuel cost per hour for coal if each pound liberates 12,600 Btu (heating value) and the unit fuel cost is $31.50 per ton, and (**d**) the fuel cost per hour for natural gas at $1.55/1000 ft^3$ if its heating value (liberated heat) is 1030 Btu/ft^3.

CARNOT CYCLE

557. A Carnot engine operating between 775 K and 305 K produces 54 kJ of work. Determine (a) the heat supplied, (b) the change of entropy during heat rejection, and (c) the thermal efficiency of the engine.

Ans. (a) 90.6 kJ, (b) −0.12 kJ/K, (c) 59.6%.

558. There are developed 10 hp by a Carnot engine operating between 1000°F and 100°F. Determine (a) the thermal efficiency, (b) the heat supplied per second, and (c) the change of entropy each second during heat rejection.

559. An engine operating on the Carnot principle receives heat from a large reservoir of water-vapor mixture in equilibrium at 1 atm and discharges 5275 kJ/hr to a large sink reservoir of water-ice mixture in equilibrium at 1 atm. If the power developed is 536 W, determine the number of Kelvin degrees separating the ice point and the absolute zero temperature.

560. In a Carnot cycle operating on nitrogen, the heat supplied is 40 Btu and the adiabatic expansion ratio is 12.5. If the receiver temperature is 60°F, determine (a) the thermal efficiency, (b) the work, and (c) the heat rejected.

Ans. (a) 63.5%, (b) 25.4, (c) 14.6 Btu.

561. Show that the thermal efficiency of the Carnot cycle in terms of the isentropic compression ratio r_k is given by $e = 1 - 1/r_k^{k-1}$.

562. Gaseous nitrogen actuates a Carnot power cycle in which the respective volumes at the four corners of the cycle, starting at the beginning of the isothermal expansion, are $V_1 = 10.10$, $V_2 = 14.53$, $V_3 = 226.54$, and $V_4 = 157.73$ ℓ. What is the thermal efficiency?

Ans. 66.7%.

563. Using the same working substance and volumes only as given in problem 562, consider a Carnot cycle receiving 21.1 kJ of heat at 593.3°C and rejecting energy to the cold body at 15.6°C. Determine (a) the work, (b) the mep. *Ans.* (a) 14.07 kJ, (b) 65 kPa.

564. A Carnot power cycle operates on 2 lb of air between the limits of 70°F and 500°F. The pressure at the beginning of isothermal expansion is 400 psia and at the end of isother-

mal expansion is 185 psig. Determine (a) the volume at the end of the isothermal compression, (b) ΔS during an isothermal process, (c) Q_A, (d) Q_R, (e) the developed hp, (f) e, (g) the mep.

Ans. (a) 7.82 ft^3, (b) 0.0948 Btu/°R, (c) 91 Btu, (f) 44.7%, (g) 15.88 psi.

565. Represent the Carnot cycle as a square on the *TS* plane. Now inscribe within this square a circle of maximum diameter D which represents a cycle. Noting that both cycles operate between the same temperature limits T_1 (source) and T_2 (sink), demonstrate that the Carnot cycle is the more efficient.

REGENERATIVE CYCLES

566. (a) A cycle with regeneration is the Stirling cycle; it is composed of two isothermal processes and two regenerative constant volume processes. See § 8.11, *Text.* Sketch this cycle on the *pV* and *TS* planes, and write expressions for Q_A, Q_R, W, e, and p_m. (b) Air is made to pass through a Stirling cycle. At the beginning of the isothermal expansion, $p_1 = 105$ psia, $V_1 = 2$ ft^3, and $t_1 = 600°F$. The isothermal expansion ratio is $r_e = 1.5$, and the minimum temperature in the cycle is $t_2 = 80°F$. Calculate (a) ΔS during the isothermal processes, (b) Q_A, (c) Q_R, (d) W, (e), and (f) p_m.

Ans. (a) 0.01487 Btu/°R, (b) 15.75 Btu, (e) 49.1%, (f) 41.7 psi.

567. Assume 2 lb of nitrogen actuate a Stirling cycle (see problem 566 for a description) between the temperature limits of 240°F and −160°F for cryogenic use. If the maximum pressure in the cycle is 200 psia and the isothermal compression ratio is $r_k = 4$, determine (a) Q_A, (b) Q_R, (c) W, (d) e, and (f) p_m.

568. Astronauts are proposing a portable Stirling cycle engine to furnish power in an environment where the heat is rejected only by radiation and subsequently is proportional to the area and the fourth power of the temperature of the radiating surface as $Q_r = KA_r T_r^4$ where K is a constant. The source of heat for the engine will be a small portable reactor. In view of the necessity for minimum mass requirements, prove that for a given power output and a predetermined maximum temperature of the engine, the radiating area A_r will be minimum when the ratio of engine temperatures is $T_{min}/T_{max} = 3/4$.

569. Demonstrate that the efficiencies of the three cycles—Carnot, Stirling and Ericsson—are identical under the same temperature restrictions and are equal to $e = 1 - T_{min}/T_{max}$.

570. An Ericsson cycle, § 8.12, *Text*, operates on 0.75 lb oxygen from 60 psia and 1200°F at the beginning of the isothermal expansion process to the lower temperature limit of 200°F. If the isothermal expansion ratio is 3, determine (**a**) Q_A, (**b**) Q_R, (**c**) W, (**d**) e and (**e**) p_m. (**f**) What is the efficiency of the same cycle without regeneration? Compare with (**d**).

571. The same as problem 570, except that the working fluid is 0.5 lb nitrogen.

Ans. (**a**) 64.6, (**b**) −25.7, (**c**) 38.9 Btu, (**d**) 60.1%, (**e**) 15.28 psi, (**f**) 20.60%.

572. The Ericsson cycle is composed of two isothermal processes and two isobaric processes, with regenerative heat exchange during the isobaric processes. Properties at the beginning of isothermal expansion are 689.48 kPaa, 142 ℓ, and 282.2°C. For a ratio of isothermal expansion of 2 and a minimum temperature of 4.4°C, find (**a**) ΔS during the isothermal process; (**b**) Q_A, Q_R, W, and e; (**c**) the volume at the end of isothermal expansion and the overall ratio of expansion; and (**d**) p_m.

Ans. (**a**) 0.122 kJ/K; (**b**) $Q_A = 67.7$ kJ, $e = 50\%$; (**c**) $r_e = 4$; (**d**) 159 kPa.

THREE-PROCESS CYCLES

573. Given these processes: isobaric, isometric, isothermal, and isentropic. Invent four different three-process cycles. Show the corresponding pV and TS diagrams for each and write expressions for Q_A, Q_R, and W from the pV-plane.

574. (STp) A thermodynamic cycle is composed of the following reversible processes: isentropic compression 1–2; isothermal 2–3; constant pressure 3–1. Sketch the pV and TS diagrams for the cycle and write expressions for (**a**) Q_A and Q_R, (**b**) net work from the pV and TS planes, and (**c**) e and p_m.

575. (STp) The cycle described in problem 574 operates on 0.25 lb of air; the compression ratio 1–2 is $r_k = 5$; $t_1 = 150°F$, $p_1 = 15$ psia. Determine (**a**) p, V, and T at each point, (**b**) Q_A and Q_R, (**c**) W from the pV plane (check by net Q), (**d**) e and p_m. (**e**) If 100 cps are completed, find the power in hp and kW.

Ans. (**b**) 44.9, −33.05, (**c**) 11.9 Btu, (**d**) 26.5%, 10.03 psi, (**e**) 1684 hp.

576. (nTS) A thermodynamic cycle is composed of the following processes: polytropic compression with $n > k$, 1–2; isothermal, 2–3; isentropic, 3–1. Sketch the pV and TS diagrams for the cycle and write expressions for (**a**) Q_A and Q_R, (**b**) net W from the pV and TS planes, and (**c**) e and p_m.

577. (nTS) The cycle described in problem 576 operates on 1.36 kg of air, for which these data apply: $p_1 = 103.4$ kPaa, $t_1 = 37.8°C$, $t_2 = 426.7°C$, $\Delta S_{23} = -0.456$ kJ/K. Determine (**a**) p, V, and T at each point, (**b**) the polytropic exponent n, (**c**) Q_A and Q_R, (**d**) W from the pV plane (check by net Q), (**e**) the thermal efficiency, (**f**) p_m. (**g**) If 50 Hz are completed, find the power in hp and kW.

578. (STp) A thermodynamic cycle is composed of the following reversible processes: isentropic expansion 1–2; isothermal 2–3; constant pressure 3–1. Sketch the pV and TS diagrams for the cycle and write expressions for (**a**) Q_A and Q_R, (**b**) net work from pV and TS planes, and (**e**) e and p_m.

579. (STp) The cycle described in problem 578 operates on 113 g of nitrogen; the expansion ratio 1–2 is $r_e = 5$; $t_1 = 149°C$, $p_1 = 689.5$ kPaa. Determine (**a**) p, V, and T at each point, (**b**) Q_A and Q_R, (**c**) W from the pV plane (check by net Q), (**d**) e and p_m. (**e**) If 100 Hz are completed, find the power in kW.

Ans. (**b**) 23.53, −16.8 kJ, (**c**) 6.73 kJ, (**d**) 73.3 kPa, (**e**) 673 kW.

580. (S, V, n) A three-process cycle of an ideal gas (for which $c_p = 1.064$, $c_v = 0.804$ kJ/kg-K) is initiated by an isentropic compression 1–2 from 103.4 kPaa, 27°C to 608.1 kPaa. A constant volume process 2–3 and a polytropic 3–1 with $n = 1.2$ complete the cycle. Circulation is a steady rate of 0.907 kg/s. Compute $\oint p \, dV$, $\oint dQ$, the thermal efficiency, and mep.

Ans. 9.5 kJ/s, 19.1%, 18.8 kPa.

581. (s, p, V) A thermodynamic cycle is composed of the following processes: isentropic compression 1–2; constant pressure, 2–3; constant volume closure, 3–1. Sketch the pV and Ts diagrams for the cycle and write expressions for (**a**) Q_A and Q_R, (**b**) net W from the pV and Ts planes, and (**e**) e and p_m.

582. (s, p, V) The cycle described in problem 581 operates on air and these values are known: $p_1 = 68.95$ kPaa, $V_1 = 425 \, \ell$, $t_1 =$

21.1°C, $p_2 = 689.5$ kPaa. Determine (**a**) p, V, t at each point, (**b**) Q_A and Q_R, (**c**) W, (**d**) e and p_m, (**e**) the power for 100 Hz.

583. (*TVn*) A thermodynamic cycle is composed of the following reversible processes: isothermal compression 1–2; constant volume heating 2–3; polytropic process 3–1, with $pV^{1.45} = C$. Sketch the pV and TS diagrams for the cycle operating on a diatomic gas and write expressions for (**a**) Q_A and Q_R, (**b**) W from the pV plane and (**c**) e and p_m.

584. (*TVn*) The cycle described in problem 583 operates on 5 lb of oxygen with $p_1 = 16$ psia and $t_1 = 105°F$. During the isothermal process 315 Btu are transferred from the working substance. Determine (**a**) the isothermal compression ratio, V_1/V_2; (**b**) p_2, p_3, and T_3; (**c**) Q_A and Q_R, (**d**) W and e; and (**e**) p_m.

Ans. (**a**) 6.02, (**b**) $p_3 = 217$ psia, 1270°R, (**c**) 555, −384.1, (**d**) 171 Btu, 30.77%, (**e**) 18.71 psi.

585. (*TSp*) A thermodynamic cycle is composed of the following reversible processes: isothermal expansion, 1–2; isentropic, 2–3; constant pressure, 3–1. Sketch the pV and TS diagrams for the cycle and write expressions for (**a**) Q_A and Q_R, (**b**) net W from the pV plane, and (**c**) e and p_m.

586. (*TSp*) The cycle described in problem 585 operates on 0.5 lb of air with $p_2 = 15$ psia, $t_2 = 90°F$. For the isothermal process, $\Delta S = 0.0475$ Btu/°R. Determine (**a**) p, V, and T at each point, (**b**) Q_A and Q_R. (**c**) net W from the pV plane (check by net Q), (**d**) COP (coefficient of performance), (**e**) p_m. (**f**) How many cycles must be completed each minute for a power requirement of 50 hp?

Ans. (**a**) $p_1 = 60$ psia, $T_3 = 817°R$, (**b**) 26.15, −32, (**c**) −5.85 Btu, (**d**) 4.47, (**e**) 6.21 psi, (**f**) 363.

587. (*SpV*) A thermodynamic cycle is composed of the following reversible processes: isentropic compression, 1–2; constant pressure, 2–3; constant volume, 3–1. Sketch the pV and TS diagrams and write expressions for (**a**) Q_A and Q_R, (**b**) net W from the pV plane, and (**c**) e and p_m.

588. (*SpV*) The cycle described in problem 587 operates on air, for which the following data apply: $p_1 = 15$ psia, $V_1 = 3$ ft^3, $t_1 = 100°F$, and $r_{k12} = 4$. Determine (**a**) p_2, T_2, and T_3; (**b**) Q_A, Q_R, and net W; (**c**) p_m and e; (**d**) ΔS for the $V = C$ process.

Ans. (**a**) $p_2 = 104.5$ psia, $T_2 = 975°R$, $T_3 = 3900°R$; (**b**) $W = 28.4$ Btu, (**c**) 68.2 psi, 18.63%; (**d**) −0.0722 Btu/°R.

589. (*TnS*) A thermodynamic cycle is composed of the following reversible processes: isothermal expansion, 1–2; polytropic ($n = 4$), 2–3; isentropic, 3–1. Sketch the pV and TS diagrams for the cycle and write expressions for Q_A, Q_R, W (from the pV and TS planes), e, and p_m.

590. (*TnS*) The cycle described in problem 589 operates on 0.25 lb of nitrogen for which the following data apply: for the process 1–2, the expansion ratio $r_e = 5$; $p_1 = 100$ psia, and $t_1 = 800°F$. Determine (**a**) p, V, and T at each point, (**b**) Q_A and Q_R, (**c**) W from the pV plane (check by net Q), (**d**) p_m, (**e**) e and compare with that of a Carnot cycle with the same temperature limits, (**f**) the cycles/min required to produce 250 hp.

591. (*npV*) A cycle is defined as: polytropic compression ($n = 1.5$) 1–2, constant pressure 2–3, constant volume 3–1. Sketch the pV and TS diagrams for a diatomic gas and write expressions for Q_A, Q_R, net W (from pV and TS planes), e and p_m.

592. (*npV*) For the cycle described in problem 591, the system is 2.5 lb of air; $p_1 = 20$ psia, $t_1 = 100°F$, $Q_R = -1682$ Btu. Solve the equations obtained in 591. Also compute the change of entropy from state 1 to state 3.

Ans. $W = 384$ Btu, $e = 18.55\%$, 106.6 psi, +0.891 Btu/°R.

593. (*VnS*) A thermodynamic cycle is composed of the following reversible processes: constant volume 1–2; polytropic 2–3, with $n = -1.1$; isentropic expansion 3–1. Sketch on the pV and TS planes and write the equations for Q_A, Q_R, net W from the pV and TS planes, thermal efficiency, and p_m for 1 Hz.

594. (*VnS*) The cycle described in problem 593 operates on 0.75 lb/sec of a gas ($R = 80$, $k = 1.30$) and the following data apply: $p_1 = 15$ psia, $t_1 = 150°F$, and the isentropic expansion ratio is $r_e = 3$. Compute (**a**) p, V, and T at each point; (**b**) Q_A, Q_R; (**c**) W in hp and kW; and (**d**) e and p_m.

Ans. (**a**) $p_2 = 209.5$, $p_3 = 62.55$ psia, $T_3 = 848°R$, $V_3 = 5.65$ ft^3, $T_2 = 8525°R$, (**c**) 310 hp, (**d**) 106 psi.

595. (*VpT*) A cycle operates on 1.5 lb of oxygen and consists of the following reversible processes: constant volume 1–2; constant pressure 2–3; isothermal expansion 3–1. The known data are: $p_1 = 15$ psia, $t_1 = 80°F$, isothermal expansion ratio is $r = 6$. Sketch the cycle on the pV and TS planes, label all points and processes, and determine: (a) p_2, V_2, T_3; (b) the work of the cycle using pV plane only; (c) the thermal efficiency; and (d) the mep.

596. (pST) Consider 1 lb of air that is heated at constant pressure from 700°R to 1100°R, whence it is processed isentropically to 700°R. Heat is then rejected isothermally to close the cycle. Sketch the pV and TS diagrams and determine (a) Q_A and Q_R, (b) the output in hp and kW if there are completed 400 cpm, and (c) e.

Ans. (a) 96, −76 Btu, (b) 188.7 hp, (c) 20.85%.

597. (VSp) A cycle operating on 0.2 lb of gas ($R = 30$, $k = 1.35$) is composed of the following reversible processes; constant volume heating 1–2; isentropic 2–3; constant pressure 3–1. Given $t_1 = 100°F$, $p_1 = 15$ psia, $Q_A = 32$ Btu. Sketch the pV and TS diagrams and determine: (a) V_1, T_2, p_2, V_3, T_3; (b) Q_R; (c) W; (d) e; and (e) p_m. (f) How many cycles must be completed each minute for an output of 30 hp?

598. (nTS) Assume 1 kg of air is expanded polytropically 1–2 from 1380 kPaa, 1110 K to 138 kPaa, 515 K; process 2–3 isothermal; 3–1 is isentropic. (a) Compute n in $pV^n = C$ for process 1–2, Q_{12}, ΔS_{12}. (b) Write equations for $\oint p\,dV$, $-\oint V\,dp$, $\oint dQ$, e, and p_m. (c) Calculate p_3, ΔS_{23}, e, and p_m. (d) What is the cycle work if the processes are all nonflow? If all are steady flow?

REVERSED, REVERSIBLE CYCLES

599. A substance executes a reversed Carnot cycle during which it receives 105.5 kJ/min of heat. Determine the work required, if the adiabatic compression process triples the initial absolute temperature. *Ans.* 3.52 kW.

600. A refrigeration cycle operates on the Carnot cycle between 244.4 K and 305.6 K with an input of 7.46 kW. Sketch the cycle on the TS plane, and determine (a) COP, (b) the tons of refrigeration (1 ton = 211 kJ/min). *Ans.* (a) 4, (b) 8.48.

601. The COP (γ) of a reversed Carnot cycle is 5.35 when refrigeration is done at 255 K; $\Delta S = 0.38$ kJ/K during the isothermal heat

interactions. Find (a) the refrigeration, (b) the temperature at which heat is rejected, (c) the net work. (d) If this cycle is used for heating (same temperature limits), what is the COP? (e) Prove that $\gamma_H = \gamma_C + 1$ where $\gamma = $ COP.

602. A Carnot system is to be used first as a power engine and then reversed and used as a refrigerator. Show that the ratio of its coefficient of performance (COP) as a refrigerator to its efficiency (e) as an engine, in terms of the respective temperatures T_{max} and T_{min}, is COP/$e = T_{max} T_{min}/(T_{max} - T_{min})^2$.

603. A refrigeration cycle operates on the Carnot cycle between −20°F and 90°F with an input of 20 hp. Sketch the cycle on the TS plane, and determine (a) COP, (b) the tons of refrigeration (1 ton = 200 Btu/min). *Ans.* (a) 4, (b) 16.96 tons.

604. It is desired to heat a space requiring 5275 kJ/min by means of a reversed Carnot engine. If the heat added to the cycle is 4220 kJ/min, what power will be required?

605. A Carnot engine with an efficiency of 30% is reversed and subsequently removes 1400 Btu from the cold body. (a) Compute the heat rejected to the hot body and the COP if the cycle is used for refrigeration. What is the Rankine temperature ratio, maximum to minimum? (b) The same as (a) except that the cycle is used for heating. *Ans.* (a) 2000 Btu, 1.43.

606. (a) Determine the horsepower required per ton (1 ton = 211 kJ/min) of refrigeration for a reversed cooling cycle with a coefficient of performance of 4. (b) If this cycle is used for heating a room, what is its COP? How much heat is transferred to the room for $Q_A = 211$ kJ/min?

607. Refrigeration is done by a reversed Carnot engine operating between 0°F and 120°F. If the total entropy change during the isothermal processes is 0.25 Btu/°R, determine (a) Q_A, (b) Q_R, and (c) COP. (d) If the engine is used for heating, instead of refrigeration, what is its COP? *Ans.* (a) 115, (b) −145 Btu, (c) 3.83, (d) 4.83.

608. Assume 4 lb of carbon monoxide execute a reversed Carnot cycle between the temperature limits of 40°F and 500°F. The minimum pressure in the cycle is 15 psia and the isothermal compression ratio is $r_k = 3$. Find (a) the volumes and pressures at the four corners, (b) Q_A, Q_R, W, and (c) the entropy change during the isothermal processes.

609. The COP (γ) of a reversed Carnot cycle is 5.35 when refrigeration is done at 255 K; $\Delta S = 0.38$ kJ/K during the isothermal heat interactions. Find (**a**) the refrigeration, (**b**) the temperature at which heat is rejected, (**c**) the net work. (**d**) If this cycle is used for heating (same temperature limits), what is the COP? (**e**) Prove that $\gamma_H = \gamma_C + 1$ where $\gamma = $ COP.

REVERSIBLE ENGINES

610. Two reversible heat engines are operating between the same temperature limits. One engine develops 50 hp and has an efficiency of 40%; the other engine receives 4240 Btu/min from the hot body. Determine the work of the second engine and the heat which each engine rejects to the cold body.

> *Ans.* 40 hp, 2544, 3180 Btu/min.

611. Prove that all reversible engines have identical efficiencies when operating within the same temperature restrictions.

612. A reversible engine operating between a high temperature source and a low temperature sink receives 63.3 kJ and produces 350 W-min of work. Determine (**a**) the thermal efficiency, (**b**) the ratio of Rankine temperatures of source and sink, (**c**) the ratio of Kelvin temperatures of source and sink, and (**d**) the sink temperature if the source temperature is 533 K.

613. The designer of a new type of engine claims an output of 225 hp with a fuel that releases 19,250 Btu/lb when burned. If the heat is supplied and rejected at average temperatures of 750°F and 145°F, respectively, estimate the lowest conceivable necessary amount of fuel for the rated output of the engine. *Ans.* 59.5 lb/hr.

614. An engine supposedly produces 139.5 kW with a fuel consumption of 19.27 kg/hr. The fuel releases 47,223 kJ/kg (heating value) when burned. Suppose that the engine receives this energy at a mean temperature of 756 K and rejects energy to the sink at a mean temperature of 339 K. Is this performance reasonable?

615. Two reversible engines R_1 and R_2 are connected in series between a heat source S and a cold body C as shown in the figure. If $T_1 = 1000$°R, $T_2 = 400$°R, $Q_A = 400$ Btu, and the engines have equal thermal efficiencies, determine (**a**) the temperature at which heat is

rejected by R_1 and received by R_2, (**b**) the work W_1 and W_2 of each engine, and (**c**) the heat rejected, Q_R, to the cold body.

> *Ans.* (**a**) 632°R; (**b**) 147.2 Btu, 93 Btu; (**c**) −160 Btu.

616. Consider the arrangement as shown in the figure with the source temperature of $T_1 = 1200$°R, the cold body temperature of $T_2 = 500$°R, and the thermal efficiency of reversible engine R_1 as twice that of the reversible engine R_2. If the work of engine R_2 is $W_2 = 100$ W-sec, determine the amount of heat in IT cal rejected by R_2 to the cold body.

617. Using a heat source, a cold body, and the two reversible engines as shown in the figure, let $Q_A = 60$ IT cal, $W_2 = 40$ W-sec, and $T_2 = 600$°R. If the engines have equal thermal efficiencies, calculate (**a**) the temperature at which R_2 receives heat, (**b**) the thermal efficiencies, (**c**) T_1, (**d**) W_1, and (**e**) Q_R.

> *Ans.* (**a**) 749°R, (**b**) 19.8%, (**d**) 49.8 W-sec.

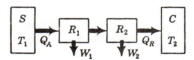

Problems 615, 616, 617

MISCELLANEOUS CYCLES

618. (**a**) Of historical interest is the Brown cycle, which operated between atmospheric pressure and some pressure less than atmospheric, consisting of a constant pressure heating 1–2, a constant volume cooling 2–3, and an isothermal compression 3–1. Sketch the pV and TS diagrams and write expressions for Q_A, Q_R, W, e, and p_m. (**b**) If 1 lb of air executes a Brown cycle between 15 psia and 5 psia with a minimum temperature during the cycle of 540°R, solve for the numerical values of the expressions obtained in (**a**).

619. (**a**) The classical Lenoir cycle consists of a constant volume heating 1–2, an isentropic expansion 2–3, and a constant pressure closure 3–1. Sketch the pV and TS diagrams and write expressions for Q_A, Q_R, W, e, and p_m. (**b**) Consider the Lenoir cycle operating on 0.2 lb air between the pressure limits of 30 psia and 15 psia, with a minimum volume in the cycle of 2 ft³, and obtain the numerical values for the expressions in (**a**).

Ans. $Q_A = 13.91$, $Q_R = -12.48$ Btu, $p_m = 6.03$ psi.

620. An imaginary engine receives and rejects heat in such a manner that the cycle on the *TS* plane may be represented by a 3-in. diameter circle where 1 in. = 100°R (temperature scale) and 1 in. = 0.05 Btu/°R (entropy scale). Calculate (**a**) the work done per cycle and (**b**) Q_A and Q_R for a thermal efficiency of 30%. (**c**) If the engine produces 75 hp, how many cpm must be completed?

Ans. (**a**) 35.3, (**b**) 117.7, −82.4 Btu, (**c**) 90 cpm.

621. An unusual type of engine operates on a cycle that appears as a 4-in. diameter circle on the *pV* plane (where vertically 1 in. = 40 psi and horizontally 1 in. = 0.1 ft³). What is the mean effective pressure?

622. A power cycle, operating on air, is composed of four reversible processes which form a rectangle on the *pV* plane. If the pressure range is from 20 psia to 80 psia, and the volume range is from 0.1 ft³ to 0.6 ft³ in the cycle, determine Q_A, Q_R, W, e, and p_m.

Ans. $Q_A = 28.73$, $Q_R = -23.17$ Btu.

623. Photon gas undergoes a cyclic (two isobarics and two isentropics) Carnot process between pressures p_1 and p_2; its pressure is a function of the absolute temperature only and is related to its internal energy and volume by $p = U/3V$. (**a**) Sketch the cycle on the *pV* and *TS* planes and find expressions for Q_A, Q_R, W, e, and p_m. (**b**) What is the functional relation between p and T?

Ans. (**b**) $T_2/T_1 = (p_2/p_1)^{1/4}$.

624. A certain reversible cycle is executed as follows: 500 Btu heat addition at 1000°R; adiabatic expansion to 800°R; 160 Btu heat rejection at 800°R; adiabatic expansion to 400°R; 40 Btu heat rejection at 400°R; closure with heat being transferred only at 700°R. Sketch the cycle on the *TS* plane and determine (**a**) ΔS for the closure only, (**b**) Q during closure only, (**c**) W and e for the cycle.

625. Temperatures on the moon are known to exist at 250°F on the dayside to −250°F on its nightside. Devise a heat engine to be used on the moon which employs these thermal conditions and discuss its feasibility to include anticipated efficiency.

626. A computer-programmed study is to be conducted on a Stirling engine operating on nitrogen. At the beginning of compression of (point 1), $p_1 = 103$ kPaa, $T_1 = 310$ K, $m = 1$ kg. Use compression ratios of 6, 8, 10, and 12 and find the work for each of the following two cases: first, account for the variation of the specific heats using data from Table I; second, use the constant specific heats as given in Item B 1. Write the program and compare results.

627–630. These numbers may be used for other problems.

9

TWO-PHASE POWER SYSTEMS

Note: Always show sketches for each problem on some convenient plane (*Ts* or *pV*). When using the Mollier chart, an *hs* sketch should be included. For the various isentropic processes, do not interpolate where two table values of entropy differ no more than 0.0005 Btu/lb-°R. A mass flow-energy diagram is particularly helpful when solving problems on the reheat-regenerative cycle and engine.

RANKINE CYCLE AND ENGINE

631. A thermodynamic cycle with elements as described in § 9.1, *Text*, operates as follows: engine produces 22.4 kW; hot body supplies 4220 kJ/min; small pump (to circulate working substance) absorbs 2 kW. Sketch the system and calculate (**a**) the net work, (**b**) the heat rejected, and (**c**) the thermal efficiency.

Ans. (**a**) 20.4 kW, (**b**) 2996 kJ/min, (**c**) 29%.

632. An experimental geothermal energy system in Baja, California consists of a hot water well, a flasher-separator-collector, and a 10,000-kW Rankine engine. The pressurized ground water at 172.4 bar, 282°C leaves the well to enter the flash chamber maintained at 13.8 bar ($h_f = 829$, $h_{fg} = 1961$ kJ/kg). The flashed vapor passes through the separator and collector to enter the turbine as saturated vapor at 13.8 bar; the turbine exhausts at 1 bar. The unflashed water runs to waste. Find the hourly amount of ground water required for continuous operation. Use Table II for the compressed liquid state.

Ans. 379,535 kg/hr.

633. The condensing pressure for a Rankine engine is 1 bar. ($h_f = 417.4$ kJ/kg). Calculate the net work for 1 kg/s of steam and the thermal efficiency when the steam at the beginning of expansion is at 50 bar and (**a**) saturated, (**b**) 350°C, (**c**) 640°C. Note the variation of efficiency and of the quality at the end of expansion. *Ans.* (**c**) 1084 kJ/s, 32.4%.

634. There are received 200,000 lb/hr steam at 310 psia, 900°F by a Rankine engine; exhaust occurs at 15 psia and $\Delta P = 0$, $\Delta K = 0$. For the engine find (**a**) W, (**b**) w, (**c**) e. For the cycle find (**d**) W, (**e**) e.

Ans. (**a**) 18,930 kW, (**b**) 10.56 lb/kW-hr, (**c**) 24.95%, (**d**) 18,850 kW, (**e**) 24.86%.

635. A turbo generator has a combined steam rate of 5.35 kg/kW-hr at its rated output of 20,000 kW. The steam supply is at 17 bar, 300°C, and the exhaust is at 0.1 bar ($h_f = 192$ kJ/kg). Calculate (**a**) the combined heat rate, (**b**) the combined thermal efficiency, and (**c**) the combined engine efficiency.

636. Steam at 750 psia, 750°F (state 1) expands in a Rankine engine to 5 psia. For 300 lb/sec of steam and considering $\Delta K = 0$, determine W, e, and w (**a**) for the cycle, (**b**) for the engine. (**c**) For an actual engine with the same specifications, the brake steam rate is $w_b = 7.88$ lb/bhp-hr and the driven electric generator has an electrical-mechanical efficiency of 93 percent. Find e_b, η_b, W_K, $x_{2'}$, the irreversibility because of friction in the turbine; $t_0 = 80°F$.

Ans. (a) 171,500 hp, 32.4 percent, 6.30 lb/hp-hr, (b) 172,300 hp, 32.67%, 6.27 lb/hp-hr, (c) 26%, 79.6%, 95,000 kW, 91.8%, 71.2 Btu/lb steam.

637. In an ideal Rankine cycle, steam is generated at 600 psia and 900°F. The condenser is at 90°F. Sketch the cycle on the *Ts* plane. Determine (a) the ideal pump work (in Btu/lb), (b) the cycle thermal efficiency. (c) For an engine with the same end states, determine its thermal efficiency, steam rate, and mep. (d) Considering the engine only, assume the brake engine efficiency to be 78%, the generator efficiency 92%, the steam flow 360,000 lb/hr; compute the output of the combined unit. (e) Compute the maximum possible work that can be done in steady flow from the initial state to liquid at 90°F and 14.7 psia. Compare with the ideal work.

Ans. (a) 1.79 Btu/lb, (b) 38.6%, (c) 4.68 lb/hp-hr, 76 psi, (d) 41,250 kW, (e) 543 Btu/lb.

638. The condensing pressure for a Rankine cycle is 0.3 bar ($h_f = 289$ kJ/kg). Calculate the net work for 1 kg/sec of steam and the thermal efficiency when the steam at the beginning of expansion is at 30 bar and (a) saturated, (b) 300°C, (c) 700°C. Note the variation of efficiency and of the quality at the end of expansion.

639. For an exhaust pressure of 2.223 psia (130°F) in a Rankine cycle, compare the heats supplied, the heats rejected, and the thermal efficiencies when at the beginning of isentropic expansion the steam is at (a) 200 psia and 600°F, (b) 400 psia and 600°F, (c) 800 psia and 600°F. Note the variation of *e*.

Ans. (a) 1224.1, −881.0 Btu/lb, 28%; (c) 1171.3, −767.5 Btu/lb, 34.5%.

640. Freon (F12) has been proposed as the working fluid for an automobile powered by a Rankine engine. Superheated Freon vapor at 500 psia enters the engine and is exhausted to the condenser as saturated vapor at 100°F. Sketch the *ph*-diagram labelling pertinent points and find (a) *W*, (b) *e*, (c) the vapor rate lb/hp-hr. (d) For a net output of 50 hp, compute the rate of flow of F12. (e) If instead of the F12, the engine used steam entering at 500 psia but exhausting as saturated vapor at one standard atmosphere, find *W*, *e*, and *w* and compare with the F12 values.

Ans. (a) 10 Btu/lb, (b) 15.15%, (c) 254.4 lb/hp-hr, (d) 12,720 lb/hr, (e) 403 Btu/lb, 29.33%, 6.31 lb/hp-hr, 315.5 lb/hr.

641. Steam at 100 bar, 600°C is received by a Rankine engine and exhausts at 2 bar ($h_f = 505$ kJ/kg); ΔP and ΔK are negligible. (a) For the ideal engine, find *W*, *ω*, *e*, and p_m. (b) For the actual engine $\eta_b = 84\%$, $\eta_{gen} = 93\%$ and the driven generator produces 30 MW. Find W_K, e_K, total throttle flow, and estimate the exhaust enthalpy $h_{2'}$.

Ans. (a) 1001 kJ/kg, 3.60 kg/kW-hr, 32.1%, 1206 kPa, (b) 782 kJ/kg, 25.1%, 138,107 kg/hr, 2780 kJ/kg.

642. (a) A Rankine engine receives saturated steam at 110 psia and exhausts it at 15 psia. Calculate the work for 1 lb. (b) Let the exhaust from the foregoing engine pass without loss through a steam separator that removes all liquid. The remaining dry and saturated steam at 15 psia expands to 1 psia in another Rankine engine. Compute the work per pound of original steam. (c) Determine the overall thermal efficiency.

643. A turbine whose steam rate is 6.1 lb/bhp-hr receives steam at 100 fps with an enthalpy of 1507.5 Btu/lb. Radiation loss is 18 Btu/lb of steam during passage to condenser where $p_2 = 2.223$ psia; discharge speed is 300 fps. Total steam flow is 305,000 lb/hr. Compute (a) the approximate quality of the exhaust, (b)·the exhaust stagnation enthalpy (would quality increase or decrease during the stagnation process?), (c) the brake power. (d) For saturated water leaving the condenser, what is the irreversibility of the heat rejection process for a sink temperature of 90°F?

Ans. (a) 95.4%, (c) 37.3 MW, (d) 536,300 Btu/min.

644. The use of mercury as a working substance for the production of power in space vehicles is being studied. Let the Hg undergo a Rankine cycle from saturated vapor at 200 psia at the throttle to a condenser pressure of 3.6319 psia ($t_{sat} = 550°F$). The energy source is an isotope (P_u^{238}). Determine (a) the mass rate of flow for a turbine fluid work of 5 kW and turbine efficiency of 55%, (b) the energy received from the isotope and the Hg cycle efficiency with pump work neglected, (c) the quality of the exhaust. (d) If the vapor at state 1 ($t_{sat} = 1017.2°F$) is heated to 1300°F, compute its entropy (datum as in Item B 34). Consider the monatomic vapor an ideal gas with $c_p = 0.02474$; also at 550°F, $h_f = 17$ Btu/lb.

Ans. (**a**) 12.3 lb/min. (**b**) 30 kW, 16.7%, (**c**) 76%, (**d**) 0.1235 Btu/lb-°R.

REGENERATIVE CYCLE AND ENGINE

645. Sketch on the Ts plane an ideal regenerative cycle with one stage of extraction feedwater heating, and write the equations for (**a**) the mass of steam bled, (**b**) the heat supplied, (**c**) the heat rejected, and (**d**) the net work.

646. The same as problem 645 except that there are two stages of regenerative heating.

647. The same as problem 645 except that there are four stages of regenerative heating.

648. A turbine, with one extraction for regenerative feedwater heating, receives steam with an enthalpy of 1450 Btu/lb and discharges it with an exhaust enthalpy of 1000 Btu/lb. The ideal regenerative feedwater heater receives 25,000 lb/hr of extracted steam at 50 psia (whose $h = 1180$ Btu/lb). The feedwater (condensate from the condenser) enters the heater with an enthalpy of 60 Btu/lb and departs saturated at 50 psia. Calculate the turbine power. *Ans.* 24,250 hp.

649. A turbine, with one extraction for regenerative feedwater heating, receives steam with an enthalpy of 3373 kJ/kg and discharges it with an exhaust enthalpy of 2326 kJ/kg. The ideal regenerative feedwater heater receives 11,338 kg/hr of extracted steam at 345 kPaa (whose $h = 2745$ kJ/kg). The feedwater (condensate from the condenser) enters the heater with an enthalpy of 140 kJ/kg and departs saturated at 345 kPaa ($h_f = 582$ kJ/kg). Calculate the turbine power. *Ans.* 18,116 kw.

650. Steam is delivered to an engine at 775 psia and 1100°F. Before condensation at 88°F, steam is extracted for feedwater heating at 90 psia. For an ideal cycle and 1 lb/sec of throttle steam, find (**a**) the amount of steam extracted, (**b**) W, and (**c**) e. For an ideal engine and the same states, compute (**d**) W and e, and (**e**) w.

Ans. (**a**) 0.1915 lb/sec, (**b**) 560 Btu/sec, (**c**) 43.9%, (**d**) 562.3 Btu/sec, 44%, (**e**) 6.07 lb/kW-hr.

651. There are received 150,000 lb/hr of steam by an ideal regenerative engine, having only one heater, of which the heater receives 33,950 lb/hr; the condenser receives the remainder at 1 psia. If the heater pressure is 140 psia, find the state (quality or °Sh) of the steam (**a**) at the heater entrance, (**b**) at the condenser entrance.

Ans. (**a**) °Sh = 6.97, (**b**) 78.5%.

652. A 10,000-kW turbogenerator operating at rated capacity receives 115,000 lb/hr of steam at 420 psia and 600°F; exhaust is at 1 psia. At 170 psia and 450°F, there is actually extracted 20% of the throttle flow for regenerative heating of the feedwater. The generator efficiency is 95%. For the ideal engine, find (**a**) the amount of steam extracted, lb/hr, (**b**) W, and (**c**) e. For the actual engine, find (**d**) the temperature of the feedwater from the open heater, (**e**) η_k, and (**f**) the approximate enthalpy of the exhaust steam.

653. A 25,000-kW turbogenerator is supplied with 281,000 lb/hr of steam at 360 psia and 752°F when developing its rated load. There are actually extracted 22,850 lb/hr at 40 psia and 18,250 lb/hr at 8.568 psia. The condenser pressure is 1 psia and the actual feedwater temperature is 260°F. For the ideal engine, find (**a**) the various percentages of extracted steam and (**b**) e. For the actual engine, find (**c**) the various percentages of extracted steam, (**d**) w_k, (**e**) e_k, and (**f**) η_k. (**g**) Find the approximate enthalpy of the exhaust if the generator efficiency is 96%.

Ans. (**a**) $m_1 = 7.81\%$, (**b**) 37.1%, (**c**) $m_1' = 8.13\%$, (**d**) 11.24 lb/kW-hr, (**e**) 26.1%, (**f**) 70.8%, (**g**) 1075 Btu/lb.

654. An ideal regenerative cycle is executed with steam generated at 1950 psia and 1100°F. Before condensation at 1 psia, steam is extracted for feedwater heating, first, at 290 psia, and second, at 145 psia. Beginning with the throttle as point 1, these enthalpies are known, Btu/lb:

$h_1 = 1537.5$	$h_5 = 69.73$
$h_2 = 1288.1$	$h_6 = 327.8$
$h_3 = 1220.1$	$h_7 = 390.6$
$h_4 = 896.7$	$h_7' = 364.4 \ (390°F)$

For a steam flow of 300,000 lb/hr, find (**a**) the amount of steam extracted at each point, (**b**) W, and (**c**) e. For an ideal engine and the same states, calculate (**d**) W, e, and w. For the actual engine, the generator efficiency is 96%, $w_k = 7.5$ lb/kW-hr, and the temperature of the feedwater from the last heater is 390°F. Find (**e**) W_K, e_K, η_K, and (**f**) the approximate enthalpy of the exhaust steam. The actual extracted steam is the same as that extracted ideally.

Ans. (**a**) 19,500, 62,700 lb/hr, (**b**) 47,650 kW, (**c**) 47.5%, (**d**) $W = 48,250$ kW, (**e**) $W_K = 40,000$ kW, (**f**) 1034 Btu/lb.

655. An ideal supercritical regenerative cycle is executed with 1,000,000 lb/hr of steam initially at 5600 psia and 1500°F. There are five stages of regenerative feedwater heating for which the respective extraction pressures are 1050 psia, 750 psia, 230 psia, 110 psia, and 15 psia. Condensation occurs at 1 psia. Find (**a**) the hourly amounts of steam extracted, (**b**) the net horsepower, and (**c**) the thermal efficiency.

656. In an ideal regenerative cycle, the steam expands in the turbine from 1100 psia and 1100°F to 80 psia, where m lb of steam is extracted for feedwater heating (open heater). The remainder continues expansion to a condenser pressure of 0.9492 psia (100°F). The throttle flow is 100 lb/sec. Compute (**a**) the cycle work and thermal efficiency, (**b**) the percentage improvement of efficiency as compared to the cycle without regenerative heating. (**c**) Consider the properties given as applying to the engine ($\Delta K \approx 0$) whose brake engine efficiency is 80%; generator efficiency is 94%. For the engine with regenerative heating, compute the power output, the combined steam rate, and the combined heat rate. (**d**) Estimate the enthalpy of the exhaust steam for the engine, assuming that the actual bled steam is $m' = 0.15$ lb/lb of throttle steam. The efficiency of the condensate pump is 50%. Show by sketch the energies and boundaries for this energy balance.

Ans. (**a**) 44.4%, (**b**) 6.2%, (**c**) 45 MW, 7.99 lb/kW-hr, 10,200 Btu/kW-hr, (**d**) 1036 Btu/lb.

REHEAT CYCLE AND ENGINE

657. Steam at 100 bar, 500°C enters an ideal engine that has one stage of reheat; exhaust is at 0.5 bar ($h_f = 138$ kJ/kg) and 85% quality. The work produced by the engine is 800 kJ/kg of steam. Determine the thermal efficiency of the engine. *Ans.* 28%.

658. Steam is delivered by the steam generating unit at 1100 psia and 900°F. After expansion in the turbine to 300 psia, the steam is withdrawn and reheated to the initial temperature. Expansion now occurs to the con-

denser pressure of 1 psia. (**a**) For 1 lb/sec of steam in an ideal cycle, find e. (**b**) For an ideal engine operating through the same states, but ignoring the pressure drop in the reheater, find W and e. (**c**) An actual turbine operates between these same state points except that the steam enters the reheater at 300 psia, 600°F and leaves at 290 psia, 900°F. The combined steam rate is 6.3 lb/kW-hr, the generator efficiency is 94%, and the heat loss through the turbine casing is 1% of the throttle enthalpy. Find the turbine efficiency and the approximate quality or °Sh of the exhaust steam.

Ans. (**a**) 41.5%, (**b**) 647.1 Btu/sec, 41.4%, (**c**) 89%, $x_{4'} = 91$%.

659. An ideal reheat steam turbine with one stage of reheating develops 280 Btu/lb of work between the throttle valve and the reheater, and 320 Btu/lb between the reheater and the condenser. After absorbing 240 Btu/lb of heat in the reheater, the steam re-enters the turbine at 180 psia and 1000°F and expands to the condenser pressure of 1 psia. Find the thermal efficiency of the turbine.

Ans. 34.5%.

660. A reheat cycle with two stages of reheating is executed, with steam expanding initially from 200 bar and 540°C. The two reheater pressures are 40 bar and 10 bar, and the steam leaves each reheater at 540°C. Condensation occurs at 60°C where $h_f = 251$ and $h_g = 268$ kJ/kg. Sketch the TS diagram. For the ideal cycle, and 1 kg/s of steam, find (**a**) Q_A, and e. (**b**) For the engine, ignore the pressure drop through the reheater, let the engine operate through the same states and compute W and e.

Ans. (**a**) 4166 kJ/s, 43.7%, (**b**) 1839 kJ/s, 44%.

661. An ideal turbine with one stage of reheat receives steam at 1150 psia, 900°F; reheat pressure is 120 psia and exhaust pressure is 1 psia. The work is 670 Btu/lb and the thermal efficiency is 41.05%. Find the temperature of the steam leaving the reheater.

Ans. 850°F.

662. In a reheat cycle steam at 2200 psia, 1000°F enters the engine and expands to 280 psia. At this point the steam is withdrawn and passed through a reheater. It reenters the engine at 1000°F. Expansion now occurs to the condenser pressure of 0.5 psia. (**a**) For the ideal cycle, find e. (**b**) A 60,000-kW turbine operates between the same state points except that the steam enters the reheater at 280 psia and 500°F, departs at 260 psia and 1000°F. The steam flow is 324,000 lb/hr; generator efficiency is 96%. For the actual engine, find e_K, w_K, η_k. (c) Determine the approximate enthalpy of the exhaust steam if the heat loss through the turbine casing is 2% of the combined work.

663. Steam at 200 bar, 760°C enters the throttle of a reheat engine and expands to 10 bar. At this point it leaves the engine, enters the reheater, and returns at 9 bar, 600°C; expansion then occurs to the condenser pressure of 0.05 bar ($h_f = 138$ kJ/kg). For a steam flow of 1 kg/s find (a) W, e of the cycle, (b) W, e, w for the ideal engine. (c) In the actual engine the steam enters the reheater at 10 bar, 300°C, and later expands to a saturated state at the exhaust to the condenser; find W, e, w.

664. A reheat cycle with two stages of reheating is executed, with steam expanding initially from 3100 psia and 1000°F. The two reheater pressures are 500 psia and 120 psia, and the steam leaves each reheater at 1000°F. Condensation occurs at 1 psia. Sketch the Ts diagram. For the ideal cycle, and 1 lb/sec of steam, find (a) Q_A, and e. (b) For the engine, ignore the pressure drop through the reheater, let the engine operate through the same states, and compute W and e.

Ans. (a) 1853.1 Btu/sec, 46.5%, (b) 868.3 Btu/sec, 46.7%.

REHEAT-REGENERATIVE CYCLE AND ENGINE

665. Assume an ideal reheat-regenerative cycle: after some expansion, steam is extracted for feedwater heating; after further expansion, there is a reheat; then expansion to exhaust. Write the equations for (a) the amount of extracted steam, (b) the net work, and (c) the thermal efficiency. The equations should refer to a Ts diagram with named points.

666. Assume an ideal reheat-regenerative cycle with, first, an extraction for feedwater heating, then later a single reheating, and finally, two extraction points for feedwater heating. Sketch the energy diagram, and write equations for (a) the amount of steam extracted at each point, (b) the work from Q_A and Q_R and the turbine work, and (c) the

thermal efficiency of the cycle. The equations should refer to a Ts diagram with named points.

667. The same as problem 666 except that the three extraction points occur after the one reheating.

668. The same as problem 666 except that two of the extraction points are before reheat and one afterwards.

669. A reheat-regenerative engine receives steam at 207 bar and 593°C, expanding it to 38.6 bar, 343°C. At this point, the steam passes through a reheater and reenters the turbine at 34.5 bar, 593°C, whence it expands to 9 bar, 427°C, at which point steam is bled for feedwater heating. Exhaust occurs at 0.7 bar. Beginning at the throttle, (point 1), these enthalpies are known (kJ/kg):

$h_1 = 3511.3$	$h_2' = 3082.1$
$h_2 = 3010.0$	$h_4 = 3205.4$
$h_3 = 3662.5$	$h_6 = 162.2$
$h_4' = 3222.9$	$h_7' = 724.2$
$h_5 = 2308.1$	$h_7 = 742.1$

For the ideal engine, sketch the events on the Ts plane, and for 1 kg of throttle steam, find (a) the mass of bled steam, (b) the work, (c) efficiency, and (d) the steam rate. In the actual case, water enters the boiler at 171°C and the brake engine efficiency is 75%. (e) Determine the brake work and the brake thermal efficiency. (f) Let the pump efficiency $\eta_p = 65\%$, and estimate the enthalpy of the exhaust steam.

670. Sketch the Ts diagram for a reheat-regenerative engine, with one reheat followed by additional expansion and one extraction. Number the points successively, starting with the throttle as point 1. The enthalpies are: $h_1 = 1351.3$, $h_2 = 1201.4$, $h_{2'} = 1214.6$, $h_3 = 1318.6$, $h_4 = 1170$, $h_{4'} = 1185$, $h_5 = 923.7$, $h_{5'} = 972$, $h_6 = 69.7$, $h_7 = 250.1$, $h_{7'} = 244$. The actual engine has a combined steam rate of 8.6 lb per kW-hr; the generator efficiency is 92%. For 1 lb of throttle steam, find (a) m_1 and m_1', (b) W and the actual fluid work W', (c) e and e_k, and (d) η_k.

Ans (a) 0.1639, 0.1563, (b) 504.5, 450.3, (c) 41.4%, 32.75%, (d) 78.7%.

671. A supercritical reheat-regenerative cycle has been designed in which the steam generator receives feedwater at 5500 psia, and the turbine receives steam at 4500 psia and 1150°F (state 1). Between the throttle and the first reheat point, 10% of the throttle steam is extracted for feedwater heating; the remainder is withdrawn at 460 psia and 550°F and is reheated to 440 psia and 1000°F. The steam reenters the engine, and another 20% of the throttle steam is extracted for feedwater heating during the subsequent expansion to the second reheat point. The remaining 70% of the throttle steam is withdrawn at 55 psia and 500°F and reheated to 50 psia and 1000°F; final expansion occurs to the condenser pressure of 1 psia. The estimated combined heat rate for the 120,000-kW engine is 8300 Btu/kW-hr. At state 1, $h_1 = 1504.5$ and $s_1 = 1.5011$; for the feedwater, $h_f = 415$. Estimate the hourly flow of steam to the throttle of the engine. *Ans.* 668,400 lb/hr.

672. A reheat-regenerative turbine operates as follows: superheated steam is received at 1650 psia and 780°F with an enthalpy of 1341; the actual expansion is to an enthalpy of 1211.2, at which point all the steam is returned to a reheater and heated to an enthalpy of 1306.2; the actual expansion continues to an enthalpy of 1222.7, where m' lb/lb throttle steam is extracted for feedwater heating; the actual expansion continues until the enthalpy is h_e, at a condenser pressure of 0.9492 psia; the condensate pump, with a 1 Btu/lb work input, delivers the water to the heater with an enthalpy of 64; there it mixes with the m' bled steam, and the water leaving the feedwater heater has an enthalpy of 311.1 (all h Btu/lb of throttle steam). When the ideal work is 489.7 Btu/lb, the brake engine efficiency is 75%. Compute the approximate percentage of moisture in the actual exhaust. In addition to an energy diagram, show the significant states on a *Ts* diagram. *Ans.* 7.43%.

673. In a supercritical steam power plant, steam leaves the superheater at 4000 psia and 1000°F. Arriving at the turbine throttle without loss, it then expands isentropically to 600 psia, where m_1 lb is extracted for (open) feedwater heating and the remainder is resuperheated to 1000°F. Next, it returns to the turbine and expands isentropically to 20 psia, where m_2 lb of steam is extracted for feedwater heating; the remainder continues the ideal expansion to 94°F. For the ideal cycle, determine (a) the mass fractions of bled steam,

(b) the thermal efficiency, (c) the rate of steam flow for 500 MW net output, (d) the heat rate. Show a *Ts* sketch with the supercritical pressure line and pump processes, and with all significant states named. (An actual plant operating between these extreme states would have several extractions; two serve to demonstrate the method.)
Ans. (a) 0.273, 0.090, (b) 50.9%, (c) 2.92 × 10^6 lb/hr, (d) 6700 Btu/kW-hr.

674. A turbine receives steam at 1100 psia, 750°F; it expands to 400 psia, where some is extracted for feedwater heating. The remainder expands to 245 psia, whence it is led through a reheater to re-enter the turbine at 240 psia, 800°F. Then the expansion occurs to the condenser pressure of 0.5 psia. In the actual turbine, the steam enters the reheater at 420°F; the water enters the boiler at 420°F. The combined steam rate is 9.7 lb/kW-hr; generator efficiency is 92%. The actual amount of steam extracted is 28% of the throttle flow. For the ideal engine: Compute (a) the percentage of throttle steam bled, (b) the thermal efficiency. For the actual engine: Compute (c) the brake work, (d) the brake and combined thermal efficiencies, (e) the approximate pump work (incompressible water) for a pump efficiency of 60%, (f) the quality of the actual exhaust steam.
Ans. (a) 31.45%, (b) 43.5%, (c) 382 Btu/lb, (d) 34.5%, 31.7%, (e) 1.423 Btu/lb throttle, (f) 95.8%.

675. In a 35,000-kW turbogenerator that receives steam at 1000 psia and 700°F, 11% of the throttle steam is actually extracted at 290 psia and 420°F, with the remainder being reheated to 260 psia and 600°F; then 20% of the throttle steam is actually extracted at 105 psia, each extraction serving an open feedwater heater. The engine exhausts to a condenser pressure of 0.69813 psia (90°F), and the temperature of the feedwater from the last heater is 400°F. The combined steam rate of the turbogenerator unit is 10.8 lb/kW-hr, and the generator efficiency is 95%. For the total throttle flow to an ideal engine, find (a) the hourly rates of extracted steam, (b) W, and (c) e. For the actual engine, find (d) e_k, (e) η_k, and (f) the enthalpy of the actual exhaust when the pump efficiency = 60%.
Ans. (a) $m_1 = 37,050$ lb/hr, (b) 437.3 Btu/lb, (c) 42.1%, (d) 30.1%, (e) 72.2%, (f) 1095 Btu/lb.

676. A 30,000-hp turbine receives steam at 600 psia and 700°F and exhausts at 1.513 psia. At the actual state of 150 psia and 400°F, the steam is withdrawn and part is used for feedwater heating, while the remainder passes through a reheater. The reheated steam reenters the turbine at 140 psia and 700°F. A second extraction for feedwater heating occurs at 20 psia and 350°F; a third extraction occurs at 5 psia and 200°F. The actual exhaust is saturated vapor at 116°F. The actual temperatures of the feedwater leaving the heaters are 160°F, 224°F, and 332°F, respectively. Assume no losses in and between the heaters, and find (**a**) the "actual" percentage extracted at each point, (**b**) the approximate hourly flow of throttle steam, (**c**) the thermal efficiency based on fluid work, and (**d**) the approximate temperature rise of the condenser cooling water if, for each pound of steam delivered to the turbine, there are circulated 50 lb of water.

Ans. (**a**) $m_1' = 10.77\%$, (**b**) 210,306 lb/hr, (**c**) 30.5%, (**d**) 16.5°F.

677. There are developed 25,000 kW at 3600 rpm by a reheat-regenerative engine (turbogenerator) which receives steam at 610 psia and 580°F and exhausts at 1 psia. At 275 psia and 420°F, part of the steam is extracted for feedwater heating, and the remainder is withdrawn for reheating. The reheated steam enters the turbine at 260 psia and 520°F and expands to 200 psia, where more steam is extracted for feedwater heating and the remainder expands to the condenser pressure of 1 psia and an actual quality of 90%. Feedwater leaves the last heater at a temperature of 405°F; the generator has an efficiency of 95%. For the ideal engine, find (**a**) the percentages of extracted steam, (**b**) W, and (**c**) e. Let the actual extracted steam masses be 85% of those for the ideal engine, and, for the actual engine, find (**d**) the total throttle flow, lb/hr, if the brake work equals the fluid work, (**e**) e_k, and (**f**) η_k.

Ans. (**a**) 0.0352, 0.2335, (**b**) 357.5 Btu/lb, (**c**) 37.2%, (**d**) 324,000 lb/hr, (**e**) 27.5%, (**f**) 73.6%.

678. An actual reheat-regenerative engine (steam turbine) develops its rated load of 50,000 kW. Steam is received at the throttle (pt 1) at 86 bar, 482°C and expands to 9 bar, 205°C. At this point (pt 2′), 23.05% of the steam is extracted for the one stage of regenerative feedwater heating; the remainder

passes through the reheater and enters the turbine at 8.3 bar, 482°C. Expansion now occurs to the condensing temperature of 27°C ($h_f = 113$ kJ/kg). Feedwater leaves the actual heater at 174°C ($h_f = 737$ kJ/kg). The combined engine efficiency is $\eta_K = 75\%$ and the generator efficiency is $e_g = 95\%$. Use Item B 16(SI) and for the ideal engine find (**a**) percentage steam extracted, (**b**) W, and (**c**) e. For the actual engine find (**d**) throttle flow, (**e**) e_k.

BINARY VAPOR CYCLES

679. In an ideal mercury-steam cycle, saturated mercury vapor enters the mercury turbine at 100 psia and is exhausted into the condenser-boiler at 1 psia ($h_f = 14$). Saturated steam at 360 psia is generated in the condenser-boiler, and the steam turbine exhausts at 1.50 in. Hg abs. ($h_f = 60$). Sketch the TS diagram, use Items B 16 and B 34, and find (**a**) the work of the mercury turbine for 1 lb Hg, (**b**) the work of the steam turbine for 1 lb of steam, (**c**) the gross work of the two turbines per 100,000 lb/hr of steam generated, and (**d**) the thermal efficiency of the binary-vapor system.

Ans. (**a**) 44 Btu/lb Hg, (**b**) 381 Btu/lb, (**c**) 26,700 kW, (**d**) 54.4%.

680. The same as problem 679 except that the steam cycle is a regenerative type with a single extraction occurring for feedwater heating at 15 psia, and further, the steam is initially superheated by the furnace for the mercury boiler to 550°F.

681. A geothermal energy system employs a binary-fluid subsystem using a secondary loop containing *n*-butane. Low temperature (182°C) ground well water is circulated through the *n*-butane boiler generating superheated *n*-butane vapor at 34.5 bar, 149°C (point 1) which expands in a Rankine engine to 2.8 bar (point 2); condensation occurs at this pressure (to point 3). These specific enthalpies are known for the *n*-butane: $h_1 = 565$, $h_2 = 479$, $h_3 = 70$ kJ/kg. The water temperature decreases by 20°C as it flows through the *n*-butane boiler. For an engine output of 1000 kW, find (**a**) mass rates of the water and *n*-butane, (**b**) thermal efficiency of the system.

682. The original Hartford, Conn., 10,000-kW mercury cycle, topping an existing 12,400-kW steam cycle, generates mercury vapor at 70 psia and 883°F and condenses at 500°F ($h_f = 15.32$ Btu/lb). The condenser-boiler receives feedwater at 150°F. Steam leaves the superheater elements at 400 psia and 700°F and is condensed at 1 psia. For the mercury turbine, the combined mercury rate is 108 lb/kW-hr. The efficiency of the mercury boiler is 86% when firing fuel oil with a heating value of $q_h = 19,200$ Btu per lb. Find (a) the ideal steam rate for the steam turbine, (b) the combined engine efficiency for the steam turbine, (c) the combined thermal efficiency for the binary-vapor system, and (d) the lb/hr of fuel oil used. See Item B 34 for specific properties of Hg.

Ans. (a) 7.63 lb/kW-hr, (b) 93.6%, (c) 46.7%, (d) 10,000 lb/hr.

INCOMPLETE EXPANSION CYCLE AND ENGINE

683. An incomplete-expansion engine has steam supplied at 180 psia and 450°F. Release occurs at 20 psia, and exhaust is at 5 psia. Test of the actual engine showed a 16.5 lb/ihp-hr steam rate and a mechanical efficiency of 87%. Find (a) the ideal work, (b) the ideal thermal efficiency, (c) the ideal steam rate, (d) the brake and indicated works, (e) the brake thermal efficiency, (f) the brake engine efficiency, and (g) the ideal and indicated mep's. (h) For the corresponding ideal cycle, what are Q_A, Q_R, w, and e?

684. An ideal incomplete-expansion cycle uses saturated steam generated at 85.3 psig. The exhaust pressure is 16 psia, and the release is at 244°F. On the basis of 1 lb, find (a) Q_A, (b) Q_R, (c) W, (d) the quality of the exhaust steam, and (e) the thermal efficiency. An engine with incomplete expansion operates under these conditions. (f) If the indicated engine efficiency is 72% and it uses 1000 lb/hr of steam, what is the ihp? (g) If the mechanical efficiency is 88%, what are the brake thermal efficiency, and the brake steam rate?

Ans. (a) 1002.9, (c) 127.2 Btu, (d) 90%, (f) 37.4 ihp, (g) 30.4 lb/ihp-hr.

685. A reciprocating steam engine with incomplete expansion receives saturated steam at 150 psia, expands it to 15 psia, where release occurs. Discharge is to a condenser at 110°F. The actual engine uses 2760 lb/hr of steam; it has a brake engine efficiency of 60% and a mechanical efficiency of 85% (= bhp/ihp). (a)

For the ideal engine, find the thermal efficiency and mep. For the actual engine, determine (b) the brake work and brake thermal efficiency, (c) the indicated thermal efficiency and indicated heat rate. (d) Compute the approximate enthalpy of the exhaust steam (at 110°F), assuming that the heat loss from the engine is 10 Btu/lb of H_2O. Sketch a complete energy diagram.

Ans. (a) 20.4%, 53.5 psia, (b) 146 bhp, 12.24%, (c) 14.4%, 17,700 Btu/ihp-hr, (d) 1023.6 Btu/lb.

686. An engine with incomplete expansion is supplied with steam at 400 psia and 500°F. Release occurs at 50 psia and the condenser temperature is 108°F. (a) If the brake engine efficiency is 60% and if 2700 lb/hr of steam are used, what is the bhp? (b) If the mechanical efficiency is 87%, what are the indicated thermal efficiency, the indicated work per pound of steam, and the indicated steam rate? (c) If the engine drives a generator whose efficiency is 92%, what are the combined thermal efficiency and the combined steam rate?

MISCELLANEOUS

687. An ideal nonexpansion engine (one in which the throttle pressure acts on the piston for the entire stroke) receives saturated steam at 145 psia and exhausts at 15 psia. Find (a) W, (b) e, (c) w, (d) mep, and (e) the specific enthalpy of the exhaust.

Ans. (a) 75 Btu/lb, (b) 7.51%, (c) 33.96 lb/hp-hr, (d) 130 psi, (e) 1118.55 Btu.

688. A $7 \times 7 \times 10$-in. double-acting duplex pump is supplied with steam at 130 psia and 98% quality. It exhausts at 15 psia, consumes 522 lb/hr of steam, makes 17 double strokes/min, and develops 5.01 ihp. (a) For the corresponding ideal nonexpansion engine, find the thermal efficiency and the steam rate. (b) Determine the indicated thermal efficiency and the approximate actual enthalpy of the exhaust steam.

Ans. (a) $e = 7.26\%$, 35.3 lb/hp-hr, (b) $e_i = 2.46\%$, 1150.4 Btu/lb.

689. A closed feedwater heater receives (steady flow) 0.1 lb/sec of extracted steam that is dry and saturated at 140 psia; 0.8 lb/sec of feedwater enters it at 150°F (from preceding heater); 0.1 lb/sec of liquid trapped from the succeeding heater also enters at 340°F. All the condensate of this heater leaves at 320°F and is pumped into the main feed line. What is the temperature to the nearest whole degree of the departing feedwater (main stream)?

Ans. 265°F.

690. (a) From the steam generator, steam enters the steam main at 600 psia and 550°F, flows adiabatically and steadily, and arrives at the turbine at a pressure of 540 psia; sink temperature is 80°F. Determine the irreversibility of the process. The cross-sectional area of the main is constant. If the steam enters the main at a speed of 100 ft/sec, what is its speed at the end and the change of kinetic energy? (b) Steam enters the main at 600 psia and 550°F and arrives at the turbine at 540 psia and 520°F. Compute the change of availability and the irreversibility. Solve by Mollier chart with large scale sketch of solution.

Ans. By full tables: (a) 5.45 Btu/lb, $v_2 = 111$ fps, (b) $\Delta \mathscr{A} = -12.26$ Btu/lb.

691. A pressurized water nuclear power plant consists of two independent loops (see figure). The water in the primary loop receives heat from the reactor and delivers it to the boiler; the secondary loop (solid lines) is through the turbine for power generation. At full load the turbine is producing 25,000 hp; pressures and temperatures are indicated on the diagram. (a) Determine the ideal thermal efficiency for the secondary loop. If the temperature rise in the primary loop is limited to 30°F, what will be the over-all thermal efficiency of the H₂O systems? (b) Regenerative feedwater heating with steam extracted at 260°F is added to the foregoing cycle (see dotted addition). Compute the thermal

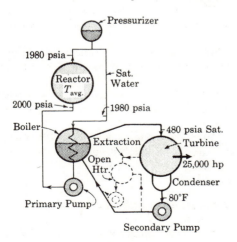

Problem 691

efficiencies as in (a). Is there an improvement? (c) Reheat (connection not shown) is provided at the extraction point in (b) and the steam that does not go to the feedwater heater is heated to 500°F at 30 psia. Other data are as already given. Is the thermal efficiency with this arrangement better than in (b) or (a)? Discuss.

Ans. (a) 35.8%, 35.4%, (b) 38.2%, 37.5%, (c) 36.1%, 35.7%.

692. A steam cycle is required to supply 50,000 lb/hr of process steam at 20 psia, dry and saturated, and to generate 5000 kW of by-product power. The process steam is not returned to the system. The turbine receives 74,100 lb/hr of throttle steam with $h_1 = 1366$ Btu/lb and expands it to the extraction state at 20 psia. There are bled 59,900 lb/hr (50,000 lb/hr to process; 9,900 lb/hr to an open feedwater heater), and the remainder expands to the condenser pressure of 1 in. Hg abs. Makeup water at 70°F to replace the process steam joins the saturated condensate from the condenser and thence flows to the open heater. A boiler-feed pump closes the cycle from the heater to the boiler. Sketch the energy diagram and determine the temperature of the feedwater to the boiler.

COMPUTER PROGRAMS

693. The effect of throttle temperature on the efficiency of a simple Rankine engine is desired. Select a specific Rankine engine, establish the throttle and condensing pressures, and then permit the throttle temperature to vary from that of saturation to a maximum value of 800°C. Find the respective values of the efficiency under these constraints and plot the curve efficiency vs throttle temperature. Program this problem.

694. A study of the economy of a regenerative engine is being conducted. It is desired to learn how the efficiency varies with the number of heaters used. Select a specific engine (this will establish a set of throttle conditions and a condensing pressure) and let the number of heaters vary from one to ten using an appropriate manner for spacing the heaters in the cycle. Find the efficiency in each case and plot the curve efficiency vs number of heaters. Write the program for this problem.

695–700. These numbers may be used for other problems.

10

IMPERFECT GASES

Note: There are numerous equations of state that attempt to resolve the nonideal qualities of a real gas; a few selected equations are presented in these problems. In addition, compressibility, fugacity, and deviation charts are in the Appendix.

EQUATIONS OF STATE

701. The van der Waals equation of state is

$$\left(p + \frac{a}{v^2}\right)(v - b) = RT$$

where a and b are constants. Its critical isotherm has a point of inflection at the critical point. (**a**) Show that these expressions for the constants must obtain: $a = 9RT_c v_c/8 = 3p_c v_c^2$, $b = v_c/3$. (**b**) Compute the approximate values of the constants a and b for the rocket fuel nonane C_9H_{20}.

702. The same as problem 701 except the equation of state is that of Berthelot:

$$\left(p + \frac{a}{Tv^2}\right)(v - b) = RT$$

the constants are $a = 27R^2 T_c^3/64p_c = 3p_c v_c^2 T_c$, $b = v_c/3$, and the fuel is propane C_3H_8.

703. The same as problem 701 except that the equation of state is that of Dieterici:

$$p(v - b)e^{a/(RTv)} = RT$$

the constants are $a = 4R^2 T_c^2/e^2 p_c$, $b = RT_c/e^2 p_c$, and the fuel is benzene C_6H_6.

704. The same as problem 701 except that the equation of state is that of Clausius:

$$\left(p + \frac{a}{T(v + c)^2}\right)(v - b) = RT$$

the constants are $a = 27R^2 T_c^3/64p_c$, $b = v_c - (RT_c/4p_c)$, $c = (3RT_c/8p_c) - v_c$, and the fuel is heptane C_7H_{16}.

705. The same as problem 701 except the equation of state is that of Redlich-Kwong:

$$\left[p + \frac{a}{T^{0.5}v(v + b)}\right](v - b) = RT$$

the constants are $a = 0.4278\ R^2 T_c^{2.5}/p_c$, $b = 0.0867RT_c/p_c$, and the fuel is butane C_4H_{10}.

706. Arrange the van der Waals equation of state in the virial form, explicit in p. See problem 701.

707. The same as problem 706 except arrange the Berthelot equation. See problem 702.

708. The same as problem 706 except arrange the Dieterici equation. See problem 703.

709. The same as problem 706 except arrange the Clausius equation. See problem 704.

710. The same as problem 706, except arrange the Redlich–Kwong equation. See problem 705.

COMPRESSIBILITY FACTOR

711. The property relation $(pv/RT) = Z$ is known as the compressibility factor for a given substance. For an ideal gas, $Z \equiv 1$ at any state. (a) Find the compressibility factor Z_c for a van der Waals gas at the critical point. (b) Using this value of Z_c, rewrite the expressions for the constants a and b excluding the property v_c. See 701.

712. The same as problem 711 except use the Berthelot gas. See problem 702.

713. The same as problem 711 except use the Dieterici gas. See problem 703.

714. The same as problem 711 except use the Clausius gas. See problem 704.

715. The same as problem 711 except use the Redlich–Kwong gas. See problem 705.

716. By manipulating the expressions for each of the respective constants a and b, determine the compressibility factor at the critical point $Z_c = p_c v_c / R T_c$ for a gas whose equation of state is (a) van der Waals, (b) Redlich–Kwong. (c) Calculate each Z_c of these two gases by substituting values of the critical properties of a given gas, say air, directly into the expression; see Item B 18 for values. (d) Compare all results with the values of Z_c given in Item B 18.

717. The pressure and temperature of given fluid are 100 atm and 633 K, respectively. Determine the compressibility factor and the density if the fluid is (a) nitrogen, (b) ammonia, (c) heptane. (d) Compare each density to that obtained assuming the gas to be ideal.

718. Determine the compressibility factor and the density of (a) nonane at 303 psia, 720°F, (b) carbon dioxide at 3480 psia, 364°F, (c) hydrogen at 35 atm, 299°F. (d) Compare each density to that obtained assuming the gas to be ideal. See Items B 19 through B 21.

719. From generalized compressibility charts, estimate the maximum pressure at which the actual density of a fluid at 108°F may be determined from the ideal gas equation with an error not exceeding 5% if the fluid is (a) nitrogen, (b) methane. *Ans.* (a) 2523 psia.

720. In a state where the pressure is 30 atm, a compressibility factor of 0.8 is noted. Determine the temperature and the mol volume if the substance is (a) air, (b) hydrogen, (c) methane. *Ans.* (a) −187.5°F, 5.35 ft³/pmole.

721. Determine the density of a fluid at $p_R = 3.0$ and $T_R = 1.3$ by locating the pseudo-relative-volume v_{Ri} on a generalized compressibility chart, and then evaluating the specific volume for the fluids (a) carbon monoxide, (b) ethane. Compare results with ideal densities and with those determined from $pv = ZRT$.
Ans. (a) 19.8 lb/ft³ (chart), 12.75 lb/ft³ (ideal).

722. A study of the compressibility charts, Items B 19 through B 21, will reveal that certain combinations of p_r and T_r will produce compressibility factors of $Z \equiv 1$, as if the gas were ideal. (a) List several of these combinations. (b) What will be the state (p psia, $t°F$) of a given fluid (other than ideal) to produce $Z \equiv 1$ if that fluid is air? Carbon dioxide? Helium?

COMPUTING PROPERTIES

723. Find the density of air at 2000 psia and 311°R, using (a) $pv = RT$, (b) $pv = ZRT$, (c) van der Waals equation. (d) Which of the three answers do you believe is more accurate?
Ans. (a) 17.37, (b) 25.9, (c) 24.85 lb/ft³.

724. Water exists at 1200°F and occupies a specific volume of $v = 0.116$ ft³/lb. (a) Find the corresponding pressure using Berthelot's equation. See problem 702. (b) Determine the percentage error between this computed pressure and that found in the steam tables at the cited temperature and volume.

725. Compute the pressure of 5 lb of carbon monoxide contained in 0.5 ft³ at 40°F, using (a) $pv = RT$, (b) $pv = ZRT$, and (c) van der Waals equation. *Ans.* (a) 1915, (b) 1825, (c) 1780 psia.

726. Methane at 600 psia, 100°F, is flowing in a pipe line at the rate of 10,000 cfm. Determine the mass flow rate using (a) ideal gas theory, (b) compressibility factor, (c) Redlich–Kwong equation.

727. There are required at least 20 kg of steam at 600 bar, 750°C to conduct an experiment; a 140-ℓ heavy duty tank is available for storage. Predict if this is adequate storage capacity using (a) the ideal gas theory, (b) the compressibility factor, (c) the van der Waals equation, (d) the Mollier chart, Item B 16 (SI).

728. Nitrogen is stored in a 0.425 m³ tank at 560 atm, 456 K. Determine the mass of nitrogen in the tank using (a) ideal gas theory, (b) the compressibility factor, (c) van der Waals equation. *Ans.* (a) 178, (b) 132, (c) 132.3 kg.

729. Find the density of air at 4000 psia and 1040°F (a) as an ideal gas, (b) as a Berthelot gas (see 702), (c) using $pv = ZRT$.
Ans. (a) 7.20, (b) 6.51, (c) 6.55 lb/ft³.

730. A hospital requires that 225 kg of medicinal oxygen be on hand at any one time. The oxygen is stored in 100-ℓ drums at 272 atm, 300 K. Determine the number of storage drums required based on (**a**) $pv = RT$, (**b**) $pv = ZRT$, (**c**) van der Waals equation, (**d**) Berthelot equation, (**e**) Redlich–Kwong equation. Which answer would you select as being the more accurate?

731. Find the density of air at 13.79 MPaa and 172.8 K, using (**a**) $pv = RT$, (**b**) $pv = ZRT$, (**c**) van der Waals equation. (**d**) Which of the three answers do you believe is more accurate?
Ans. (**a**) 278.2, (**b**) 415.8, (**c**) 398 kg/m³.

732. If a 5-ft³ drum contains CO_2 at 350 atm and 140°F, determine the moles in it in accordance with (**a**) the Dieterici equation (see problem 703), (**b**) ideal gas equation, (**c**) the principle of corresponding states.

733. What volume will be required to contain 100 lb CO_2 at 364.5 atm pressure, 327°F? Find the volume using (**a**) ideal gas theory, (**b**) compressibility factor, (**c**) van der Waals equation.

734. Methane is being pumped at the rate of 100 lb/sec at 183.2 atm pressure, 56°F. Find the volumetric flow, cfs, using (**a**) ideal gas theory, (**b**) compressibility factor, (**c**) van der Waals equation.
Ans. (**a**) 12.82, (**b**) 10.39, (**c**) 10.0 cfs,

GENERALIZED EQUATIONS

735. (**a**) Transform the van der Waals equation of state to reduced coordinates. See problem 701. (**b**) Modify this reduced equation by introducing the ideal critical volume $v_{ci} = RT_c/p_c$ and the ideal reduced volume $v_{ri} = v/v_{ci}$. (**c**) Develop an expression for the compressibility factor $Z = pv/RT$ based on the reduced equation of van der Waals.

736. The same as problem 735 except that the Berthelot equation is to be transformed and then modified. See problem 702.

737. The same as problem 735 except that the Dieterici equation is to be transformed and then modified. See problem 703.

738. The same as problem 735 except that the Clausius equation is to be transformed and then modified. See problem 704.

739. The same as problem 735 except that the Redlich–Kwong equation is to be transformed and then modified. See problem 705.

740. For each of the five reduced equations of state (problems 735–739), plot these isotherms ($T_R = 0.5$, $T_R = 1.0$, $T_R = 1.5$) on a $v_R p_R$ chart and compare curves. Suggest use value ranges of v_R: 0.5–2, p_R: 0–2.

741. The same as problem 728 except solve using (**a**) the reduced van der Waals equation and (**b**) the modified reduced form. See problem 735. Compare answers with those given in problem 728.

742. Assume 5 lb of ethane are contained in a 1-ft³ tank at 80°F. Determine the pressure by means of the reduced Berthelot equation and compare this value to that obtained through the ideal gas theory and the compressibility factor.

743. Steam at 10,000 psia, 1200°F occupies 5 ft³. Find its mass using (**a**) steam table data (Item B 15), (**b**) ideal gas equation, (**c**) compressibility factor, (**d**) van der Waals equation, (**e**) reduced form of van der Waals equation, (**f**) modified reduced form of van der Waals equation.
Ans. (**a**) 66.1, (**b**) 50.6, (**c**) 67.5, (**d**) 71.5, (**e**) 113.1, (**f**) 70 lb.

744. Determine the mass of nitrogen occupying a 425-ℓ vessel at 560 atm, 456 K. Use (**a**) ideal gas equation, (**b**) compressibility factor, (**c**) van der Waals equation, (**d**) reduced van der Waals equation, (**e**) modified reduced van der Waals equation.

745. Superheated vapor tables show that at 5500 psia, 1200°F the density of water vapor is 6.6 lb/ft³. Determine the percentage error involved if the density is calculated by using (**a**) the modified reduced van der Waals equation, (**b**) the ideal gas theory.
Ans. (**a**) 7.73%, (**b**) 15.60%.

ENTHALPY AND ENTROPY DEVIATIONS

746. (**a**) What are the enthalpy and internal energy of N_2 at 360°R and 70 atm measured from an ideal gas base of zero at 0°R and 1 atm? (**b**) What is the absolute entropy of N_2 at 360°R and 70 atm? Use the deviation charts.

747. Air is compressed isothermally from 40 atm, 520°R to 220 atm; the process is steady flow, steady state; $\Delta K = 0$, $\Delta P = 0$. (**a**) Use the deviation charts and find Q and W. (**b**) Use ideal gas theory and find Q and W. (**c**) Solve for Q and W using Item B 2. Compare all answers.

748. An ideal turbine receives nitrogen at 300 atm, 500 K and expands it in a steady flow manner to 5 atm; the flow rate is 2 kg/sec. Assume the nitrogen obeys the Redlich-Kwong equation of state and calculate the power ouput of the turbine. See Table I for the specific heat c_p for the nitrogen.

749. Steam at 9000 psia, 1200°F, is expanded to 3000 psia, 1000°F, in a steady flow adiabatic manner; $\Delta K = 0$. Use the deviation charts and determine (**a**) Δh, (**b**) Δs, (**c**) v_1. Compare answers with values as obtained from vapor tables.

750. Air at 1800 psia, 40°F is heated to 540°F in a steady flow constant pressure manner; $\Delta K = 0$. For a flow of 10 lb/sec, determine the required heat and the change of entropy, accounting for the variation of specific heat: (**a**) for ideal-gas air, (**b**) for imperfect-gas air considering the deviations.

751. A gas turbine receives 1 lb/sec air at 300 atm, 450°R and expands it reversibly to 30 atm in an adiabatic steady flow manner; $\Delta P = 0$; $\Delta K = 0$. (**a**) Use the deviation charts and find the exit air temperature and the work. (**b**) Solve using ideal gas theory and compare with foregoing answers.

Ans. (**a**) 247°R, 45.1 Btu/sec, (**b**) 233°R, 52.1 Btu/sec.

752. If 1 pmole of oxygen is confined in a rigid tank while being refrigerated from 1500 psia, 450°R, to 300°R, determine (**a**) the final pressure, (**b**) the heat, (**c**) the change of entropy. Use the deviation charts.

Ans. (approx.) (**a**) 50.5 atm, (**b**) −945 Btu, (**c**) −2.57 Btu/°R.

753. There are throttled 2.27 kg/s of nitrogen from 200 atm, 200 K to 15 atm; sink temperature $t_0 = 15.6°C$. Compute (**a**) the final temperature, (**b**) ΔS, (**c**) the change of availability. Use the deviation charts. For this temperature range, use c_p from Item B 1.

ISOBARIC PROCESS

754. (**a**) Integrate the expression $\int p\, dv$ for a van der Waals fluid undergoing an isobaric nonflow process. (**b**) Let the fluid have properties similar to those of butane C_4H_{10} and determine the nonflow work of 1 kg-mole as it expands isobarically and reversibly from 75 atm, 850 K to 2778 K.

755. Propane at a pressure of 150 atm undergoes an isobaric nonflow process from 720°R to 990°R. For this range use an average low-pressure specific heat of 26.3 Btu/mole-°R. For 1 pmole, compute (**a**) the work, (**b**) the change of enthalpy and entropy, (**c**) the heat and the internal energy change.

Ans. (**a**) 800, (**b**) 9890, 11.76, (**c**) 9890, 9090 Btu/mole.

756. Saturated steam at 200 bar is to be heated at constant pressure to 650°C. Using appropriate deviations, determine Δh, the heat added, Δs, and the specific volume at state 2. Compare results with values read from the Mollier chart, Item B 16(SI).

757. Oxygen at 1500 psia, 450°R is to be further refrigerated during a steady flow process ($\Delta K = 0$) through a heat exchanger to a temperature of 300°R. Neglect pressure drop. For 1 pmole determine (**a**) the heat transferred, (**b**) the change of entropy, (**c**) the final volume. Consider using the deviation charts.

Ans. (approx.) (**a**) −2400 Btu, (**b**) −6.8 Btu/°R, (**c**) 0.81 ft³.

758. Gases at the bottom-hole of a deep gas well have properties similar to those of methane CH_4 and often are in a state of 7500 psia, 400°F. Further, it is thought that these gases conform closely to the Berthelot equation of state. If these gases are processed without pressure drop to 140°F, find the value of the expression $\int p\, dv$ for each 1 mole/sec. What is the significance of this answer?

759. If 1 kg-mole of acetylene is at 310 atm, 463 K, find the slope of this isobar on the Tv plane at this particular state assuming that the gas acts like a van der Waals fluid. See Item B 18 for constants. Compare this slope to that if the acetylene were considered to be ideal.

ISOMETRIC PROCESS

760. A 142-ℓ insulated and rigid pressure vessel containing oxygen initially at 100 atm, 278 K, receives internal paddle work ($Q = 0$) that increases the pressure to 300 atm. Find (**a**) the paddle work, (**b**) ΔS, (**c**) the change of availability of the gaseous system for $T_0 = 277$ K.

761. Methane CH_4 is stored in a rigid vessel at 200 atm, 450°R. It is permitted to cool to 90 atm. The average molal specific heat for the temperature range and 1 atm is assumed to be

$c_p = 8.1$ Btu/pmole-°R. Determine (a) $\bar{v}_1$, $\bar{v}_{ri1}$, T_2, (b) Δh per mole, (c) Q.

Ans. (a) 1.165, 0.213 ft³/mole, 375°R, (b) −848, (c) −284 Btu/mole.

762. (a) Integrate the expression $-\int v\,dp$ for a van der Waals fluid undergoing an isometric process. (b) Let the fluid have properties similar to those of ethylene C_2H_4 and determine the value of the integral as 1 mole of the fluid changes state isometrically from 10.1 atm, 500°R to 101 atm. Is there any significance to this value?

763. A 10-ft³ rigid tank contains O_2 at 100 atm and 320°R. The contents are agitated by paddle work until the temperature becomes 460°R. Using the compressibility factor and gas tables, compute (a) the mass of O_2, (b) the final pressure, (c) the change of stored energy, and (d) the change of entropy of the system. (e) If the actual work input is 12,000 Btu, compute the heat and ΔS for the surroundings at 400°R. (f) What quantity of the energy added to the system is available energy with respect to a 400°R sink and a cyclic operation?

ISOTHERMAL PROCESS, FUGACITY

764. Find the $\int p\,dv$ for a van der Waals gas undergoing a nonflow isothermal process. Assume 1 lb of air occupying a volume of 0.4 ft³ under a pressure of 1000 psia undergoes this process until the pressure becomes 200 psia. Determine the nonflow work done if the air is considered to be (a) an ideal gas, (b) a van der Waals gas.

765. Integrate the expression $-\int v\,dp$ for a van der Waals fluid undergoing a steady flow reversible isothermal process. Now using the same numerical data as given in problem 764, determine the steady flow isothermal work and compare to that obtained by ideal gas theory; $\Delta P = 0$, $\Delta K = +5$ Btu/lb flowing.

Ans. 115.5, 114.5 (ideal) Btu/lb.

766. Using the Berthelot equation of state as given in problem 702, find the work of 16 lb of O_2 undergoing an isothermal nonflow process from 100 atm, 500°R to 10 atm. For the O_2, $a = 59,300$ atm-(ft³/mole)²-°R, $b = 0.397$ ft³/lb mole. Compare with results obtained assuming the gas to be ideal.

Ans. 1140, 1141 Btu (ideal).

767. (a) Integrate the expression $-\int v\,dp$ for a Berthelot fluid (see problem 702) undergoing an isothermal change of state in a reversible steady flow manner. (b) Using the numerical data of problem 766 let the mass flow be 16 lb/sec ($\Delta P = 0$, $\Delta K = -2$ Btu/lb) and find the steady flow isothermal work between the two state points.

768. Ethane is compressed in a steady-flow compressor at the rate of 100 lb/min from 30 atm to 100 atm during an isothermal process at 116°F; $\Delta P = 0$, $\Delta K = 0$. Determine the entropy change, the enthalpy change, and the steady flow work.

Ans. −7.02 Btu/mole-°R, −111,600 Btu/min, 40.5 kW.

769. Ethane is compressed reversibly and isothermally from 1 atm, 560°R, to 70 atm in a steady flow manner and at a rate of 1 mole/sec. Using the deviation charts, Appendix, determine (a) the work, (b) the heat transferred, (c) the change of entropy, (d) the increase in availability for a sink temperature of 60°F. Account for the variation in c_p for this temperature range. (e) Find the work by van der Waals equation and compare with (a).

770. Show that the fugacity of a van der Waals gas is given by the expression

$$\ln f = -\ln(v-b) - \frac{2a}{RTv} + \frac{b}{v-b}$$

771. Chilled drinking water, say at 1 atm, 283 K represents the state of a compressed liquid. Show that the fugacity of this compressed liquid is approximately equal to the fugacity of the liquid in its saturated state at the same temperature.

772. A booster station compresses 50 kg/sec of methane from 14 atm, 285 K to 98 atm in a reversible and isothermal steady-state, steady-flow manner. Use the generalized fugacity coefficient chart (Item B 37) and calculate the compression work and the heat transfer. Now solve using ideal gas theory and compare answers.

773. (a) Dry air at 1 atm, 80°F is compressed isothermally and steady flow to 3000 psia. Using the principle of corresponding states, compute the change of entropy, the heat, the work per pmole ($\Delta P = 0$, $\Delta K = 0$). (b) What mass of this compressed air would be contained in a 6-ft³ receiver? (c) The compressed air in the receiver is now heated at constant pressure to 1200°R. What is the heat required, the change of entropy, and the final density? (d) If the receiver full of air at 3000 psia is heated at constant volume to 1200°R, what heat is required?

Ans. (**a**) −11.29 Btu/mole-°R, −6090, −5648 Btu/mole, (**b**) 89.3 lb, (**c**) 15,700 Btu, 19.55 Btu/°R, 6.22 lb/ft³, (**d**) 9890 Btu.

ADIABATIC PROCESSES

774. In preliminary estimates for the performance of a high-pressure steam power plant, the enthalpy change during an $S = C$ process from 20,000 psia, 1500°F to 6000 psia is desired. (**a**) Determine Δh. (**b**) Compute the specific volume of the steam in state 1.

775. There are compressed 10 lb/min of air from 750 psia, 280°R, to 3000 psia in a steady flow isentropic manner; $\Delta K = 0$. Determine the final temperature and the required work: (**a**) by ideal gas theory, (**b**) accounting for deviations. For this temperature range, use $c_p = 0.24$.

Ans. (approx.) (**a**) 415°R, −323 Btu/min. (**b**) 388°R, −242 Btu/min.

776. Oxygen at 100 atm and 320°R is compressed adiabatically to 300 atm and 500°R in steady flow with $\Delta K \approx 0$; $\dot{m} = 90$ lb/min. Compute (**a**) the horsepower, (**b**) the change of entropy, (**c**) the temperature at the end of an isentropic compression and the compressor efficiency.

Ans. (**a**) 117, (**b**) 8.08 Btu/°R-min, (**c**) 394°R, 30%.

777. Assume 1 lb/sec of nitrogen is compressed adiabatically from 75 atm, 500°R (state 1) to 300 atm. For the compressor, $\eta_c = 70$ per cent. Compute (**a**) $t_{2'}$, (**b**) ΔS, (**c**) $v_{2'}$, (**d**) W'.

778. Butane at 150 atm, 440°F is throttled to 5 atm. For 1 mole/sec, compute its final temperature, change of entropy, and change of availability for $t_0 = 60$°F. For iteration, use a constant specific heat for about 340°F.

Ans. 759°R (approx.), 4.96 Btu/sec-°R, −2580 Btu/sec.

779. Methane CH_4 undergoes an expansion from 100 atm, 540°R to 10 atm, 360°R. For this temperature range, the average specific heat is $C_p = 8.05$ Btu/mole-°R at low pressure. (**a**) For steady flow of 10 lb/sec through a turbine ($\Delta P = 0$, $\Delta K = 0$) with $Q = +25$ Btu/mole, calculate the work. (**b**) Compute ΔS. (For comparison purposes only, a table for CH_4 gives $\Delta h = -902$ Btu/mole.) (**c**) What is the turbine efficiency?

Ans. (**a**) 348 Btu/min, (**b**) 2.05 Btu/mole-°R, (**c**) 57.3%.

780. Oxygen undergoes a steady flow adiabatic process from 1000 atm, 600°R to 250 atm, 460°R; $\Delta P = 0$, $\Delta K = 0$. Compute (**a**) the work, and (**b**) the irreversibility for a sink at 460°R.

Ans. (**a**) 43.9 Btu/lb, (**b**) 299 Btu/mole.

781. In processing oxygen during a liquefying process, the O_2 is compressed adiabatically from 200 atm, 360°R to 600 atm, 500°R. Compute the steady flow work and the change of availability for a sink of 500°R; $\Delta P = 0$, $\Delta K = 0$.

782. Hydrogen is throttled adiabatically from 300 atm, 350°R (state 1) to 75 atm at a rate of 1 lb/sec. Compute (**a**) $t_{2'}$, (**b**) ΔS, (**c**) the change in availability for $t_0 = 60$°F.

783. The last stage of a compressor receives CO_2 at 100 atm, 120°F and delivers it at 250 atm. If the compression is steady-flow isentropic, compute the final temperature and the work done per 1 pmole/sec.

Ans. 675°R (approx.), −727 Btu/sec.

COMPUTER PROGRAMS

784. Write a computer program for a van der Waals gas using its virial form and let enthalpy h and entropy s be calculated at selected pressures and temperatures. Account for the variation of the specific heat $c_p = \alpha + \beta T + \gamma T^2$.

785. A manufacturer of pressurized gas containers desires to obtain a plot of pressure vs volume at selected temperatures. Use one of these three equations of state on the reduced basis, van der Waals, Redlich–Kwong, Berthelot, and write the computer program.

786–790. These numbers may be used for other problems.

11

RELATIONS OF THERMODYNAMIC PROPERTIES

Note: In numerical solutions, the units must be consistent. Where tables and charts are used for finite differences, resulting answers may be in error because the tabulated properties are not carried to sufficient places to make small differences accurate; further, the selected finite difference may be too great.

THERMODYNAMICS AND BASIC MATHEMATICS

791. Test the following expressions and state which of them have characteristics of a property, that is, are point functions: (**a**) $p\,dv$, (**b**) $(p\,dv + v\,dp)$, (**c**) $(3v^2/p^2)\,dv - (2v^3/p)\,dp$, (**d**) $(2x^2y + 5)\,dx + (2/3x^3 + 7)\,dy$, (**e**) $x^3y + 3xy$ where x and y are general properties.

792. Prove that neither work W nor heat Q is a property. Apply the exactness test to a closed gaseous system undergoing a reversible process. In the case of work, the process can also be made adiabatic.

793. Employ the exactness test and determine if the differential $dz = (x + 3y)\,dx + (x + 3y)\,dy$ is exact. Integrate it clockwise around the square whose corners are $(0, 0)$, $(0, 2)$, $(2, 2)$, $(2, 0)$. Assuming that dz is an exact differential, what would be the value of this cyclic integration?

794. Demonstrate the validity of equation (11-4, *Text*), $(\partial x/\partial y)_z(\partial y/\partial z)_x(\partial z/\partial x)_y = -1$, by replacing the x, y, z functions with p, v, T properties and then evaluating the three derivatives from (**a**) the ideal gas equation of state (**b**) the Redlich–Kwong equation of state given in problem 705.

795. Mathematics dictates that four point-function variables x, y, z, v are related by the expression $(\partial z/\partial x)_y(\partial x/\partial v)_y(\partial v/\partial z)_y = 1$. Demonstrate the validity of this statement using water properties in the region of 20 bar, 300°C; replace x, y, z, v with t, p, s, h.

796. Replace the x, y, z functions in the mathematical relation in problem 794 with p, T, S; thence evaluate each of the partial derivatives for steam in the region of 50 bar, 500°C, using appropriate finite intervals (Δp) for differentials $(dp, \partial p)$. Is the product of these three ratios in keeping with the equality?

797. Prove that $V = c$ lines are more steep than $p = c$ lines when both are shown on a TS-plane. State all assumptions used.

798. Considering an ideal gas undergoing a nonflow reversible process, how much greater will be the slope of an adiabatic path than that of an isothermal one through a common point on the pv-plane?

MAXWELL RELATIONS, OTHER FUNCTIONS

799. Develop expressions for the four exact total derivatives which in turn serve as the base for the analytical development of the four Maxwell relations.

800. During the analytical development of the Maxwell relations, four other pairs of equalities are noted and equal respectively to T, v, $-p$, $-s$. Derive these relations.

801. Employing Maxwell relation I, $(\partial T/\partial v)_s = -(\partial p/\partial s)_v$, and the mathematical relation from problem 794, develop the remaining three Maxwell relations.

802. Demonstrate the validity of each of the four Maxwell relations by evaluating the eight derivatives for steam in the region of 20 bar 400°C, using finite intervals (Δp) for differentials (dp, ∂p).

804. A study of the compressed liquid water table reveals that for an increase in pressure with a constant temperature of 32°F, the entropy increases; conversely, at 100°F and above, an increase in pressure will cause a decrease in entropy with the temperature held constant. Use one of the Maxwell relations and justify this. What significance do you place on this opposite effect that pressure has on entropy for some temperatures between 32°F and 100°F.

805. Simultaneous values of h and s for steam ($p = C$) are: $h_1 = 1204.2$, $s_1 = 1.6410$; $h_2 = 1210$ Btu/lb, $s_2 = 1.6481$ Btu/lb-°R. Calculate the approximate mean temperature between these states. *Hint*: start with the definition of enthalpy and use a partial derivative.
Ans. (approx.) 355°F.

806. Compute the Gibbs function for about four states of superheated steam at 300°C, plot the Gp curve at constant T, and show that $(\partial G/\partial p)_T = v$, numerically (approximating the differentials by finite intervals). Use 1 bar pressure intervals for the plot.

807. Compute the Helmholtz function A for four states of superheated ammonia at 200°F, plot the Av curve at constant T, and show that $(\partial A/\partial v)_T = -p$, numerically (approximating the differentials by finite intervals).

CLAUSIUS–CLAPEYRON EQUATION

808. For a vapor obeying the ideal gas equation, show that the change in the saturation vapor pressure is given by $dp/p = h_{fg} \, dT/(RT^2)$ if the volume of the saturated liquid is assumed to be negligible.

809. Using the Clapeyron relation, check the latent heat h_{fg} for steam at 170°F using pressure, temperature, and volume data taken from Item B 13.

810. Plot the saturated liquid-vapor curve on the pT-plane for steam and estimate the slope at a temperature of 100°F. Then on the assumption that steam is an ideal gas, compute the latent heat of vaporization. Discuss any deviation from the table value of h_{fg} from the viewpoint of error in measurement of the plotted slope or error in assumption of ideal gas.

811. Compute the approximate pressure needed to maintain an ice-water mixture in equilibrium at 31°F. Assume that Δv and Δh are independent of pressure. From Keenan and Keyes *Steam Tables* we find $v_f = 0.01602$, $v_i = 0.01747$ ft³/lb, and $h_i = -143.8$; assume $h_f = -1$ Btu/lb; the initial $p_1 = 0.0847$ psia.
Ans. 1084 psia.

812. Find the equilibrium temperature of a mixture of ice and liquid water when the pressure is changed from that at the triple point value to that of one atmosphere. See problem 811 for pertinent data.

COEFFICIENTS AND MODULI

813. Express the coefficients of expansion and compressibility in terms of density instead of specific volume.

814. Starting with the basic relation $\beta = (1/v)(\partial v/\partial T)_p$ determine the coefficient of expansion for a gas whose equation of state is

(a)
$$pv = RT$$

(b)
$$\left(p + \frac{a}{v^2}\right)(v - b) = RT$$

(c) Now develop the expressions for the two coefficients of compressibility, isothermal and isentropic, for these two gases. Assume constant specific heats.

815. Demonstrate that the equation of state for a pure substance may be written in the differential form: $dv/v = \beta dT - K_T dp$. Remember, $v = f(T, p)$. Now let $\beta = 1/T$ and $K_T = 1/p$ and find the equation of state.

816. Prove that the coefficient of volumetric expansion may be expressed as $\beta = 1/(T - \tan \theta)$ where θ is the slope angle of an isotherm on the Mollier (hs) chart and T is the absolute temperature.

817. A fluid has the equation of state $p(v - b) = RT$; b is a constant. Find the expression for its compressibility coefficient $\beta = (1/v)(\partial v/\partial T)_p$. What would β become if $b = 0$?
Ans. $\beta = R/pv$.

818. From the relationship $v = f(T, p)$, express the differential dv as the sum of two partial quantities and show that $(\partial T/\partial p)_v = K_T/\beta$.

819. Determine the coefficient of volumetric expansion β for a fluid at 1 bar, 200°C if that fluid is (a) an ideal gas, (b) water.

820. Show that the difference between the two compressibility coefficients is given by the expression $\kappa_T - \kappa_s = T\beta^2 v/c_p$ for an ideal gas.

821. Prove that the slope of an isotherm on the βp-plane is equal to and opposite (in signs) the slope of an isobar on the $\kappa_T T$-plane. State any assumptions.

822. (a) For a van der Waals fluid, verify each of the following coefficients:

$$\beta = \frac{Rv^2(v-b)}{RTv^3 - 2a(v-b)^2}$$

$$\kappa_T = \frac{v^2(v-b)^2}{RTv^3 - 2a(v-b)^2}.$$

(b) What is the value of κ_T/β expressed in its simplest form? (c) What do the above relations become when $a = 0$, $b = 0$ (ideal gas)?

823. Show for an ideal gas that κ_T is k times the value of κ_s where $k = c_p/c_v$.

824. A fluid in a given state has a coefficient of volumetric expansion of $\beta = 1/v(\partial v/\partial T)_p = 0.007$. If 100 cm³ of this fluid be cooled 10 K at constant pressure, what will be the final total volume? The value of β is based upon the initial volume.

825. (a) Write the differential of v for $v = f(p, T)$ and express the volume change in terms of the isothermal compressibility and the expansion coefficient. (b) Compute the volume change for a unit mass of copper for which $K_T = 0.776 \times 10^{-12}$ cm²/dyne, $\beta = 49.2 \times 10^{-6}$/K and density is $\rho = 8888$ kg/m³; the pressure is increased from 690 kPaa to 137.9 MPaa while the temperature remains constant at 300 K. *Ans.* -1.20×10^{-7} m³/kg.

ENTROPY, INTERNAL ENERGY, AND ENTHALPY

826. (a) Start with the entropy function $s = f(T, v)$ and derive the general expression for the entropy change

$$ds = c_v \frac{dT}{T} + \left(\frac{\partial p}{\partial T}\right)_v dv$$

(b) Now use the function $s = f(T, p)$ and obtain the general expression

$$ds = c_p \frac{dT}{T} - \left(\frac{\partial v}{\partial T}\right)_p dp$$

827. Using the expression for ds in problem 826(a), show that the entropy change along an isotherm takes the form of $ds_T = \beta\, dv/K_T$ for an ideal gas.

828. Develop the general equations for du and dh employing the expressions given in problem 826.

829. Find the expression (in simplest form) for the partial derivative $(\partial u/\partial p)_T$ for a fluid whose equation of state (a) $pv = RT$, (b) $pv = RT + Ap$ where A is a function of temperature only.

830. The expression $(\partial h/\partial s)_p = T$ should be familiar. Demonstrate its validity by using finite differences for steam in the region of 100 bar, 500°C; solve for T and then compare it to 500°C. What percentage error is noted?

831. Evaluate the change of entropy along an isotherm for 1 kg of steam in the region of 50 bar, 400°C using the two general expressions in problem 826. Use finite differences and compare the results of each to the values as taken directly from Item B 16(SI).

832. Start with the definition of enthalpy and show that $v = (\partial h/\partial p)_s$. Compute v for steam at 35 psia, 275°F from this expression using finite differences. *Ans.* 12.15 ft³/lb.

833. (a) Apply each of the two general entropy equations (see problem 826), to a van der Waals gas undergoing a process and derive an equation for the change of entropy. (b) Now apply the general equations (11–24) and (11–26), *Text*, to the gas and determine the changes of internal energy and enthalpy for the process. *Ans.* (a) $ds = c_v\, dT/T + R\, dv/(v-b)$, (b) $du = c_v\, dT + a\, dv/v^2$.

834. Find the changes of entropy, internal energy, and enthalpy for 2 kg acetylene undergoing a state change from 15 atm, 278 K, to 30 atm, 556 K, assuming that the acetylene conforms to van der Waals equation of state. Use the general expressions developed in problem 833 and compare with ideal gas theory.

835. Consider 5 lb of ammonia at 220°F that are compressed isothermally from 100 psia to 200 psia. Assuming that van der Waals equation applies, compute the changes of internal energy, enthalpy, and entropy. See problem 833.

836. Start with the equation $dQ = dh - v\,dp$, and show that a general expression for heat during a reversible process is

$$dQ = c_p\,dT + \left[\left(\frac{\partial h}{\partial p}\right)_T - v\right]dp$$

Now apply the exactness test to this expression and show that Q is not a point function.

837. Assuming that N_2 conforms to van der Waals equation, compute its internal energy and enthalpy from a zero datum of ideal gas at $0°R$ and 1 atm (*Gas Tables*), when it is at $310°R$ and 50 atm (Btu/mole). See problem 833.

838. Assume that methane behaves in accordance with the van der Waals equation and changes state from $150°F$ and a specific volume of 1.5 ft^3 to $80°F$ and $v_2 = 5$ ft^3. **(a)** Compute the change in internal energy, enthalpy, and entropy. The needed equations are to be found in problem 834. **(b)** If the second state is reached steady flow by an adiabatic expansion through a throttle valve and then a heat flux, what is the heat $(\Delta K \approx 0)$?

839. Estimate the change of enthalpy for 1 lb of steam at $500°F$ undergoing an isothermal process between 50 psia and 400 psia; use only pvT data from the vapor tables and the general equation (11–26, *Text*) for dh. *Hint*: plot $p = C$ curves on the vT-plane; obtain the slope at the desired T and then find the bracketed part in the general equation between the desired pressures at suitable pressure intervals; finally plot a curve of the bracketed value vs pressure—the area under this curve is the graphical integration of $\int dh_T$.

ENTROPY AND ENTHALPY DEVIATIONS

840. **(a)** Start with the general expression for entropy change ds as given in problem 826 and develop the expression for entropy deviation

$$\Delta S_d = \int_{p^0}^{p}\left[\left(\frac{\partial v}{\partial T}\right)_p - \frac{R}{p}\right]dv$$

(b) Transform the expression for ΔS_d given in **(a)** using $pv = ZRT$ and reduced properties thus obtaining

$$\Delta S_d = R\int_{p_R^0}^{p_r}\left[Z - 1 + T_R\left(\frac{\partial Z}{\partial T_R}\right)\right]\frac{dp_R}{p_R}$$

841. **(a)** Derive the expression for the enthalpy deviation

$$\Delta h_d = \int_{p^0}^{p}\left[v - T\left(\frac{\partial v}{\partial T}\right)_p\right]dp_T$$

(b) Transform the foregoing expression for Δh_d using $pv = ZRT$ and reduced properties thus obtaining

$$\frac{\Delta h_d}{T_c} = RT_R^2\int_0^p\left(\frac{\partial Z}{\partial T_R}\right)_p d(\ln p_R)$$

Discuss how this integral may be evaluated.

842. Steam at $400°C$ is compressed isothermally from 35 bar to 110 bar. Determine the changes of enthalpy and entropy by each of these methods and compare: **(a)** extract the enthalpy and entropy values directly from the Mollier chart, Item B 16(SI); **(b)** use the deviation charts.

843. Gaseous CO_2 is compressed isentropically from 110 atm, 304 K to 729 atm for storage purposes; the flow rate is 1 kg/min. Use the deviation charts and find **(a)** the final temperature and **(b)** the work required. **(c)** If the gas behaved in an ideal manner, what would be the final temperature and work? Compare answers.

844. Acetylene (C_2H_2) is stored at 3000 psia, $208°F$. In this state, how much does its entropy and enthalpy deviate from that of the ideal gas? *Ans.* $\Delta S_d = 0.1404$ Btu/lb-°R.

JOULE-THOMSON COEFFICIENT

845. **(a)** Develop the expression for the Joule-Thomson coefficient as follows:

$$\mu = \left(\frac{\partial T}{\partial p}\right)_h = \left(\frac{v}{c_p}\right)[T\beta - 1].$$

(b) In the case of the Joule-Thomson coefficient being constant $(\mu = c)$ for a given fluid, prove that the following expression must hold: $h = f(T - \mu p)$.

846. Determine the Joule-Thomson coefficient for a gas whose equation of state is **(a)** $pv = RT$, **(b)** $p(v - b) = RT$, **(c)** $(p + a/v^2)(v - b) = RT$.

847. Study Item B 34 and state whether the Joule-Thomson coefficient for mercury is positive or negative. Give reasons for your answers.

848. Steam at 9000 psia, $1100°F$ is throttled slowly and adiabatically to standard atmospheric pressure. Use Item B 15 and compute the Joule-Thomson coefficient $\mu = (\partial T/\partial p)_h$. What is its final temperature?

849. Through an adiabatic porous plug steam is throttled from 700 bar, 650°C to 40 bar; the sink temperature is 38°C. Determine **(a)** the average Joule-Thomson coefficient, **(b)** the change in availability of the flowing steam.

Ans. **(a)** +0.3332 K/bar, **(b)** −348 kJ/kg.

850. **(a)** Using the mathematical relation (11–14) in problem 794, replace the x, y, z functions with h, p, T properties and note the relationship of three quantities: specific heat at constant pressure c_p; Joule-Thomson coefficient μ: a constant-temperature coefficient $c_T = (\partial h/\partial p)_T$. **(b)** Find a corresponding relationship for three other quantities formed by replacing the x, y, z functions with u, v, T properties. *Ans.* **(a)** $c_T = -c_p\mu$.

851. Develop an expression for the inversion temperature for each of the fluids whose equations of state are given in problem 846.

852. Estimate the inversion temperature for steam and hydrogen, each at zero pressure, assuming that van der Waals equation of state governs each fluid.

SPECIFIC HEATS

853. Derive the relation for the difference of specific heats which states that $c_p - c_v = vT\beta^2/\kappa_T$. For an ideal gas, show that $vT\beta^2/\kappa_T = R$, the gas constant.

854. **(a)** Derive the relation for the difference in specific heats:

$$c_p - c_v = T\left(\frac{\partial p}{\partial T}\right)_v\left(\frac{\partial v}{\partial T}\right)_p$$

(b) Show that for a van der Waals gas,

$$c_p - c_v = \frac{TR^2}{[TR - 2a(v-b)^2/v^3]}.$$

(c) The same as **(b)** except that equation $pv = RT - Kp^n$ applies, where K is a constant.

Ans. **(c)** $R/[1+(n-1)Kp^n/(RT)]$.

855. Derive the relation for the ratio of specific heats, $c_p/c_v = k = \kappa_T/\kappa_s$ where κ_T and κ_s are the compressibility factors, isothermal and isentropic, respectively.

856. Using basic concepts, show all steps in developing the relation

$$c_p = -\frac{[\partial(v\tau)/\partial\tau]_p}{\mu_J}$$

where $\tau = 1/T$ and μ_J is the Joule-Thomson coefficient.

857. Start with the basic definition of c_v and develop the expression which shows that the rate of change of c_v with respect to volume along an isotherm is $(\partial c_v/\partial v)_T = T(\partial^2 p/\partial T^2)_v$.

858. The same as problem 857 except that the rate of change of c_p with respect to pressure along an isotherm is shown to be $(\partial c_p/\partial p)_T = -T(\partial^2 v/\partial T^2)_p = -Tv\beta^2$.

859. From the generalized Berthelot equation, (see problem 736) find

$$\frac{c_p - c_p^0}{R} = \frac{81 p_R}{T_R^3}$$

860. Along an isotherm, determine the rate of change of c_p with pressure for steam in the region of 100 psia, 900°F.

861. **(a)** Using the two state points for steam 2600 psia, 900°F and 2900 psia, 1000°F, compute $c_v = T(\partial s/\partial T)_v$. **(b)** Determine c_p in this region, say between 900°F and 1000°F at 2700 psia. **(c)** Determine k from these two specific heats.

Ans. **(a)** 0.474, **(b)** 0.732, **(c)** 1.545.

862. The Linde equation of state $v = RT/p - (a + bp)/T^3 + d + ep$ in.^{3}/lb applies reasonably well to naphtha with the constants: $R = 157$, $a = 7234(10)^7$, $b = 102(10)^7$, $d = 20$, $e = 0.52$ for p psi, T°R, and v in.^{3}/lb. At low pressure, say zero pressure the specific heat of naphtha is given by $c_p^0 = 0.000504(t + 670)$ Btu/lb-°F, for t°F. Find the approximate specific heat value at 500 psia, 400°F.

Ans. 0.933 Btu/lb-°R.

863. **(a)** Apply the exactness test to equation (11–18A), *Text*, a general equation for entropy change, and show that for $T = C$,

$$\Delta c_p = c_{p2} - c_{p1} = -T\int_1^2\left(\frac{\partial^2 v}{\partial T^2}\right)_p dp_T$$

(b) Find Δc_p for a Callendar gas whose equation of state is (a, b, are constants):

$$v = \left(\frac{RT}{p}\right) + b - \left(\frac{a}{T^{3.33}}\right)$$

Ans. **(b)** $\Delta c_p = 14.4 a(p_2 - p_1)/T^{4.33}$.

864. Show that (for G = Gibbs function, A = Helmholtz)

$$c_p = -\left(\frac{\partial^2 G}{\partial T^2}\right)_p \quad \text{and} \quad c_v = -T\left(\frac{\partial^2 A}{\partial T^2}\right)_v$$

865. Show that the relation $(\partial c_p/\partial p)_T = -T(\partial^2 v/\partial T^2)_p$, takes the form $(\partial c_p/\partial p)_T = -Tv\beta^2$ for a constant expansion coefficient β.

866. In this exercise, c_p, c_v, and k for steam will be computed. (a) Locate these two state points on Item B 16(SI): 20 bar, 400°C and 30 bar, 450°C. Obtain data and compute $c_v = T(\partial s/\partial T)_v$ using finite differences. (b) Determine $c_p = (\partial h/\partial T)_p$ in this region say between 400°C and 450°C at 25 bar. (c) Now determine $k = c_p/c_v$ from these two specific heat values.

WORK PROCESSES, LIQUID

867. This is an exercise with compressibilities and the expansion coefficient from finite differences. Let the pressure on saturated water at 200°F be increased to 1000 psia. (a) Using the compressed liquid table for H_2O, compute the average isothermal compressibility. (b) Using saturation values at 190°F and 210°F, estimate the expansion coefficient at 200°F. (c) Show that $\kappa_T - \kappa_s = T\beta^2 v/c_p$ and compute κ_s. Estimate c_p from $(\Delta h/\Delta T)_p$ at 190°F and 210°F. (d) If the increase in pressure is brought about nonflow, show that $dW_n = -\kappa_s vp \, dp$, and compute the nonflow work W_n. (e) Compute the isentropic rise in temperature. (f) Show that the steady flow work $dW_{sf} = dW_n - d(pv)$, and compute W_{sf}.

868. The same as problem 867 except that let the pressure on saturated water at 200°F be increased to 3000 psia.

869. Assume 10 lb of liquid water at 200°F are isothermally decompressed to a saturated state; the process is accompanied with a decrease in enthalpy of 30 Btu. Estimate the initial pressure. *Ans.* 1337 psia, approx.

870. (a) For the steady flow pumping of liquid water, show that if the process is considered to be reversible and adiabatic, the temperature rise during this process will be $dT = T\beta v \, dv/c_p$. (b) Estimate the temperature rise of water being compressed isentropically from saturated liquid at 100°F to 2000 psia. Assume the values of $T\beta v$ and c_p to remain constant. *Ans.* 1°F.

871. Assume that liquid mercury conforms to the van der Waals equation of state wherein its volume is given by $v = b + RTb^2/(a + pb^2)$. Find the steady flow work required to pump 1 lb/sec of liquid mercury from 1 to 5000 atm while its temperature remains constant at 32°F.

Constant values are: $a = 5100$ atm-ft^6/(pmole)^2, $b = 1.070$ ft^3/pmole.

GENERAL SYSTEMS

872. A 100-lb cube of copper at 40°F is permitted to expand reversibly and isothermally from 1200 atm to 1 atm. Average values of pertinent properties of the copper are: $\rho = 555$ lb/ft^3, $\kappa_T = 5.40 \times 10^{-8}$ in.^{2}/lb, $\beta = 2.75 \times 10^{-5}$/°R. Determine (a) the work, (b) the change of entropy, (c) the heat, (d) the change of internal energy.

873. A force B acts on a tight rubber band of length L and does a differential amount of work $dW = B \, dL$ in a reversible process. By manipulation of fundamental mathematical relations, show that $(\partial u/\partial L)_T = B - T(\partial B/\partial T)_L$.

874. The equation of state of a given rubber rod is $f(F, T, L) = 0$ where F tensile force, T temperature, and L length are fundamental properties. The following are measured quantities pertinent to the rod: $(\partial F/\partial L)_T = 50$ g/cm, $(\partial L/\partial T)_F = -0.025$ cm/°C, $(\partial F/\partial T)_L = 1.3$ g/°C. Estimate the accuracy of these measurements.

875. An elastic wire of cross-sectional area A and length L is subjected to a tensile force F. (a) Show that the availability function is $\mathscr{A} = -(1/AE_y)(\partial F/\partial T)_\varepsilon$. (b) The equation of state for the wire ($K = $ constant) is

$$\sigma = \frac{KT}{A}\left[\frac{L}{L_0} - \left(\frac{L_0}{L}\right)^2\right]$$

where L_0 is the free (unloaded) length. Show that at constant temperature, Young's modulus is $E_y = \sigma + (3KT/A)(L_0/L)^2$. (c) Using ds given in equation (p), § 11.28, *Text*, and equation (11-38), *Text*, show that $dU = (\partial U/\partial T)_\varepsilon \, dT + [\sigma + T\mathscr{A}E] \, d\varepsilon$.

MISCELLANEOUS

876. Relevant to the Mollier (hs) diagram, prove that the constant pressure lines thereon are parallel to each other at their points of intersection with a common isotherm.

877. Given the characteristic functional relation $A = F(v, T)$, express the remaining basic properties, p, s, u, h and G in terms of only the three embraced by the function.

878. Start with the functional relation $u = f(v, s)$ and develop expressions in terms of u, v, s only for the properties T, p, h, A, G.

Ans. $T = (\partial u/\partial s)_v$, $p = -(\partial u/\partial v)_s$, $h = u - v(\partial u/\partial v)_s$.

879. The same as problem 878 except that start with $G = f(p, T)$ and develop expressions in terms of G, p, T only for v, s, u, h, A.

880. Derive the Tv and pv relations for a van der Waals gas in an isentropic process. Let specific heats be some constant average values.

Ans. $T(v - b)^{R/c_v} = C$, $(p + a/v^2)(v - b)^{(c_v + R)/c_v} = C$.

881. Given the eight basic coordinates p, v, T, s, u, h, A, and G, which two will form a plane on which the slope of an isentropic trace will be given by the density ρ?

882. We have studied and used these following basic coordinates (properties): p, v, T, s, u, h, A, G. Which two will form a plane on which the slope of an isotherm $(T = c)$ is given by the absolute value of the pressure? Sketch the plane and show direction of slope on this plane.

883. Using the Gibbs primitive surface as described in the *EVS*-region (see §11.24, *Text*) develop the Maxwell relations through trigonometric and descriptive geometric manipulations.

884. Find the expression for the partial derivative $(\partial u/\partial p)_T$ for a fluid whose equation of state is (a) $pv = RT$, (b) $pv = RT + Ap$, where A is a function of temperature only.

885. A compressible fluid undergoes a change of state in accordance with the relation $pv^n = c$. Sketch path traces on the pv-plane depicting this change for values of n of 0, -0.5, -1, -2.

886. For an internally reversible process, we know that $dQ = dh - v\, dp$. Prove that in general the heat is given by $dQ = c_p\, dT + [(\partial h/\partial p)_T - v]\, dp$. From this expression prove that Q is not a property.

887. A gas obeys the equation of state $p(v - b) = RT$. (a) Is the difference $c_p - c_v$ variable or constant? Increase or decrease? (b) Is the internal energy change or the enthalpy change dependent in any way on the pressure change? (c) Will the temperature of this gas change in a throttling process? Increase or decrease? (d) Find equations for: the inversion temperature, the expansion coefficient, the isothermal compressibility coefficient; (e) the

Tv relation for an isentropic process, with specific heats constant; (f) the isentropic compressibility coefficient.

888. Since the details of the solution of this problem are in the *Text*, this may be considered programmed study. Refer to *Text* only when you must have help over an obstacle. The symbols are as previously defined. (a) Starting with the definition of the Gibbs function, derive the corresponding Maxwell relation. (b) Write the expression for $ds = s(p, T)$; use the definition of c_p and the Maxwell relation in (a), and find $ds = c_p\, dT/T - v\beta\, dp$. (c) Using results above and $pv = ZRT$, derive the equation for the entropy deviation, $(s^* - s)_{T,}$ in terms of reduced properties. (d) Find an expression for c_p from ds in (b). Then show that $k = \kappa_T/\kappa_s$. (e) Show that the nonflow isentropic work is given by $dW_n = -vp\kappa_s\, dp$.

889. Apply the functional relation $V = f(p, t, m)$ to a heterogenous system $[m = f(m_1, m_2 \cdots m_i)]$ and show that the partial property $v_i = (\partial v/\partial m_i)_{p,T,m(-)}$ is exactly the same as the specific property v, that is, $v_i = v$.

890. Given the two traces, isothermal and isentropic, on the pV-plane, show that the relation between their slopes and the heats for a reversible isothermal process and a reversible isometric process is

$$(\partial p/\partial v)_s/(\partial p/\partial v)_T = 1 - (dQ/dp)_T/(dQ/dp)_v$$

891. The (specific volume)–(temperature) relation for liquid water is shown by the figure (Bridgman's data). What do these data in the figure indicate concerning the frequently made statement that "all constant pressure lines on the Ts-plane are concurrent (point convergence) on the saturated liquid line at 4°C"?

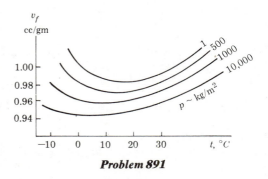

Problem 891

COMPUTER PROGRAMS

892. An isothermal trace, less than that of critical, is to be plotted on the pV-plane for a van der Waals gas. Select the constants for a given gas from Item B 18, write the virial form of the van der Waals equation, use a pressure range of 1–50 atm, and calculate the various volumes at each pressure and for the selected temperature. Write this computer program.

893. The Joule-Thomson coefficient for water is being studied to compare the effect of throttling on the two separate phases, liquid and vapor. Let each separate phase begin saturated at 3200 psia and vary the respective down stream pressures from 3000 psia to 500 psia in equal pressure increments of 500 psia. Plot a curve of the coefficient versus pressure reflecting this comparison. Program this problem.

894. Values of these three coefficients are desired: coefficient of volumetric expansion β, isentropic compressibility coefficient K_S, and the isothermal compressibility coefficient K_T. The study involves air and steam each measured at 15 psia over the temperature range 300–1100°F using equal increments of 200°F. Find the respective coefficients for each fluid and compare. Program this problem.

895–900. These numbers may be used for other problems.

12

MIXTURES OF GASES AND VAPORS

Note: Solve the problems using vapor tables unless instructed otherwise, and then check computations where possible by a psychrometric chart. By doing this you will become familiar with both the basic theory and the commercial manner of obtaining a solution. A Ts diagram and, in process problems, an energy diagram should accompany all solutions. These molecular weights will prove helpful in many of the problems: $C = 12$, $O_2 = 32$, $H_2 = 2$, $N_2 = 28$, $S = 32$, dry air = 29.

KNOWN GRAVIMETRIC ANALYSIS

901. The gravimetric analysis of dry air is approximately $O_2 = 23.1\%$ and $N_2 = 76.9\%$. Calculate (a) the volumetric analysis, (b) the gas constant, (c) the respective partial pressures, and (d) the specific volume and density at 1 atm, 15.6°C. (e) How many kilograms of O_2 must be added to 2.27 kg air to produce a mixture which is 50% O_2 by volume?

Ans. (a) 20.81% O_2, (b) 288.2 J/kg-K, (c) 21.08 kPaa for O_2, (d) 0.821 m³/kg, (e) 1.471 kg.

902. (a) How many kilograms of nitrogen must be mixed with 3.60 kg of carbon dioxide in order to produce a gaseous mixture that is 50% by volume of each constituent? (b) For the resulting mixture, determine M_m, R_m, and the partial pressure of the N_2 if that of the CO_2 is 138 kPaa.

903. One mol of a gaseous mixture has the following gravimetric analysis: $O_2 = 16\%$, $CO_2 = 44\%$, $N_2 = 40\%$. Find (a) the molecular weight of the mixture, (b) the mass of each constituent, (c) the moles of each constituent in the mixture, (d) R_m, and (e) partial pressures for $p_m = 30$ psia.

Ans. (a) 34.13 lb/mole, (b) 5.48 lb O_2, (c) 0.171 mole O_2, (d) 45.2 (e) 5.13 psia (O_2).

904. A gaseous mixture composed of 25 kg of N_2, 3.6 kg of H_2, and 60 kg of CO_2 is at 200 kPaa, 50°C. Find the respective partial pressures and compute the volume of each component at its own partial pressure and 50°C.

905. Assume 4 lb of oxygen are mixed with 6 lb of an unknown gas. The resulting mixture occupies a volume of 42 ft³ at 40 psia and 150°F. Determine (a) R and M of the unknown gas constituent, (b) the volumetric analysis, and (c) the partial pressures.

Ans. (a) $R = 33.75$ ft lb/lb°R, (b) 48.8% O_2, (c) 19.52 psia (O_2).

906. An 8-ft³ drum contains a gaseous mixture of CO_2 and CH_4, each 50% by mass, at $p_m = 100$ psia, 100°F; 2 lb of O_2 are added to the drum with the mixture temperature remaining at 100°F. For the final mixture, find (a) the gravimetric analysis, (b) the volumetric analysis, (c) c_p, (d) p_m.

Ans. (**a**) 30.58% CO_2, (**b**) 18.2% CO_2, (**c**) 0.3096 Btu/lb-°R, (**d**) 147.2 psia.

KNOWN VOLUMETRIC ANALYSIS

907. Assume 5 mole of a gaseous mixture are comprised of 1.5 mole of nitrogen, 2.75 mole of oxygen, and 0.75 mole of carbon dioxide. Find (**a**) the volumetric analysis, (**b**) the mass of the mixture, and (**c**) the equivalent molecular weight of the mixture.

Ans. (**a**) 30% N_2, (**b**) 163 lb, (**c**) 32.6.

908. A 283-ℓ drum contains a gaseous mixture at 689.48 kPaa and 37.8°C whose volumetric composition is 30% O_2 and 70% CH_4. How many kilograms of mixture must be bled and what mass of O_2 added in order to produce at the original pressure and temperature a mixture whose new volumetric composition is 70% O_2 and 30% CH_4?

Ans. Bleed 0.90 kg, add 1.381 kg O_2.

909. The same as problem 908 except that the original composition is to be changed to the final composition by replacing some of the original mixture with an equal mass of O_2; also, a new pressure will obtain.

910. A gaseous mixture has the following composition by volume: 20% N_2, 30% CO_2, 50% CH_4. Determine (**a**) the gravimetric analysis, (**b**) the molecular weight of the mixture, (**c**) R_m, (**d**) the specific heat C_p for the mixture, and (**e**) the partial pressure of the N_2 if that of the CH_4 is 9 psia.

Ans. (**b**) 26.8, (**e**) 3.6 psia.

911. A rigid tank containing 3 lb of a gaseous mixture of nitrogen and carbon dioxide (each 50% by volume) at 40 psia and 150°F receives 1 lb more of nitrogen with the temperature remaining at 150°F. For the resulting 4 lb, determine (**a**) the gravimetric and volumetric analyses, (**b**) the pressure, and (**c**) the molecular weight.

Ans. (**a**) For N_2: $f = 54.2\%$, $X = 65\%$; (**b**) 57.1 psia; (**c**) 33.6 lb/mole.

912. A gaseous mixture of CH_4, N_2, CO, and O_2 occupies a vessel at the respective partial pressures of 140, 55, 70, and 15 kPaa. Find (**a**) the volumetric and gravimetric analyses, (**b**) M_m and R_m, (**c**) the specific heats c_p and c_v for the mixture, and (**d**) the volume occupied by 45 kg of the mixture at p_m and 32°C.

PROPERTIES OF AIR–STEAM MIXTURES

913. Atmospheric air is at 14.65 psia, $t_d = 94°F$, and $t_w = 68°F$. Find (**a**) the partial pressure of the water vapor, (**b**) the humidity ratio, (**c**) the dew point, (**d**) the relative humidity, (**e**) the volumetric and gravimetric percentages of the H_2O, and (**f**) the volume occupied by the H_2O in 1 lb da.

Ans. (**a**) 0.2027 psia, (**b**) 0.00873 lb v/lb da, (**c**) 52.5°F, (**d**) 25.6%, (**e**) 1.38% by vol, (**f**) 14.20 ft³.

914. The humidity ratio of atmospheric air at 1 atm, 26.7°C is 0.016 kg v/kg da. Find (**a**) p_v, (**b**) ϕ, (**c**) the dew point, (**d**) ρ_m, (**e**) the volumetric and gravimetric percentages of the H_2O, and (**f**) the mass of H_2O in 28.32 m³ of the atmospheric air.

Ans. (**a**) 2.54 kPaa, (**b**) 72.6%, (**c**) 21.3°C, (**d**) 1.166 kg/m³, (**e**) 2.51% by vol, (**f**) 0.52 kg.

915. The temperature in a steam condenser is 32.2°C, and there are 0.075 kg da/kg H_2O present. If the H_2O is saturated vapor, find (**a**) ω, (**b**) the condenser vacuum for a 1-bar barometer, (**c**) ρ_m, (**d**) the percentage by volume and the percentage by mass of the air.

Ans. (**a**) 13.31 kg v/kg da, (**b**) 96.29 kPa vac, (**c**) 0.0368 kg/m³, (**d**) 4.46%, 6.98%.

916. (**a**) Calculate the vacuum in a steam condenser in which the temperature is 90°F and into which air has leaked so that there are 0.15 lb da/lb v; barometer is 29.92 in. Hg. (**b**) Also, for the condition given, find the dew point temperature and the humidity ratio.

917. A low-pressure, air-steam mixture at 150°F has a dew point of 80°F. If the steam/air mass ratio is 4/100, find (**a**) ϕ, (**b**) p_m, (**c**) ρ_m, (**d**) the volumetric percentage of the H_2O, and (**e**) the volume occupied by the dry air in 1 lb vapor.

Ans. (**a**) 13.65%, (**b**) 17.072 in. Hg abs, (**c**) 0.0363 lb/ft³, (**d**) 6.05%, (**e**) 711 ft³.

918. The gravimetric percentage of water in atmospheric air is 1.5%. Also, $t_d = 100°F$, $p_m = 14.60$ psia. Find (**a**) ω, (**b**) p_v, (**c**) ϕ, (**d**) the dew point, and (**e**) the volume occupied by 100 lb atmospheric air.

Ans. (**a**) 0.01523 lb v/lb da, (**b**) 0.349 psia, (**c**) 36.8%, (**d**) 68.9°F, (**e**) 1435 ft³.

919. The enthalpy for steam vapor at low pressures, and within the temperature range 10–60°C, may be obtained from the expression $h_v = 2500 + 1.817\, t_v$, kJ/kg, where t_v is in °C.

Demonstrate that this equation results from plotting h_g for steam on rectangular coordinate paper and noting that a straight line results. See Item B 16(SI) for values.

920. The same as problem 919 except use Item B 13, a temperature range of 50–150°F, and find that $h_v = 1061 + 0.445\ t_v$, Btu/lb.

921. A gaseous mixture at 137.9 kPaa, 93.3°C has the following volumetric analysis: 35% CO_2, 50% N_2, 15% H_2O. With respect to the H_2O, find (a) the humidity ratio, (b) the dew point, (c) the relative humidity, and (d) the degree of saturation. (e) What is the density of the mixture?

Ans. (a) 0.092 kg v/kg dg, (b) 60.8°C, (c) 26%, (d) 0.13, (e) 1.45 kg/m³.

ADIABATIC SATURATION PROCESS

922. Atmospheric air at 28.50 in. Hg abs has a 20°F wet-bulb depression from 88°F db. Find (a) the humidity ratio from the adiabatic saturation equation, (b) p_v and ϕ, (c) the dew point, (d) the density of the atmospheric air, and (e) the mass of dry air in 5000 cfm of the atmospheric air. (f) Check the value of p_v above by Carrier's equation and by the psychrometric chart.

Ans. (a) 0.01081 lb v/lb da, (b) 36.5%, (c) 58°F, (d) 0.0686 lb/ft³, (e) 339 lb/min.

923. An adiabatic evaporative process occurs as follows: 6.8 kg/s da at 1 bar, 104.4°C and 0.454 kg/s wet steam ($y = 10\%$) at 1 bar each enter an adiabatic chamber and leave after mixing as a gas-vapor mixture at 1 bar; all liquid initially in the steam evaporates during mixing to form added vapor. Sketch an energy diagram of the steady flow system and for the exit mixture find (a) the temperature, (b) the humidity ratio, (c) the relative humidity. (d) What is the entropy production and the irreversibility for the mixing process if $t_0 = 15.6$°C?

924. Atmospheric air at 14.55 psia and 80°F db undergoes an adiabatic saturation process to a final temperature of 58°F. For the state of the air just prior to the adiabatic process, find (a) t_w, (b) p_v, (c) ϕ, (d) ω, and (e) ρ_m. (f) For the state after the process, what are p_v, t_w, ω, and ρ_m?

925. If an open pan of water be placed in a $16 \times 20 \times 9$-ft room where $p_m = 14.50$ psia, $t_d = 78$°F, $t_w = 54$°F, approximate the maximum loss of water from the pan that may occur.

Neglect infiltration and exfiltration losses, except assume that the total pressure and the dry bulb temperature remain constant.

Ans. 3.65 lb.

926. The state of the atmospheric air is $p_m = 29.60$ in. Hg abs, $t_d = 80$°F, $t_w = 60$°F. (a) Find, ω, p_v, ϕ, and the dew point, using principle of adiabatic saturation. (b) Check p_v by Carrier's equation. (c) Solve (a), using the psychrometric chart (show all chart readings on a sketch).

Ans. 0.00659 lb v/lb da, 0.31 in. Hg abs, 30%, 45.9°F.

PSYCHROMETRIC CHART

927. There are conditioned 5000 cfm of atmospheric air ($p_m = 14.7$ psia, $t_{d1} = 80$°F, $t_{w1} = 60$°F) at constant relative humidity until the dry bulb temperature becomes $t_{d2} = 100$°F. Make a psychrometric chart sketch and find (a) ϕ_1, (b) p_{v1}, (c) ω_2, (d) h_{wb1}, (e) t_{w2}, (f) v_{m1}, (g) m_{da}, lb/min, (h) final dew point, (i) p_{v2}, (j) moisture added, lb/min.

Ans. (a) 30%, (d) 26.5 Btu/lb da, (g) 326 lb/min.

928. Saturated atmospheric air at 14.7 psia, $t_d = 54$°F undergoes a constant pressure humidifying process until its relative humidity is halved while its humidity ratio is doubled. Make a psychrometric chart sketch and find (a) final t_d, t_w, and dew point temperatures, (b) moisture added to 2000 cfm of initial atmospheric air, lb/min, (c) heat required, Btu/min.

929. To 5000 cfm of atmospheric air measured at 14.7 psia, 90°F db, $\phi_1 = 30\%$, there are added 25 grains of water vapor to each pound of dry air involved; the wet bulb temperature remains constant during this process. Show the process on a psychrometric chart sketch and determine (a) t_{d2}, (b) ϕ_2, (c) moisture change, lb/min.

930. There are heated 1350 cfm of atmospheric air initially saturated at 14.70 psia, 65°F db until the final dry bulb temperature is $t_{d2} = 90$°F; the dew point temperature remains constant during this heating process. Use the psychrometric chart only (show sketch) and find (a) ϕ_2, (b) the initial mass of atmospheric air, lb/min, (c) heat required, Btu/min.

931. For a given state, the atmospheric conditions are $p_m = 14.7$ psia, $t_d = 89$°F, $t_w = 74$°F. Making the solution from the psychrometric chart only, find (**a**) the dew point, (**b**) ω, (**c**) p_v, (**d**) ϕ, and (**e**) the specific volume. (**f**) How many pounds of water vapor are present in 15,000 ft^3 of this air? (**g**) How many pounds of water are required to saturate the 15,000 ft^3 of air at 74°F if t_w remains constant? If t_d remains constant? Assume that the total pressure remains unchanged.

Ans. (**a**) 68°F, (**b**) 0.01458 lb v/lb da, (**c**) 0.3035 psia, (**d**) 50%, (**e**) 14.15 ft^3/lb da, (**f**) 15.46 lb, (**g**) 3.63 lb for $t_w = C$.

932. Atmospheric air, 1500 cfm, at 92°F db and 60% relative humidity is to be conditioned to 75°F db and 40% relative humidity. Using a *psychrometric chart*, find (**a**) the dew points, wet-bulb temperatures, and vapor pressures for the atmospheric air and for the conditioned air; (**b**) the amount of moisture removed; and (**c**) the net transferred heat. (**d**) Solve the problem without using the chart.

Ans. (**b**) 1.27 lb/min. (**d**) −1810 Btu/min.

MIXTURES OTHER THAN AIR–STEAM

933. There are added (by mass) 2 parts of benzene vapor to 13 parts of dry air to form a gas-vapor mixture at 15 psia, 110°F. Find the relative humidity ϕ, dew point, and degree of saturation μ, all based upon the benzene vapor.

934. Mix 6 lb of ethyl alcohol vapor with 18 lb oxygen to form a gas-vapor mixture at 20 psia, 140°F. Find (**a**) gravimetric analysis, (**b**) volumetric analysis, (**c**) relative humidity, (**d**) dew point temperature.

Ans. (**a**) 75% O_2, (**b**) 81.2% O_2, (**c**) 57%, (**d**) 119°F.

935. A gas/vapor mixture at 20 psia, 130°F is formed as follows: an unknown mass of benzene (C_6H_6) vapor is mixed with 10 lb of oxygen gas. The relative humidity of the mixture based upon the benzene vapor is 25%. Find (**a**) the mass of benzene vapor ($R = 19.8$) in the mixture, and (**b**) the dewpoint temperature. Make appropriate sketches showing the vapor state on the Ts-plane and the tp-chart from which data were taken.

936. To each 25 lb of dry air there are added 2 lb of octane vapor (C_8H_{18}, $R = 13.55$) to form a gas-vapor mixture at 30 psia, 160°F. Sketch the Ts diagram depicting the condition of the vapor in the mixture and find (**a**)

gravimetric analysis f, (**b**) volumetric analysis X, (**c**) relative humidity, (**d**) dew point temperature.

937. The volumetric composition of a mixture is 90% He and 10% H_2O for the state $p_{ml} = 20$ psia, $t_{ml} = 140$°F. (**a**) Find ϕ_1, ω_1, and the dew point for this state. (**b**) If this mixture is cooled at constant total pressure to 60°F at the rate of 1000 cfm measured at state 1, find the rate at which condensation occurs.

Ans. (**a**) 69.2%, 0.503 lb v/lb dg, 126°F, (**d**) 5.0 lb/min.

938. A gaseous mixture at 20 psia and 200°F has the following volumetric analysis: 35% CO_2, 50% N_2, 15% H_2O. With respect to the H_2O, find (**a**) the humidity ratio, (**b**) the dew point, (**c**) the relative humidity, and (**d**) the degree of saturation. (**e**) What is the density of the mixture?

Ans. (**a**) 0.092 lb v/lb dg, (**b**) 141.5°F, (**c**) 26%, (**d**) 0.13, (**e**) 0.0907 lb/ft^3.

939. Through the manifold of an automobile engine there moves 15 lb/min dry air, 1 lb/min octane vapor, and 0.20 lb/min water vapor, all mixed at 12 psia and 130°F. Find the relative humidity and the dew point of the mixture (**a**) with respect to the octane vapor and (**b**) with respect to the water vapor.

Ans. (**a**) 17.21%, 68°F, (**b**) 11.21%, 59.1°F.

940. Atmospheric air at 80°F db, 29.92 in. Hg abs, and 50% relative humidity is drawn through a carburetor and mixed with octane fuel in the proportions 15.11 lb da/lb octane (approximately 100% ideal air for combustion). In the manifold, $p_m = 12$ psia and $t_m = 120$°F. (**a**) What mass of water vapor passes through the carburetor, lb v/lb da? For the mixture in the manifold, find (**b**) the masses of water vapor and octane vapor per pound of dry air; (**c**) the partial pressures of the dry air, water vapor, and octane vapor; (**d**) the relative humidity and the dew point with respect to the octane vapor; and (**e**) the relative humidity and dew point with respect to the water vapor.

941. The same as problem 940 except that the fuel is methyl alcohol and there are 6.46 lb da/lb fuel.

Ans. (**a**) 0.0109 lb v/lb da; (**b**) 0.155 lb alcohol/lb da; (**c**) alcohol $p_v = 1.454$ psia; (**d**) 19.8%, 61°F; (**e**) 10.71%, 51.2°F.

942. An adiabatic saturation process occurs as follows; dry oxygen at 10 psia enters a constant pressure adiabatic saturation chamber in which the liquid is octane (C_8H_{18}).

Oxygen and octane vapor leave the chamber in a saturated state at 77°F, the adiabatic saturation (wet-bulb) temperature of the O_2 and C_8H_{18}. (a) At what temperature does the oxygen enter? (b) Compute the lb O_2 per lb C_8H_{18} at the exit.

Ans. (a) 144°F, (b) 10.7 lb O_2/lb C_8H_{18}.

943. There are enclosed 2 lb O_2 and 0.1 lb H_2O in a 10-ft^3 vessel at 140°F. Assume that the gaseous contents act as ideal gases and determine (a) the mass of liquid H_2O present, (b) the pressure p_m of the mixture, (c) the humidity ratio of the gaseous components, (d) the quality of the H_2O considering the total amount, (e) the volumetric fraction of O_2.

ISOBARIC PROCESS

944. The volumetric percentages of a gas-vapor mixture are 90% H_2 and 10% H_2O when the temperature and total pressure are 150°F and 20 psia. This mixture is cooled with constant total pressure at the rate of 1000 cfm, measured at the initial state, to 60°F. Determine the initial relative humidity and the rate at which condensation occurs.

Ans. 53.8%, 2.475 lb/min.

945. Atmospheric air is at 14.7 psia, 70°F and 50% relative humidity. The air is now cooled in a steady flow constant pressure manner until its temperature is 40°F. For a flow of 1000 cfm of initial air, find (a) the final relative humidity, (b) the moisture removed lb/min. Solve both by analytical method and by use of the psychrometric chart. A *TS* diagram and a sketch of the chart are required.

946. A spray of chilled water receives 2000 cfm of atmospheric air at 29.85 in. Hg abs, 100°F and a relative humidity of $\phi = 60\%$; the air leaves saturated at 60°F. Use the psychrometric chart only (showing sketch as part of your solution) and solve for (a) the dry air processed, lb/min; (b) the moisture change for the air, lb/min; (c) the dew points for both air conditions; (d) the change of wet bulb enthalpy, Btu/min.

947. A frictionless, constant-pressure, piston-and-cylinder arrangement contains 1 lb of a gaseous mixture whose volumetric analysis is 70% N_2, 10% O_2, and 20% CO_2. Use the gas tables and find (a) the heat to cool the mixture from 3000°F to 300°F, (b) the work, and (c) ΔS.

Ans. (a) −765.8, (b) −168.8 Btu, (c) −0.4239 Btu/°R.

948. Atmospheric air at 29.80 in. Hg abs, 80°F db, and 50% relative humidity is heated at constant pressure to 110°F. Find (a) the relative humidity after heating, (b) Δh_m, (c) Δh_{wb} (use chart), and (d) the dew point of the original air and of the heated air. (e) How much heat will be required for 1500 cfm atmospheric air?

Ans. (a) 19.90%, (b) 7.34, (c) 7.40 Btu/lb da, (d) 59.7°F (original), (e) 793 Btu/min.

949. Assume 1000 ft^3 of a gaseous mixture, whose gravimetric analysis is 20% CO_2, 15% O_2, 65% N_2, are at 15 psia and 300°F. Find (a) the volumetric analysis, (b) the respective partial pressures, (c) R_m and M_m, (d) the moles of mixture and of each constituent, and (e) the heat with no change in pressure to reduce the temperature 150°F, (f) the volume the mixture occupies after the cooling.

950. The volumetric percentages of a gas-vapor mixture are 90% H_2 and 10% H_2O when the temperature and total pressure are 65.6°C and 137.9 kPaa. This mixture is cooled with constant total pressure at the rate of 28.32 m^3/min, measured at the initial state, to 15.6°C. Determine the initial relative humidity and the rate at which condensation occurs.

Ans. 53.8%, 1.122 kg/min.

951. For summer comfort, atmospheric air in state 1, at $p_m = 24.45$ in. Hg, 80°F db, and 70% relative humidity, is to be cooled at constant total pressure to 50°F (state 2). Then the air-vapor mixture at 2 is heated to state 3 at 70°F (by heat flux into the space). For a flow of 1000 cfm at 1, compute: (a) the lb/min of dry air, (b) the humidity ratios at 1, 2, and 3, (c) the lb/min of H_2O condensed, (d) the dew-point temperatures at 1, 2, and 3, (e) the heat removed from state 1 to 2, Btu/min, (f) the relative humidity at state 3. (g) Solve the problem by psychrometric chart, specifying also the wet-bulb temperatures at 1, 2, and 3. Show solution on a large sketch. Is there a theoretical reason for the answers by chart not being the same as those computed? Discuss.

Ans. (a) 58.2 lb/min, (b) 0.019, 0.00936, (c) 0.56 lb/min, (d) 69.2°F, 50°F, (e) 1032 Btu/min, (f) 49.1%.

952. Air at 110°F, $\phi = 10\%$ in a desert location ($p_m = 13$ psia) is cooled by contact with water (steady flow through wet screens). The air leaves the cooler at 76°F, $\phi = 80\%$. (a) If the water enters at 80°F and cools to 70°F as it leaves the unit, how much is supplied to the system (considered adiabatic) per pound of incoming air? (**b**) How much make-up water is needed during 1 hr for 1000 cfm of incoming air? Sketch an energy balance.

Ans. (**a**) 0.369 lb, (**b**) 41.5 lb/hr.

ISOMETRIC PROCESS

953. Consider 4 lb of CO and 2 lb of CH$_4$ at 90°F that are in a 20-ft^3 rigid drum. Find (**a**) p_m, (**b**) the volumetric analysis, (**c**) the partial pressures, and (**d**) the heat to cause a temperature rise of 100°F.

Ans. (**a**) 78.9 psia, (**b**) 53.5% CO, (**c**) 42 psia (CO), (**d**) 153 Btu.

954. A mixture of the two gases O$_2$ and N$_2$ occupies a given volume at 30 psia and 200°F. If the partial pressure of the O$_2$ is twice that of the N$_2$, find (**a**) the volumetric and gravimetric analyses, (**b**) R_m, (**c**) the density, and (**d**) the final pressure and temperature if 80 Btu/lb of heat are absorbed with no change in volume.

955. There are heated 2 m^3 of air-steam mixture, initially saturated at 1 bar, 20°C, at constant volume. If the final temperature is 65°C, find (**a**) the masses of dry air and water vapor, (**b**) the relative humidity and partial pressures for the final state, (**c**) the heat.

956. To what temperature must saturated air at 1 bar and 30°C be heated at constant volume in order to quarter its initial relative humidity?

957. Assume 20 ft^3 of an air-steam mixture are initially at 14.70 psia, 96°F db, and 100% relative humidity. The air is cooled at constant volume to 40°F. Find (**a**) ω_1, (**b**) the partial pressures at the final state, (**c**) ω_2, (**d**) the temperature at which condensation started, (**e**) the total amount of vapor condensed, and (**f**) the heat.

Ans. (**a**) 0.03775 lb v/lb da, (**b**) 12.45, 0.1217 psia, (**c**) 0.006075 lb v/lb da, (**d**) 96°F, (**e**) 0.0427 lb, (**f**) −57.3 Btu.

958. Atmospheric air is compressed and stored in a 30-ft^3 rigid tank wherein initially $p_1 = 60$ psia, $t_1 = 140$°F, $\phi = 40$%. Sometime later the temperature is $t_2 = 60$°F. For the final state determine (**a**) the humidity ratio, (**b**) the relative humidity. (**c**) How much heat was rejected during this cooling period?

959. Consider 10 lb of a mixture of dry air and octane vapor ($\phi_1 = 50$%) at $p_m = 20$ psia that are cooled at constant volume from 170°F

to 70°F. Determine (**a**) the masses of air and vapor initially present, (**b**) the total volume occupied, (**c**) the mass of vapor condensed, (**d**) the final pressure of the mixture.

ISOTHERMAL PROCESS

960. Assume 10 lb of an air-steam mixture, initially saturated at 75 psia and 90°F, are *expanded* isothermally until the partial pressure of the vapor becomes 0.178 psia. For the final state, find (**a**) the partial pressure of the air, (**b**) the relative humidity, (**c**) the dew point, (**d**) the heat.

Ans. (**a**) 18.93 psia, (**b**) 25.5%, (**c**) 50°F, (**d**) 516 Btu.

961. Atmospheric air, initially saturated at 15 psia, 110°F, is *compressed* isothermally until the final pressure is $p_{m2} = 45$ psia. Sketch the Ts diagram and for 20 lb atmospheric air find (**a**) the final relative humidity, (**b**) the amount of moisture condensed, lb.

962. Twenty pounds of a dry air-steam vapor mixture are at 30 psia, 90°F and $\phi_1 = 80$%. The air *expands* isothermally until $\phi_2 = 20$%. Sketch the Ts diagram showing this process for the vapor and find (**a**) final mixture pressure, (**b**) final humidity ratio, (**c**) final dewpoint, (**d**) the total entropy change of the vapor.

Ans. (**a**) 7.5 psia, (**b**) 0.0118 lb v/lb da, (**c**) 43.6°F, (**d**) 0.0356 Btu/°R.

963. A gas-vapor mixture is formed at 10 psia, 120°F by mixing octane (C$_8$H$_{18}$) vapor and gaseous oxygen until the relative humidity based upon the octane vapor is 20%. The mixture is now *compressed* isothermally until the mixture pressure becomes 80 psia. Find the amount of vapor condensed for 100 lb of initial mixture. Use the saturation tp-chart found in appendix.

964. There are *compressed* isothermally 100 m^3/min of a dry air-steam from $p_{m1} = 1$ bar, $t_{d1} = 100$°C, $\phi_1 = 20$% to a saturated state. Use Item B 16 (SI), show both Ts and hs diagrams, and find (**a**) initial p_v, (**b**) ω_1, (**c**) initial and final dewpoint temperatures, (**d**) final p_m. (**e**) If the compression process is continued after the saturation state has been reached until $p_m = 10$ bar, find the mass of vapor condensed.

965. There are *compressed* 1000 cfm of atmospheric air measured at 29.60 in. Hg abs,

96°F db, 86°F wb. After compression, the air is cooled to a state where $p_2 = 90$ psia, $t_2 = 96$°F. (a) How much vapor will be condensed? (b) If the compression process takes place at $T = C$ to 90 psia, what is the heat? (c) If it takes place isentropically to 90 psia and then cools at $p = C$, what is the heat? (d) If condensed vapor is removed and the cooled air expanded to atmospheric pressure and temperature, find the resulting relative humidity.

966. Atmospheric air at 14.7 psia, 90°F and a relative humidity of 50% is *compressed* isothermally until the air becomes saturated (100% relative humidity). Sketch the *TS* diagram for the process and find (a) final pressure, (b) initial and final humidity ratios. (c) initial and final dew point temperatures. Solve analytically; your psychrometric chart is of no use in this problem.

Ans. (a) 29.40 psia, (b) 0.01512 lb v/lb da, (c) 68.85, 90°F.

967. An air-steam mixture, 4.535 kg and initially saturated at 517.11 kPaa, 32.2°C, is *expanded* isothermally until the partial pressure of the vapor becomes 1.227 kPaa. For the final state, find (a) the partial pressure of the air, (b) the relative humidity, (c) the dew point, (d) the heat.

Ans. (a) 130.52 kPaa, (b) 25.5%, (c) 10°C, (d) 544 kJ.

MIXING STREAMS

968. There are mixed 8500 cfm of saturated air at 14.7 psia, 48°F db, with 6600 cfm of air at 14.6 psia, 92°F db, 60% relative humidity, in a steady flow adiabatic process. For the resulting mixture, determine (a) ω, (b) t_d, (c) ϕ (d) the dew point, (e) ρ, and (f) μ.

Ans. (a) 0.0123 lb v/lb da, (b) 66.3°F, (c) 88.7%, (d) 62.9°F.

969. Assume 1 lb/min of steam is mixed with 750 cfm of atmospheric air in a steady flow constant pressure manner. Initially for the air, $t_a = 90$°F, $\phi = 20\%$, barometer = 28.25 in. Hg. Determine (a) the humidity ratio for the air prior to mixing, (b) the humidity ratio after mixing, (c) the final relative humidity if the temperature remains at 90°F; $p_m = C$.

970. There are mixed 600 lb/min of atmospheric air at 29.92 in. Hg barometer, 96°F db, 75°F wb with 400 lb/min of recirculated air at 29.92 in. Hg, 70°F db, 70% relative humidity, all in an adiabatic steady flow manner. For the resulting mixture, determine (a) the humidity ratio (b) t_d, (c) t_w.

Ans. (a) 0.01277, (b) 85.3°F, (c) 70.8°F.

971. In an air-conditioning system, there are mixed adiabatically two steady flow streams; $\Delta P = 0$, $\Delta K = 0$. One stream A is atmospheric air at 29.92 in. Hg abs, 90°F db, $\phi = 38\%$, 500 lb/min; the other stream B is recirculated air at 29.92 in. Hg abs, 70°F db, $\phi = 70\%$, 400 lb/min. Determine (a) the humidity ratio of each stream A, B, C (the resulting mixture), (b) the dry bulb temperature and dew point of stream C, (c) the entropy production of the mixing process.

Ans. (a) 0.0114, 0.01094, 0.0112 lb v/lb da, (b) 82°F, (c) 374 Btu/°R-min.

972. With 150 m³/min of saturated air at 1 bar, 10°C, there are mixed 100 m³/min of air at 1 bar, 40°C db, 60% relative humidity in a steady flow adiabatic process. For the resulting mixture determine (a) ω, (b) t_d, (c) ϕ, (d) dewpoint, and (e) ρ.

973. Two flow lines merge at an adiabatic mixing point. One line transports 105 m³/min of CO at 140 kPaa and 90°C; the other transports 175 m³/min of CH_4 at 140 kPaa and 15°C. Considering velocity effects to be negligible, find (a) the temperature of the resulting mixture, (b) the gravimetric and volumetric analyses of the mixture, (c) R_m and M_m, and (d) the entropy production.

WATER AND AIR STREAMS

974. An induced-draft *cooling tower* is required to cool 9020 gpm of entering water from 84°F to 68°F. The average condition of the atmospheric air is 29.75 in. Hg abs, 70°F db, and 60°F wb. It leaves the tower saturated at 80°F. Sketch the energy diagram, and find (a) the volume of air required and (b) the hourly make-up for the evaporation losses.

Ans. (a) 965,000 cfm, (b) 57,960 lb/hr.

975. Water enters a *cooling tower* at 110°F and leaves at 76°F. The tower receives 500,000 cfm of atmospheric air at 29.75 in. Hg abs, 70°F db, 40% relative humidity; the air leaves the tower at 95°F db, $\phi = 95\%$. Find (a) the mass per min of dry air passing through the tower, (b) the volume of incoming water cooled, gpm, and (c) the amount of water evaporated each hour.

976. A mechanical draft *cooling tower* receives 250,000 cfm of atmospheric air at 29.60 in. Hg abs, 84°F db, 45% relative humidity and discharges the air saturated at 98°F. If the tower receives 3500 gpm of water at 104°F, what will be the exit temperature of the cooled water? *Ans.* 83°F.

977. In a forced-draft *cooling tower*, 2740 lb/min of water are received at 106°F and cooled to 82°F with an evaporation loss of 3630 lb/hr. The tower receives 25,000 cfm of air at 14.7 psia, 100°F db, 76°F wb. Find the temperature of the exit air if it is in a saturated state.

978. An *air washer* receives 1500 cfm of atmospheric air at $t_1 = 40°F$ db, $\phi_1 = 20\%$ and delivers the conditioned air at $t_2 = 80°F$ db, $\phi_2 = 50\%$ in the following manner: The atmospheric air is initially saturated to the dew point of the conditioned state by passing it through a spray of warm water. It is then heated to the final state. (a) Using steam tables and an algebraic solution, find ω_1, ω_2, Δh_{12}, $\Delta H_{wb\,12}$, the mass of warm water evaporated, the air temperature from the spray, and the heat transferred to the saturated air. (b) Using the psychrometric chart insofar as possible, solve the problem. Show a large sketch of your solution.

Ans. (a) 0.001032, 0.01091, $\Delta h = 20.45$, 70.62 lb/hr, 59.68°F, 580 Btu/min.

979. Atmospheric air at 96°F db and 60% relative humidity is to be conditioned to 70°F db and 50% relative humidity. This is to be done by first *cooling* the incoming free air in a spray of chilled water to the dew point of the desired state and then heating the resulting mixture. The temperature of the spray water increases from 38°F to 48°F. For 6000 cfm of incoming free air, find (a) the temperature of the air leaving the spray, (b) the amount of vapor removed from the free air, (c) the amount of spray water required, and (d) the tons of refrigeration required to chill the spray water back to 38°F.

Ans. (a) 50.46°F, (b) 5.93 lb/min, (c) 1105 lb/min, (d) 55.2.

MISCELLANEOUS

980. Show that if atmospheric air be expanded (or compressed) isentropically without condensation of the water vapor (ideal gas components), the respective variations in entropy of the two components, dry air and water vapor, will be other than zero—but equal and opposite such that the entropy of the mixture remains constant.

981. The thermodynamic system shown in the figure is an insulated rigid container divided internally with a partition. Initially, side A contains 1 lb of N_2 at 15 psia and 100°F, and side B contains 2 lb of CH_4 at 50 psia and 300°F. If the partition is removed and the gases mix, determine (a) p_m and t_m for the mixture and (b) the changes in internal energy and entropy for the system AB.

982. In a divided adiabatic chamber (see figure), there are 11.338 kg of dry air on one side at 1 bar, 99.6°C and 0.454 kg of saturated water vapor on the other side at 1 bar. The partition is removed and mixing occurs to equilibrium. For the final state, determine (a) the partial pressure of the water vapor, (b) the relative humidity. (c) For the system as a whole, find the change of internal energy and of entropy caused by the mixing process.

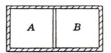

Problems 981–986

983. In the figure shown, there is O_2 in compartment A and CO in B, each gas being at 50 psia and 150°F; $V_A = V_B = 3$ ft³. The partition is removed and the gases mix. What is the change of entropy? *Ans.* +0.06295 Btu/°R.

984. Compartment A in the figure contains 2 lb of O_2 at 50 psia and 100°F; B contains 5 ft³ of a gaseous mixture with a volumetric composition of 12% CO_2 and 88% N_2 at 14.7 psia and 80°F. The partition is removed and the gases mix. For equilibrium conditions, find (a) the volumetric and gravimetric analyses, (b) R_m and M_m, (c) p_m and t_m, (d) the partial pressure of each constituent, and (e) the change of entropy.

Ans. (a) 84.01% O_2, 2.83% CO_2 13.16% N_2 by mass, (b) 48.8, 31.66, (c) 35.9 psia, 97°F, (d) 29.8 psia for O_2; (e) 0.0867 Btu/°R.

985. In a divided adiabatic chamber (see figure), there are 25 lb of dry air on one side at 15 psia, 213°F and 1 lb of saturated water vapor on the other side at 15 psia. The partition is removed and mixing occurs to equilibrium. For the final state, determine (**a**) the partial pressure of the water vapor, (**b**) the relative humidity. (**c**) For the system as a whole, find the change of internal energy and of entropy caused by the mixing process.

986. Given n_a mole of gas A and n_b mole of $B(X_a, X_b$ mole fractions) at the same temperature and pressure, separated by a partition in a closed adiabatic system. See figure. The partition is removed and the gases mix. Show that the increase of entropy for the mixing process is $\Delta S = -\bar{R}(n_a \ln X_a + n_b \ln X_b)$ Btu/mole-°R. Also generalize for any number of gases i that $\Delta S = -\bar{R}\Sigma(n_i \ln X_i)$.

987. There are 2 ft³ of air in a closed vessel at 600 psia and 100°F. This vessel connects with another in which there are 3 lb of argon at 100 psia. When the valve separating these two vessels is opened, the resulting equilibrium mixture is at 267 psia and 86°F. (**a**) What initial volume did the argon occupy at what temperature? (**b**) Determine the partial pressures of the components. (**c**) What is the change in entropy?

Ans. (**a**) 4.03 ft³, 500°R, (**b**) 194 psia (air), (**c**) +0.503 Btu/°R.

988. A thermodynamic system consists of two thin-walled adiabatic closed cylinders, each with a volume of 1 ft³, constructed so that one may slide inside the other without friction (see figure). The inner end of one is closed by a membrane M permeable to CO_2 but not to CH_4. The inner end of the other is closed by a membrane N permeable to CH_4 but not to CO_2. Initially the cylinders are not integral but membranes are touching; each cylinder is filled respectively with gaseous CO_2 or CH_4 at 1 atm, 100°F. The cylinders are now pushed together until only a 1 ft³ mixture of CO_2 and CH_4 remains at 2 atm, 100°F (temperature maintained constant). (**a**) Determine the work required to cause this mixing process. (**b**) Is this process reversible? (**c**) If the cylinders are permitted to move apart thus expanding the mixture isothermally to its original separated state, what would be the work?

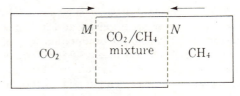

Problem 988

COMPUTER PROGRAMS

989. The effects of gravimetric analysis and temperature on the specific heats of a given gaseous mixture are being studied. Mix together two gaseous compounds from Table I, vary each gravimetrically in increments of 10%, and for each given analysis vary the temperature from 500°R to 5000°R using an increment of 500°R. Calculate the various values of the specific heats c_v and c_p for the mixture under these constraints. Write the program for this problem.

990. Atmospheric air at a given barometric pressure and dry bulb temperature is being studied. It is desired to learn the effects of the wet bulb depression on the relative humidity ϕ and the humidity ratio ω. Let the wet bulb depression vary from zero $(t_w = t_d)$ to a maximum value of 50°F using an increment of 5°F and compute the various values of ϕ and ω under these constraints; use Carriers equation. Program this problem.

991–1000. These numbers may be used for other problems.

13

REACTIVE
SYSTEMS

Note: Review the note at the beginning of the problems in Chapter 12; it has helpful information. Stoichiometric air is also referred to as ideal air and 100% air; theoretical air may be deficient, stoichiometric, or an excess amount. Product tables for a hydrocarbon fuel $(CH_2)_n$ in 200% and 400% stoichiometric air are in the appendix.

COMPOSITION OF FUELS, AIR

1001. (a) The volumetric analysis of air is 21% O_2, 79% N_2. Find the moles of N_2 per mole O_2. What is the ratio kg N_2/kg O_2? (b) Air is mixed with propane in the ratio 15 kg air/kg C_3H_8. In 1 kg of this mixture, find the grams of C, H_2, O_2, N_2.

1002. Gaseous fuel flowing in a pipeline is composed volumetrically of 75% CH_4, 15% C_2H_6, 6% O_2, and 4% CO. (a) Convert this to a percentage mass basis. (b) In 1 kg of this fuel mixture, find the grams of C, H_2, O_2.

1003. A gravimetric analysis of a typical automotive gasoline gives 86% C and 14% H_2. What average chemical formula in the form C_xH_y approximates this fuel?

1004. An ultimate analysis of a bituminous coal as received is 77.5% C, 3.7% H_2, 1.5% N_2, 4.3% O_2, 0.5% S, 6.5% ash, 6.0% H_2O. (a) Convert this analysis to a dry basis. (b) Find the analysis on a dry-and-ashless basis. (c) If this fuel as received is burned at the rate of 100 metric tons/hr and the refuse is analyzed as being 10% combustible (carbon in the ash), how many kilograms of refuse must be handled each hour?
Ans. (a) 82.45%, (b) 88.57% C, (c) 7222 kg/hr.

SIMPLE REACTIONS

1005. Set up the simple combustion equation for each of the basic combustibles C, H_2, S in stoichiometric air and note the amount of air required to burn each element.
Ans. Air required: C/11.5, H_2/34.3, S/4.3 lb air/lb element.

1006. Write the combustion equation for hydrogen in 120% stoichiometric air. Show relative weights and volumes, and compute (a) the pounds of air required to burn 50 lb of hydrogen, (b) the mass of products formed from the 50 lb of hydrogen, and (c) the air/fuel and fuel/air ratios.
Ans. (a) 2068, (b) 2118 lb, (c) 0.0242 lb f/lb air.

1007. Two moles of CO are burned in 5.76 moles air. Write and balance the theoretical combustion equation and find (a) the mass of CO_2 formed, (b) the percentage excess air, (c) the air/fuel ratio.

1008. Pure carbon reacts with all the O_2 in 80% of ideal air. Balance the resulting theoretical combustion equation, and find the masses of CO and CO_2 formed per 100 kg of air supplied. *Ans.* 10.21 kg CO, 24.05 kg CO_2.

1009. Set up the necessary combustion equations and determine the amount of air theoretically required to burn 1 kg of pure carbon (a) to equal masses of CO and CO_2, (b) to where the mass of CO_2 is double that of the CO. *Ans.* (a) 7.98 kg air.

1010. Consider 1000 ℓ of a gaseous mixture that has the following gravimetric analysis: 30% O_2, 70% CO. Is there sufficient oxygen present to support complete combustion of the CO?

1011. Assume 1 lb of carbon is burned so that $\frac{1}{2}$ lb of C goes into CO_2 and $\frac{1}{2}$ lb into CO. Set up the combustion equation and find (a) the pounds of air used per pound of carbon, (b) the volume of this air at 65°F and 14.7 psia, (c) the volumetric and gravimetric composition of the products, (d) the volume of the products at 65°F and 14.7 psia, and (e) the partial pressure of each of the products.

Ans. (a) 8.63, (b) 114 ft³, (c) 13%, 19% for CO_2, (e) 1.91 psia for CO_2.

1012. In a rigid vessel at 1-atm pressure and 100°F, there are 1 lb of H_2 and 28 lb of O_2. The H_2 reacts completely to H_2O. Determine (a) the volume of the vessel, (b) the temperature at which the H_2O is on the point of condensing (use steam tables), (c) the amount of condensation when the contents are cooled to 80°F, (d) the partial pressure of the O_2 at the final state.

Ans. (a) 562 ft³, (b) 170°F, (c) 8.11 lb, (d) 0.511 atm.

COMBUSTION OF HYDROCARBONS, CARBOHYDRATES

1013. A hydrocarbon fuel $(CH_x)_n$ requires equal masses of oxygen for a complete reaction of each of its components carbon and hydrogen, respectively. Determine x and n on the basis of 1 mole of $(CH_x)_n$. *Ans.* 4, 1.

1014. Consider the process wherein octane is burned with 80% stoichiometric air, and assume that CO is the only combustible appearing in the products. Find the products analysis by volume and by mass.

Ans. CO_2: 5.49% vol., 8.86% grav.

1015. The same as problem 1014 except that the only combustibles in the products are CO and CH_4 which appear in equal volumes.

1016. If 5 mole/hr of propane C_3H_8 are completely burned in the stoichiometric amount of air, determine (a) the volume (m³/min) of air required measured at 1 atm,

25°C, (b) the partial pressure of the CO_2 in the products, measured at 1 atm, 149°C, (c) the volume (m³/min) of the products measured at 1 atm and 149°C, and (d) the dew point of the H_2O in the products.

Ans. (a) 48.50 m³/min, (b) 11.8 kPaa, (c) 74.43 m³/min, (d) 55°C.

1017. Ethane burns in 20% excess stoichiometric air. Write the theoretical combustion equation and find (a) the mass of CO_2 formed per pound of fuel, (b) the partial pressure of the H_2O vapor formed if the total pressure of the products is 16 psia, (c) the volumetric analysis of the dry products, (d) the dew point of the products.

1018. A gaseous mixture of 4 moles CH_4 and 9 moles O_2 is ignited. Write the theoretical combustion equation and find (a) the volumetric analysis of the products, (b) the equivalent amount of air represented by the O_2, (c) the percentage excess of O_2 in the mixture and, if excess, how much more CH_4 could have been burned to completion, (d) the dew point of the products if the mixture pressure is 20 psia.

Ans. (a) $X_{CO_2} = 30.76\%$, (b) 42.84 moles equivalent air, (c) 12.5% excess, 0.5 mole CH_4, (d) 203.2°F.

1019. In the combustion of a hydrocarbon fuel at 1 atm, 19 lb da/lb f are supplied. The humidity ratio of the air supply is $\omega = 0.015$ lb v/lb da. The combustion process produces 1.4 lb H_2O/lb f. For the products from dry air, $M = 28.9$. What is the dew point of the products? *Ans.* 123°F.

1020. (a) Set up the chemical equation for the combustion of propane C_3H_8 in stoichiometric air. Show the relative masses and volumes, and compute the air/fuel ratio. (b) The same as (a) except that combustion occurs in 15% excess air. (c) The same as (a) except that combustion occurs in 90% of the stoichiometric air and the H_2 reacts completely to H_2O. (d) Determine the gravimetric percentages of carbon and hydrogen in the fuel. (e) For the reaction in (a), determine the gravimetric and volumetric analyses of the products with $H_2O(g)$.

Ans. (a) 15.61, (b) 17.95, (c) 14.05 lb a/lb f, (d) 81.8% C, (e) CO_2: 11.62% vol, 18.07% grav.

1021. The same as problem 1020 except that the fuel is octene, C_8H_{16}.

Ans. (a) 14.7, (b) 16.9, (c) 13.23, (d) 80.7% C, (e) CO_2: 13.08% vol, 20% grav.

1022. The same as problem 1020 except that the fuel is nonane, C_9H_{20}, a rocket fuel.

1023. The same as problem 1020 except that the fuel is ethyl alcohol, C_2H_6O.

Ans. (a) 8.92, (b) 10.25, (c) 8.04, (d) 52.2% C, (e) CO_2: 12.28% vol, 19.30% grav.

1024. Assume 5 mole/hr of propane C_3H_8 are completely burned in the stoichiometric amount of air. Determine (a) the volume (cfm) of air required, measured at 14.7 psia and 77°F, (b) the partial pressure of the CO_2 in the products, $H_2O(g)$, (c) the volume (cfm) of the products, measured at 14.7 psia and 300°F, and (d) the dew point of the H_2O in the products.

1025. The same as problem 1024 except that the fuel is octene, C_8H_{16}.

Ans. (a) 1855 cfm, (b) 1.92 psia, (c) 2810 cfm, (d) 124.6°F.

1026. The same as problem 1024 except that the fuel is nonane, C_9H_{20}, a rocket fuel.

1027. The same as problem 1024 except that the fuel is ethyl alcohol, C_2H_6O.

Ans. (a) 466 cfm, (b) 1.80 psia, (c) 754 cfm, (d) 137.5°F.

1028. Hydrogen peroxide $H_2O_2(g)$, sometimes used as an oxidizer for rocket fuels, reacts with nonane $C_9H_{20}(g)$ to produce only CO_2 and $H_2O(g)$ products at 1 atm pressure. Balance the equation for a stoichiometric reaction and determine (a) the mass of H_2O_2 used per kilogram of fuel, (c) the partial pressure of the H_2O in the products, (d) the dewpoint of the water in the products, (e) the volume of the products at 226.7°C, (f) the gravimetric percentage of carbon in the nonane.

Ans. (a) 7.43, (b) 5.34 kg, (c) 81.91 kPaa, (d) 94.2°C, (e) 1930 m³, (f) 84.4%.

1029. A gaseous mixture composed of 30% CH_4O and 70% C_3H_8, percentages by volume, is burned in 200% ideal air at 14.7 psia. (a) Write and balance the combustion equation. There are no combustibles in the products. (b) Find the dew point of the products.

1030. Butane C_4H_{10} is burned in air. Write and balance the theoretical combustion equations for this action under each condition. (a) Stoichiometric (100% ideal) air is supplied, (b) 15% excess air is supplied, (c) 15% deficient air is supplied with CH_4 being the only combustible in the products.

1031. A Signal Hill, California, gas sample has the following volumetric analysis: 62.5%

CH_4, 32.9% C_2H_6, 3.6% H_2, 1.0% CO_2. Balance the chemical equation for this gas burned in the stoichiometric amount of air, and find (a) the air/fuel ratio, by mass and volume, and (b) the volumetric and gravimetric analyses of the products. *just CO_2*

Ans. (a) 16.4 lb a/lb f, 11.52 ft³/ft³ f, (b) CO_2: 10.21% vol, 16.12% grav.

1032. There are burned 141.6 m³/min of coke-oven gas (measured at 1 atm, 65.6°C) in the stoichiometric amount of air. The gas has the following volumetric composition: 36.9% CH_4, 52% H_2, 5% CO, 0.5% O_2, 4.2% N_2, 1.4% CO_2. What volume of air measured at 1 atm, 65.6°C is required?

Ans. 625.6 m³/min.

COMBUSTION OF COAL

1033. Two hundred metric tons per hour of coal are burned in 125% (25% excess) stoichiometric air; the as-fired ultimate analysis is 75% C, 4% H_2, 0.5% S, 6% O_2, 1.5% N_2, 8% H_2O, 5% ash. Find (a) the mass of air required, kg/hr, (b) the mass of refuse collected if all ash shows in the refuse which tests 25% combustible. (c) What is the carbon content of the coal on a dry basis?

Ans. (a) 2.442×10^6 kg/hr, (b) 13,340 kg/hr, (c) 81.5%.

1034. A Grimes County, Texas lignite coal, as-received, has the following ultimate analysis: 32% C, 2.4% H_2, 1.5% S, 9.6% O_2, 0.5% N_2, 39% H_2O, 15% ash. Balance the combustion equation for this coal burned as-received in 85% stoichiometric air; the only combustible in the products is CO. Find (a) the air/fuel ratios as-received and for dry coal, (b) the mass of dry gaseous products per kilogram of the as-received fuel burned.

1035. An anthracite coal has the following dry-basis ultimate analysis: 81.63% C, 2.23% H_2, 0.48% S, 2.92% O_2, 0.80% N_2, 11.94% ash. (a) Balance the combustion equation for stoichiometric air, and find the air/fuel ratio on the dry basis; also on the as-received basis if the moisture content is 3.43%. (b) The same as (a) except that the air supplied is 90% of the stoichiometric amount. Assume that CO is the only combustible element in the products and find its mass per pound of dry fuel and per pound of fuel as received.

Ans. (a) 10.06 (dry), (b) 9.05 lb a/lb f (dry), 0.408 lb CO/lb f.

1036. The ultimate analysis of a bituminous coal as-fired is 79.1% C, 4.3% H_2, 1.4% N_2, 3.4% O_2, 1.1% S, 6.7% ash, 4.0% H_2O. Convert this gravimetric analysis to a dry basis. For "100% air," find (a) the mass of dry flue gas per pound of carbon in the fuel and per pound of dry coal, (b) the volumetric percentage of CO_2 in the hot dry flue gas, (c) the partial pressure of the H_2O in the hot products, and (d) the air/fuel ratio on a dry basis and on an as-fired basis (no combustible in the ash).

1037. There are supplied 10.2 kg air per kilogram of coal whose sample analysis is: 71% C, 2.5% H_2, 1.5% S, 3% N_2, 5% O_2, 9% H_2O, 8% ash. Find (a) the percentage of excess air supplied, (b) the percentage carbon in the fuel on a dry-ashless basis.

1038. The ultimate gravimetric analysis of a coal as-received is: 74% C, 1.5% H_2, 1% S, 6% O_2, 2.5% N_2, 5.5% H_2O, 9.5% ash. (a) What is the percentage carbon on a dry-ashless basis? (b) Find the air/fuel ratio (100% ideal air) required to burn the fuel as-received. (c) If 100 metric ton/hr of the as-received coal are burned and the refuse shows 20% combustible, find the kg/hr refuse collected.

ANALYSIS OF PRODUCTS

1039. The following is a gravimetric (ultimate) analysis of a coal: 70.85% C, 4.48% H_2, 2.11% S, 6.36% O_2, 1.38% N_2, 12.3% ash, 2.52% H_2O. During actual combustion, the following volumetric analysis of the stack gases was obtained: 12.1% CO_2, 0% CO, 7.2% O_2, 80.7% N_2. Determine (a) the percentage excess or deficiency of air and (b) the mass of dry products per kilogram of coal fired.
Ans. (a) 49.8% excess, (b) 14.78 kg.

1040. (a) The volumetric analysis of the dry products from the coal described in problem 1039 is: 11.8% CO_2, 7.8% O_2, 0.2% CO, 80.2% N_2. Find the percentage excess or deficiency of air. (b) A sample of the refuse pit was later analyzed and showed 18% C and 82% ash by mass. Find the mass of unburned carbon in the pit per kilogram of fuel and the mass of actual air supplied per kilogram of fuel.

1041. Consider 100 ton/hr of pulverized coal that are burned. Coal analysis by mass showed: 76% C, 6% H_2, 7% O_2, 2% N_2, 4% H_2O, 5% ash. Stack gas analysis by volume showed: 13% CO_2, 1.5% CO, 5.5% O_2, 80%

N_2. Refuse pit analysis by mass showed: 23% C, 77% ash. Find (a) the volume of actual air measured at 14.7 psia and 90°F, (b) the refuse collected each hour, and (c) the volume of dry products at $p_m = 14.7$ psia and 310°F.
Ans. (a) 605,000 cfm, (b) 6.49 tons/hr, (c) 880,000 cfm.

1042. The burning of a hydrocarbon fuel $(CH_x)_n$ in an automotive engine results in a dry exhaust gas analysis, percentage by volume, of: 11% CO_2, 0.5% CO, 2% CH_4, 1.5% H_2, 6% O_2, and 79% N_2. Find (a) the actual air/fuel ratio, (b) the percentage excess air, and (c) the mass of water vapor formed per pound of fuel.
Ans. (a) 15.35, (b) 4.71%, (c) 0.719 lb.

1043. An analysis of the dry products resulting from burning a C_xH_y fuel in air is, % vol.: 13.5% CO_2, 1.5% CO, 4% O_2, 79% N_2, 1.2% CH_4, 0.8% H_2. (a) Write the combustion equation and find x and y. (b) What is the dew point of the products that are at 1 bar, 200°C? Use Item B 16(SI).

1044. The dry products of combustion from a hydrocarbon fuel burned in air, percentages by volume, are: 13.6% CO_2, 0.8% CO, 0.4% CH_4, 0.4% O_2, 84.8% N_2. Write the theoretical chemical equation, and find (a) the values of x and n in $(CH_x)_n$, (b) the mass of air supplied per kilogram of fuel, (c) the percentage of excess or deficiency of air, and (d) the mass of dry products per kilogram of fuel burned.
Ans. (a) $[CH_{2.31}]_{14.8}$, (b) 14.75 kg, (c) 2.7% def., (d) 14.25 kg.

1045. The same as problem 1044 except that the volumetric analysis of the dry products is: 12.3% CO_2, 0.7% CO, 1.1% CH_4, 0.4% H_2, 4% O_2, 81.5% N_2.

HEATING VALUES

1046. Start with the two equalities $-h_{rp}^0 = q_p^0$ and $-u_{rp}^0 = q_v^0$, and show that the difference between the two heating values is given by the expression $q_p^0 - q_v^0 = (\bar{R}T^0/M_f)(n_r - n_p)$ where n_r and n_p are the moles of reactants and products, respectively, and M_f is the molecular weight of the fuel.

1047. Gaseous octene (C_8H_{16}) is to be burned in air. (a) Relevant to its higher heating value, which is the larger, q_p or q_v? (b) Relevant to its lower heating value, which is the larger, q_p or q_v? (c) How much water is formed from burning a kilogram of octene?

1048. Consider liquid benzene and state whether its heating values at constant pressure (q_h and q_l) are greater than, equal to, or less than its respective constant volume heating values (q_h and q_l).

1049. (a) If propane $C_3H_8(g)$ is mixed with the stoichiometric air, what are the higher and lower heating values ($p = C$) per pound of the mixture and per cu ft of mixture at $p_m = 14.7$ psia and 77°F? (b) Find q_h and q_l ($p = C$) per lb fuel, at 200°F and at 0°R. (c) Find q_h and q_l per lb fuel, at 77°F when $V = C$.

Ans. (a) q_h: 1303 Btu/lb, 98.3 Btu/ft³, (b) $q_h = 21,624$ Btu/lb at 200°F, (c) $q_{hv} = 21,573$, $q_{lv} = 19,953$ Btu/lb.

1050. The same as problem 1049 except that the fuel is octene ($c_p = 0.39$ Btu/lb-°R), $C_8H_{16}(g)$.

Ans. (a) $q_h = 1305$ Btu/lb, 101.1 Btu/ft³, (b) $q_h = 20,490$ Btu/lb, 200°F, (c) $q_h = 20,510$ Btu/lb.

1051. The same as problem 1049 except that the fuel is nonane $C_9H_{20}(g)$.

1052. The same as problem 1049 except that the fuel is ethyl alcohol, $C_2H_6O(l)$; $c_p = 0.58$ Btu/lb-°F.

Ans. (a) q_h: 1327 Btu/lb, 108.3 Btu/ft³, (b) $q_h = 13,097$ Btu/lb at 200°F, (c) $q_{hv} = 13,138$ Btu/lb.

1053. The volumetric analysis of a natural gas fuel is 22.6% C_2H_6 and 77.4% CH_4. Find (a) the mass of stoichiometric air per pound of fuel, (b) the mass of CO_2 and H_2O formed per pound of fuel, (c) the gravimetric percentage of C and H_2 in the fuel and in the stoichiometric air-fuel mixture, and (d) the higher and lower heating values at 77°F, per pound of fuel and per pound of stoichiometric air-fuel mixture.

Ans. (a) 16.8 lb, (b) 2.81 lb CO_2, (c) 4.31% C, 1.30% H_2, (d) $q_h = 25,050$ Btu/lb f, $q_h = 1406$ Btu/lb mix.

1054. The dry exhaust from an automotive engine, fuel $(CH_x)_n$, has a volumetric analysis of 12.5% CO_2, 3.1% O_2, 0.3% CO, and 84.1% N_2. Balance the chemical equation, and find (a) the air/fuel ratio, (b) the volumetric percentages of H_2O and CO_2 in the hot products, (c) the partial pressure of the N_2 if the total pressure is 14.7 psia, (d) the volume of products at 3000°R in ft³/lb fuel and in ft³/mole fuel, and (e) gravimetric percentages of C and H_2 in the fuel. (f) Estimate the higher and lower heating values of the fuel.

Ans. (a) 17.05, (b) 11.72%, 11.07%, (c) 10.9 psia, (d) 1380 ft³/lb fuel, (e) 85.4% C, (f) $q_l = 18,800$ Btu/lb.

COMBUSTION TEMPERATURE, HEAT

1055. Compare the maximum adiabatic flame temperature of H_2 versus CO when each fuel is burned to completion (no dissociation) in a steady flow system with 200% air; the reactants enter at 1 atm, 77°F.

Ans. 2967°R (H_2), 3185°R (CO).

1056. Gaseous nonane (C_9H_{20}) is burned in 200% ideal air at constant pressure and steady flow. The reactants enter at 77°F. Find the theoretical adiabatic flame temperature using Item B 9 for the products.

1057. The same as problem 1056 except that the fuel is gaseous butane (C_4H_{10}) in 400% air; use Item B 8.

1058. Gaseous octane and 200% air react in a steady flow manner; the reactants cross the boundary at 100°F and the products leave at 2000°F. For the process, $\Delta K = 0$, $W = 0$. Determine the heat for a fuel flow of 1 mol/sec. Do not neglect the sensible enthalpy of the fuel; use Item B 9.

1059. A mixture of octane vapor C_8H_{18} and 200% stoichiometric air (100% excess) is burned at constant volume. If combustion starts at 1185°R, compute the temperature of the products after adiabatic combustion, using Item B 9. Sketch energy diagrams; for fuel, $c_v = 0.39$ Btu/lb-°F. *Ans.* 3826°R.

1060. Ethane $C_2H_6(g)$ reacts with 200% stoichiometric air in a steady flow process, maintained at 1 atm. The reactants enter at 77°F; the products leave at 2000°R. The fuel flow is 30 lb/sec. Solve for the rate of heat transfer (a) assuming that the products have properties as given in Item B 9, (b) considering the individual constituents in the products.

Ans. −216,000 Btu/sec.

1061. A Diesel engine burns dodecane $C_{12}H_{26}$ in 200% stoichiometric air (100% excess). At the end of the compression process (initial point of fuel injection—fuel at 77°F) the air temperature is 1080°F. Using Item B 9, compute the temperature of the products after constant-pressure combustion if the combustion efficiency is 94%. Sketch energy diagrams.

1062. Consider a stoichiometric reaction of nonane $C_9H_{20}(l)$ and hydrogen peroxide $H_2O_2(g)$ to $CO_2(g)$ and $H_2O(l)$. If the process begins and ends at 77°F and 1 atm, determine (a) the enthalpy of reaction, (b) the change of entropy. (c) If the nonane reacts instead with pure O_2, is more or less energy released? Compare this $-h_{rp}$ with that given in Item B 12.

Ans. (a) $-34,800$ Btu/lb f, (b) -504 Btu/°R for 1 mole nonane.

1063. A torpedo propulsion system involves a reaction of methyl alcohol $CH_4O(l)$ and hydrogen peroxide $H_2O_2(g)$. Using Δh_f^0 and/or ΔG_f^0, determine the maximum work that can be done for constant p, T, at $p_m \doteq$ 1 atm and 77°F. What are the entropy change and heat? Compare the heat of this reaction with the heating value from Item B 12.

ENTHALPY OF FORMATION

1064. Let octane $C_8H_{18}(l)$ be burned adiabatically in 400% air with the reactants initially at 77°F; steady flow obtains. Determine the theoretical flame temperature (a) using Item B 8, (b) using the enthalpies of formation of each compound.

1065. (a) Using the enthalpies of formation, determine the standard enthalpy of combustion, $-h_{rp}^0$, of ethane $C_2H_6(g)$ with liquid H_2O in the products. Compare with Item B 12. (b) Using enthalpies of reaction, compute the enthalpy of formation. Compare with Item B 11.

Ans. (a) $-22,320$ Btu/lb, (b) $-36,400$ Btu/mole.

1066. Using the enthalpy of combustion given in Item B 12, compute the internal energy of combustion (constant volume heating value) at 77°F (liquid H_2O) for ethane $C_2H_6(g)$. *Ans.* 22,210 Btu/lb.

1067. Methane is burned completely in a steady flow manner through an adiabatic system with 200% stoichiometric air; the fuel enters at 1 atm, 77°F; the air at 700°R. Find the theoretical flame temperature (a) using Item B 9, (b) using the enthalpies of formation and gas tables where pertinent. *Ans.* 2787°R.

1068. Into a 0.5-ft³ bomb calorimeter, filled with air at 1 atm and 77°F, are placed 0.0001 pmole of methanol (methyl alcohol, CH_4O). Complete adiabatic combustion occurs. For no dissociation, compute the final pressure.

1069. Using Item B 11, calculate the enthalpy of combustion and the internal energy of combustion for CO at 1 atm, 77°F. *Ans.* $-121,745$, $-121,203$ Btu/lb-mole.

1070. (a) Determine the standard enthalpy of combustion $-h_{rp}^0$ of propane $C_3H_8(g)$, with $H_2O(l)$ in the products from the enthalpies of formation. (b) Use only the enthalpies of reaction and determine the enthalpy of formation of propane.

1071. Penta-borane $B_5H_9(l)$ a rocket fuel, reacts with hydrogen peroxide $H_2O_2(l)$ to give only $B_2O_3(s)$ and $H_2O(g)$ in the products. Values of enthalpy of formation, Btu/mole are: 13,930 for $B_5H_9(l)$, $-80,712$ for $H_2O(l)$, and $-549,610$ for $B_2O_3(s)$; see Item B 11. Determine the enthalpy of combustion at the standard state. *Ans.* $-2,136,005$ Btu/mole f.

1072. The same as problem 1071 except that hydrazine $N_2H_4(l)$ reacts with the $H_2O_2(l)$ to give the products $N_2(g)$ and $H_2O(g)$; for hydrazine, $\Delta h_f^0 = 21,690$ Btu/mole.

1073. Determine quantitatively the effect of the phase (liquid versus vapor) of the water in the products on the enthalpy of combustion $\bar{h}_{rp}^0$ for gaseous n-octane reacting in air at 1 atm, 77°F. Use Item B 11.

Ans. $\bar{h}_{rp}^0$ Btu/mole: $-2,371,407$, $H_2O(l)$; $-2,200,992$, $H_2O(g)$.

ENTROPY, GIBBS FUNCTION

1074. Compute the Gibbs function of formation of CO_2 at 1 atm and 77°F, using $G = H - TS$ and the enthalpies of formation and compare with the values given in Item B 11.

1075. Determine the Gibbs function of methane $CH_4(g)$ at 5 atm, 140°F measured from the same datum as the Gibbs function of formation given in Item B 11. Assume the specific heat to be constant as given in Item B 1. *Ans.* $-22,786$ Btu/mole.

1076. Suppose that acetylene $C_2H_2(g)$ could be made to undergo a stoichiometric reaction with oxygen O_2 in a fuel cell (only CO_2 and $H_2O(l)$ to be in the products) at the constant conditions 1 atm, 77°F. Determine (a) the ideal work produced by the cell, (b) ΔS for the reaction. (c) What does the ΔS value signify regarding a spontaneous process?

1077. Benzene $C_6H_6(g)$ is burned with 300% air in a steady flow manner. The reactants are at 1 atm, 77°F. Determine the maximum work possible if the reaction occurs isothermally.

1078. Gaseous octane $C_8H_{18}(g)$ reacts with 400% stoichiometric air at 1 atm, 77°F. Determine ΔS, ΔG, and W_{max} if the H_2O in the products is liquid.

1079. (a) Using Δh_f^0, compute ΔG_f^0 for hydroxyl $OH(g)$ and check with value in Item B 11. (b) Using the value from (a), compute the Gibbs function of formation at 400 K. (c) Using enthalpy of formation, Gibbs function of formation, and the absolute entropies of the elements, compute the absolute entropy of $OH(g)$ in the standard state; compare with table value.

1080. If a way were found to make gaseous ethane C_2H_6 react with O_2 in an ideal fuel cell at 140°F and 1 atm, compute ΔS for the reaction and determine the ideal work for $H_2O(l)$.
Ans. −69.5 Btu/°R-mole f, 20,860 Btu/lb.

EQUILIBRIUM AND DISSOCIATION

[*Note*: Long-hand or machine calculations are often necessary to give significant answers for dissociation problems.]

1081. Determine the equilibrium constant K_p for the reaction at 77°F: (a) $CO + H_2O = CO_2 + H_2$; (b) $CO_2 + H_2 = CO + H_2O$. See Item B 11 for $\Delta \bar{G}_f^0$. *Ans.* (a) 98,100.

1082. Calculate the equilibrium constants for the following reactions occurring at 77°F: (a) $H_2 + 0.5 O_2 = H_2O$; (b) $CO_2 = CO + 0.5 O_2$.

1083. If H_2O is heated at a pressure of 10 atm until it is 6% dissociated into molecular hydrogen and oxygen, what is its equilibrium temperature (chemical equilibrium)?

1084. Compute the adiabatic flame temperature for the combustion of CO in stoichiometric oxygen at a constant pressure of 5 atm, starting from 77°F and allowing dissociation. *Suggestion.* Try 5400°R first.

1085. When an object enters the earth's atmosphere at high speed, the temperature behind the shock wave in the vicinity of the object may be quite high. Suppose that the temperature is 7200°R, the total pressure is 0.034 psia, and it is desired to estimate the extent of dissociation of the oxygen. For the reversible reaction $O_2 \rightleftharpoons 2 O$ at 7200°R, the equilibrium constant is $K_p = 2.4094$. *Hint*: Let the reaction equation be

$$3.76 N_2 + O_2 \rightarrow n_1 O + n_2 O_2 + 3.76 N_2$$

which assumes that the dissociation of the N_2 is negligible. Define K_p in terms of n_2.
Ans. mole $O_2 = 0.0007$.

1086. The same as problem 1085 except that the temperature is 8100°R and the dissociation of the N_2 is desired on the assumption that the O_2 is entirely dissociated. For $N_2 \rightleftharpoons 2$ N, the value of $K_p = 0.03683$. *Ans.* 6.87 N.

1087. (a) Assume 1 mole of $H_2O(g)$ is heated to 6300°R at constant $p = 1$ atm and maintained there in equilibrium. How many moles of O_2 are present? (b) A stoichiometric mixture of H_2 and O_2 are heated to 6300°R at constant $p = 1$ atm, after which p, T remain constant. How many moles of O_2 are present per mole of H_2? *Ans.* (a) 0.167.

1088. Hydrogen is burned in 200% stoichiometric air during a steady flow process occurring at $p_m = 5$ atm. If the temperature of the products is maintained at 5000°R, determine the heat (a) when the reactants enter the process at 77°F, (b) when the reactants enter at 1540°F.
Ans. (a) 103,936, (b) 41,531 Btu/mole H_2.

1089. Assume 1 mole of carbon (graphite) and 2 moles of O_2 are placed in a constant-pressure chamber that is and remains at 5000°R and 2 atm pressure. Consider that the products consist only of CO_2, CO, O_2. Determine the number of moles of each of the products and specify the degree of dissociation.
Ans. $n(CO) = 0.122$ mole.

1090. Pure H_2O is heated to 5400°R and maintained there at 10 atm. Determine the equilibrium composition if there are present only H_2O, OH, H_2. See Item B 13.

1091. Determine the adiabatic flame temperature for CO burning in 100% ideal air at 5 atm in a steady flow manner and with dissociation; the reactants enter the process at 537°R. *Ans.* 4300°R (approx.).

1092. Methane $CH_4(g)$ is burned in "90% air" in a steady flow adiabatic process; the reactants enter at 77°F. Consider dissociation of CO_2 and H_2O, except assume that there is no O_2 in the products (a simplification involving small error in this case). Estimate the adiabatic flame temperature. *Hint*: Use only the water gas reaction for the solution.

1093. An object falls to earth creating a shock wave and resulting high temperatures in its path. At one point of this path in the earth's atmosphere, the temperature is 5400°R; the pressure is 1 atm. Estimate the dissociation of oxygen at this point. For the reversible reaction $O_2 \rightleftharpoons 2\,O$ at 5400°R, $K_p = 0.01441$. See problem 1085. *Ans.* 0.248 mole O.

MISCELLANEOUS

1094. During the recent energy crisis it was proposed to utilize cattle manure from large feed-lots by hydrogasifying it and burning the resulting gaseous mixture in power plants. The following compositions are known: raw cattle manure before gasification, percent mass: 35.4 C, 4.6 H_2, 0.2 S, 30.1 O_2, 3.4 H_2O, 0.7 N_2, 25.6 ash; product gas resulting from gasification of raw manure, percent volume: 78.76 CH_4, 19.02 C_2H_6, 1.07 H_2, 1.15 CO_2. Find the heating value of each composition and determine the stoichiometric air required for each.

1095. Develop the relation between fugacity f and the compressibility factor Z as follows: $\ln f/p = \int_0^p (Z-1)\,dp/p$. Start with the change of Gibbs function for an isothermal process considering ideal and real gas conditions.

1096. Find the fugacity f (see Item B 37) for each of the following fluids at 2940 psia, 440°F: (**a**) water, (**b**) propane, (**c**) hydrogen.

1097. Show that for a reversible isothermal steady-flow, steady state process, the work is given by $W = G_1 - G_2 = -RT \ln (f_2/f_1)$ where $\Delta K = 0$, $\Delta P = 0$, G is the Gibbs function, and f is the fugacity.

1098. There are compressed 4.54 kg/min of propane from 1282 kPaa, 60°C to 12,790 kPaa in a reversible isothermal, steady-state, steady-flow manner with $\Delta P = 0$, $\Delta K = 0$. Find the work W by means of fugacities; see § 13.43, *Text*, and Item B 37.
Ans. −206.6 kJ/min.

1099. In industry, the CO_2 content of the products of combustion is conveniently used as an index of the combustion efficiency and/or the percentage excess air for a given fuel. Plot the curve "percentage CO_2 (by volume) versus percentage air (theoretical)" for methane CH_4, allowing the amount of air to vary from 50% ideal to 150% ideal. For deficient air, assume that by volume the CO content is twice that of the H_2. Note that the resulting curve may be used to indicate the percentage air supplied when the CO_2 content only is known.

1100. Let octane $C_8H_{18}(l)$ be burned in 400% air during steady flow at 1 atm, adiabatically and with the reactants initially at 77°F. (**a**) Determine the theoretical flame temperature for no dissociation by using Item B 8. (**b**) Compute ΔS from reactants to products at the flame temperature (each component separately). (**c**) What reversible work $(-\Delta\mathcal{A})$ could be done by these products in steady flow to 77°F and 1 atm. (**d**) Compute the change of availability of the reaction as defined. (**e**) Let the reaction of the octane occur reversibly at T, p constant ($p_m = 1$ atm, 77°F) in a fuel cell and compute the change of Gibbs function. Observe that for a sink at 77°F, this $\Delta G = \Delta\mathcal{A}$. Does the sum of your values of $\Delta\mathcal{A}$ for the original combustion and the steady flow of the products, parts (**c**) and (**d**), check the ΔG of part (**e**)?
Ans. (**a**) 1735°R, (**b**) 20.5 Btu/°R-lb f, (**c**) 9199 Btu/lb f, (**d**) −1,257,700 Btu/pmole f, (**e**) −2,304,000 Btu/pmole f.

1101. Prove that the Orsat analyzer ignores the water vapor and reports the exact analysis of the gaseous mixture as if for a dry gas. *Hint*: Assume a mixture of CO_2, N_2 and water vapor—then follow one of the components (say the CO_2) through the Orsat absorption process.

COMPUTER PROGRAMS

1102. It is desired to determine the effect of excess air on the dewpoint temperature of the products resulting from burning a selected hydrocarbon in air at constant pressure ($p = 14.7$ psia). Select a fuel from Item B 12 and burn it theoretically in air varying from that of stoichiometric to 400% excess. Plot a curve depicting dewpoint temperature versus percentage excess air. Write the computer program for this problem.

1103. The adiabatic flame temperature resulting from burning propane C_3H_8 in theoretical air is to be analyzed. Let the reactants be at 77°F and let the percentage excess air vary from 0% to 400%. Graph the curve depicting adiabatic flame temperature versus percentage excess air. Program this problem using Table I (variable specific heats) as needed.

1104–1110. These numbers may be used for other problems.

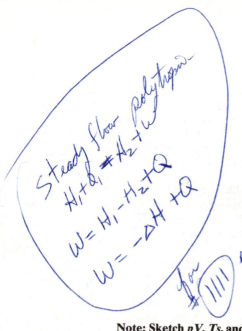

steady flow polytropic

$H_1 + Q_1 \neq H_2 + W$

$W = H_1 - H_2 + Q$

$W = -\Delta H + Q$

for #1111 part b

14

GAS COMPRESSORS

Note: Sketch pV, Ts, and energy diagrams. Where the working substance closely conforms to $pv = RT$, answers obtained from the gas tables (Items B 2 through B 10) are more accurate; some answers are based on Item B 1 and are so designated.

COMPRESSOR WORK

1111. A steady flow compressor handles 113.3 m³/min of nitrogen measured at intake where $p_1 = 97.22$ kPaa and $t_1 = 26.7°C$. Discharge is at 310.27 kPaa. The change of kinetic energy is negligible. For each of the following cases, determine the temperature t_2 and the work if the process is (**a**) an isentropic, (**b**) an internally reversible polytropic with $n = 1.34$, (**c**) an irreversible adiabatic with a compressor efficiency of $\eta_c = 80\%$, (**d**) an isothermal. Solve this problem from the viewpoint of energy diagrams. Does $-\int V\,dp$ represent anything asked for?

Ans. (**a**) −15,454, (**b**) −15,168, (**c**) −19,318, (**d**) −12,783 kJ/min.

1112. There are required 1902.3 kW of compressor power to handle air adiabatically from 1 atm, 26.7°C to 304.06 kPaa. The initial air velocity is 21 m/s; the final is 85 m/s. (**a**) If the process is isentropic, find the volume of air handled, m³/min measured at inlet conditions. (**b**) If the compression is an irreversible adiabatic to a temperature of 157.2°C, with the capacity found in (**a**), find the kilowatt input.

Ans. (**a**) 899 m³/min, (**b**) 2377 kW.

1113. The adiabatic power input required to compress 50 lb/min of air from 14 psia, 80°F to a higher pressure is 60.4 hp where $\Delta K = 0$.

If the process is reversible, find the discharge pressure.

1114. Water, circulating at the rate of 52 lb/min around the cylinder of an air compressor, enters at 70°F and leaves at 80°F, all heat received coming from the air in the cylinder. The compression is internally reversible from 14.7 psia, 80°F to 330°F; $\Delta K = 0$. For an air flow of 50 lb/min, find (**a**) the work, (**b**) ΔS for the air, (**c**) the available part of the heat with respect to the air and again as it was received by the water if $t_0 = 60°F$.

Ans. (**a**) 83 hp, (**b**) −0.791 Btu/°R-min, (**c**) 109, 14.3 Btu/min.

1115. Demonstrate that the compressor work obtained from the analysis of a conventional card with clearance and polytropic processes for the reciprocating compressor is identical to that obtained from the analysis of a reversible steady flow rotary compressor wherein m' pounds of a gas are compressed from p_1, t_1 to p_2 in accordance to $pV^n = C$.

SINGLE-STAGE RECIPROCATING COMPRESSORS

1116. There are compressed 6.542 m³/min of oxygen from 1 atm, 26.7°C to 310.27 kPaa by a 35.56×35.56-cm single-stage, double-acting compressor operating at 100 rpm. Compression and reexpansion processes are isentropic and $\Delta K = 0$. Find the volumetric efficiency, the work done on the oxygen, and the heat removed. Solve first by using the conventional indicator card; check by using an energy diagram and considering steady flow.

Ans. 92.6%, 14.53 kW, 14.57 kW.

1117. Find the volumetric efficiency and estimate the approximate clearance of a 45.75×45.75-cm, double-acting, single-cylinder compressor that is turning at 150 rpm and pumping 19.82 m³/min of a gas from 1 atm, 26.7°C to 675.7 kPaa. Compression and reexpansion are polytropic with $pV^{1.32} = C$.

1118. A 14×14-in., horizontal, double-acting air compressor with 5% clearance operates at 120 rpm, drawing in air at 14.4 psia and 88°F, and discharging it at 57.6 psia. The compression and reexpansion processes are polytropic with $n = 1.33$. Sketch the conventional card and determine (**a**) the conventional volumetric efficiency, (**b**) the mass of air discharged, (**c**) the horsepower input to the air. (**d**) How much is $-\int V \, dp$ for the compression process?

Ans. (B1), (**a**) 90.8%, (**b**) 19.3 lb/min, (**c**) 29 hp.

1119. Oxygen is compressed by a 35.56×35.56-cm single-stage, double-acting, motor-driven compressor operating at 100 rpm. These data apply: $p_1 = 101.35$ kPaa, $t_1 = 26.7$°C, $p_2 = 310.27$ kPaa. Compression and reexpansion are polytropic with $n = 1.31$. Determine (**a**) the conventional volumetric efficiency, (**b**) compressor capacity in m³/min measured at state 1, (**c**) the work done on the oxygen in kW, (**d**) the kW input by the driving motor for an overall adiabatic efficiency of 72%.

COMPRESSOR EFFICIENCIES

1120. Gas is compressed polytropically $pV^n = C$ with $n = 1.27$ from 98 kPaa, 27°C to 613 kPaa. Calculate the percentage clearance of the compressor if its volumetric efficiency is (**a**) 90%, (**b**) 86%, (**c**) 82%.

1121. The same as problem 1120 except that the compression is (**a**) isothermal, (**b**) isentropic with $k = 1.4$.

1122. A reciprocating air compressor with a clearance of 6% draws in 4.25 m³/min of air measured at suction conditions of 100 kPaa, 57.2°C. For a discharge pressure of 300 kPaa and an over-all adiabatic efficiency of 68%, determine the power of the driving motor.

Ans. 13.43 kW.

1123. The steady flow compressor of a Brayton-cycle turbine breathes in 45,000 cfm of air at 15 psia, 60°F and compresses it through a pressure ratio of 9.5; the compressor efficiency is 82%. Use Item B 2 and find (**a**) discharge temperature, (**b**) compression work, hp, (**c**) irreversibility and change in availability for $p_0 = 15$ psia, $t_0 = 60$°F.

1124. A compressor handles 3500 cfm of carbon dioxide measured at intake where $p_1 = 14.2$ psia and $t_1 = 75$°F. At discharge, $p_2 = 28.4$ psia and $t_2 = 178$°F. The initial velocity is 40 fps and the final velocity is 150 fps. The process is an irreversible adiabatic. Find (**a**) $\Delta H'$, $\Delta U'$, $\Delta S'$, (**b**) W', (**c**) η_c.

Ans. (**a**) 8150, 6400 Btu/min, 2.06 Btu/°R-min, (**b**) −8309 Btu/min, (**c**) 82%.

1125. There are compressed 2300 cfm of methane from 15 psia and 75°F to 15 psig by a steady flow compressor. The process is an irreversible adiabatic and the initial velocity is 50 fps with the final of 300 fps. If the compression efficiency is $\eta_c = 82.7$%, find (**a**) t_2, (**b**) ΔS, (**c**) W. (**d**) How much is $-\int V \, dp$? What does it represent? (**e**) What is the change of availability per pound of methane flowing if the lowest available temperature is $t_0 = 40$°F?

Ans. (**a**) 186.5°F, (**b**) 1.515 Btu/°R-min, (**c**) −5880 Btu/min, (**e**) 53.3 Btu/min.

1126. The same as problem 1125 except that the working substance is air.

1127. A 14×12-in., single-cylinder, double-acting air compressor with 5.5% clearance operates at 125 rpm. The suction pressure and temperature are 14 psia and 100°F, respectively. The discharge pressure is 42 psia. Compression and reexpansion processes are isentropic. Considering the conventional compressor and neglecting the piston-rod effect, determine (**a**) the volumetric efficiency, (**b**) the mass and volume at suction conditions handled each minute, (**c**) the work in horsepower, (**d**) the heat rejected, and (**e**) the indicated air horsepower developed if the compression efficiency is 75%.

1128. Gas, whose properties are similar to those given in Item B 8, is under study for use in a nuclear reactor-gas turbine system. The compressor receives the gas at 540°R and delivers it at 1120°R; the pressure ratio across the compressor is $r_p = 10$. Compute the compressor efficiency and work required for a mass rate of 4.4 mole/sec.

Ans. 82.3%, 26,115 hp.

1129. A 7×8-in., double-acting, single-cylinder gas compressor with a clearance of 5% operates at 150 rpm and compresses air from 15 psia, 90°F to 40 psia in an isentropic manner. Sketch the conventional card and find (**a**) conventional volumetric efficiency, (**b**) air delivered, lb/min, (**c**) air ihp developed if the adiabatic compression efficiency is 80%.

1130. From a test of an air compressor driven directly by a steam engine, the following data and results were obtained: capacity, 800 cfm; suction at 14.7 psia; discharge at 110 psia; ihp of air compressor, 155; ihp of steam engine 172. Calculate (**a**) the compression efficiency, (**b**) the overall efficiency.

Ans. (**a**) 89.9%, (**b**) 81%.

1131. An air compressor with a clearance of $c = 4\%$ compresses 14.73 m³/min of air from 97 kPaa, 27°C to 462 kPaa. If the overall adiabatic efficiency is 61%, determine the ihp of the directly connected driving steam engine.

COMPRESSOR CYLINDER DIMENSIONS

1132. Find the cylinder dimensions of a single-cylinder, double-acting compressor handling 30 ℓ/rev of nitrogen from 100 kPaa, 37°C to 725 kPaa. Compression and reexpansion are in accordance with $pV^{1.35} = C$. Use the conventional volumetric efficiency; $c = 5\%$; $L/D = 1$.

1133. A single-cylinder, double-acting gas compressor running at 200 rpm has a piston speed of 600 fpm. It compresses 60 lb/min of ~~... 14~~ psia, 60°F to 95 psia; clearance is ~~... compression, find (a)~~ η_v, ~~...ventional card;~~ ~~...he compressor.~~ ~~...roperties from~~ ~~...ompare.~~

~~...m, (b) 29.9 psi,~~

~~...with $c = 7\%$~~ ~~...17°C and dis-~~

charges it at 1800 kPaa. The mass rate is 20 kg/min; let the process be isentropic. Find (**a**) the temperature at the end of compression, (**b**) the work, (**c**) the displacement, (**d**) the volume measured at intake, and (**e**) the bore and stroke for $n = 90$ rpm and $L/D = 1.25$.

1135. A compressor is to be designed with 6% clearance to handle 500 cfm of air at 14.7 psia and 70°F, the state at the beginning of compression stroke. The compression is isentropic to 105 psia. (**a**) What displacement in cfm is necessary? (**b**) If the compressor is used at an altitude of 6000 ft and if the initial temperature and the discharge pressure remain the same as given above, by what percentage is the capacity of the compressor reduced? (**c**) What should be the displacement of a compressor at the altitude of 6000 ft to handle the same mass of air as in (**a**)?

MULTI-STAGE RECIPROCATING COMPRESSORS

1136. For a two-stage reciprocating compressor with intercooler, prove that the work will be minimum when the pressure between cylinders (intercooler pressure) is $p_i = (p_1 p_2)^{0.5}$. Here p_1 is compressor inlet pressure and p_2 is compressor discharge pressure. Further, let the intercooler return the air to the compressor inlet temperature.

1137. Methane is compressed in a two-stage, double-acting compressor which is electrically driven at 165 rpm. The low pressure cylinder (30.5×35.5-cm) receives 6.85 m³/min of air at 96.53 kPaa, 43.3°C, and the high pressure cylinder (20.3×35.5-cm) discharges the methane at 717.06 kPaa. Piston rods are 5.1 cm in diameter and the isothermal overall efficiency is 74%. Find (**a**) the volumetric efficiency, (**b**) the kW of the driving motor.

1138. There are compressed 11.33 m³/min of air from 103.42 kPaa, 26.7°C to 827.36 kPaa. All clearances are 8%. (**a**) Find the isentropic power and piston displacement required for a single stage compression. (**b**) Using the same data, find the minimum ideal horsepower for two-stage compression when the intercooler cools the air to the initial temperature. (**c**) Find the displacement of each cylinder for the conditions of part (**b**). (**d**) How much heat is exchanged in the intercooler? (**e**)

For a compressor efficiency of 78%, what driving motor output is required?

Ans. (a) 55.4 kW, 15.58 m³/min, (b) 47.46 kW, (c) 12.43 m³/min, 4.39 m³/min, (d) 1423 kJ/min, (e) 61.5 kW (2-stage).

1139. A two-stage air compressor without clearance delivers 90 lb min at 140 psia. At the intake, $p_1 = 14.3$ psia and $t_1 = 60°F$. Compression follows $pV^{1.31} = C$, and the intercooler cools the air back to 60°F. Find (a) the optimum intermediate pressure, (b) the conventional work, (c) the heat of the various processes (sketch these processes on the *TS* plane). (d) What horsepower would be required for isentropic compression in a single-stage machine? (e) What is the saving due to the cooling process? Does this appear to be worth while? (f) If the temperature of the cooling water in the intercooler rises 15°F, what mass of water is required?

Ans. (a) 44.75 psia, (b) −198 hp, (c) −717, −3483, −717 Btu/min, (d) −243 hp, (e) 45 hp, (f) 232 lb/min.

1140. Air is compressed in a two-stage, double-acting compressor from 14.3 psia, 90°F to 185 psia; the mass rate is 90 lb/min. The barometric conditions are 14.63 psia, 80°F. The pressure drop in the intercooler is 3 psi and the temperature of the air at the intercooler exit is 90°F; $n = 210$ rpm and $pV^{1.34} = C$ for both compression and reexpansion, $c = 5\%$. The cooling water temperature increases 18°F. Find (a) cfm of free air handled, (b) discharge pressure of LP cylinder for minimum work, (c) the temperature at discharge from both LP and HP cylinders, (d) the mass rate of cooling water to be circulated around each cylinder and through the intercooler, (e) the conventional horsepower. (f) If, for the LP, cylinder $L/D = 0.68$ and if both cylinders have the same stroke, what should be the cylinder dimensions? Neglect piston rod effects. (g) Let the actual volumetric efficiency be 88% and the size of the compressor be as found in (f), and find the actual mass of air delivered each minute. (h) If the adiabatic compression efficiency is 78%, and if the mechanical efficiency of the compressor is 85%, what should be the horsepower output of the driving motor? (i) What is the change in availability of the gas ($pV^{1.34} = C$) as it passes through the LP cylinder and as it passes through the HP cylinder?

FANS, BLOWERS, AND ROTARY COMPRESSORS

1141. A large forced-draft fan is handling air at 1 atm, 43.3°C under a total head of 26.6 cm wg (at 43.3°C). The power input to the fan is 224 kW and the fan is 75% efficient. Compute the volume of air handled each minute. Local gravity acceleration is $g = 9.71$ m/s².

Ans. 3908 m³/min.

1142. Air is removed from a large space and given a velocity of 63 fps by a fan. The air density is $\rho = 0.075$ lb/ft³ and the work done on the air is 0.0155 hp-min/lb air. Find the static head on the fan, in. wg (at 100°F).

1143. A small blower handles 43.33 m³/min of air whose density is $\rho = 1.169$ kg/m³. The static and velocity heads are 16.38 and 1.22 cm wg (at 15.6°C), respectively. Local gravity acceleration is $g = 9.741$ m/s². (a) Find the power input to the air from the blower. (b) If the initial velocity is negligible, find the final velocity.   *Ans.* (a) 1.24 kW, (b) 854 m/min.

1144. Carbon dioxide is handled by a rotary type compressor from 15 psia, 90°F through a compression ratio of 7 with a compressor efficiency of 75%; $\Delta K = 0$. Find the discharge temperature. Solve using Item B 1 and check answer using gas tables Item B 3.

Ans. (B 1) 1100°R, (B 3) 1009°R.

1145. A low-pressure, water-jacketed, steady flow, rotary compressor compresses 15 lb/min of air from 14.7 psia and 70°F to 5 psig and 110°F. (a) Let the process be polytropic, neglect the change in kinetic energy, and find the work. What mass of water is circulated? The temperature rise of the cooling water is 6°F. How much is $-\int V\,dp$ in this system and what does it represent? (b) Consider the process as an irreversible adiabatic (no water jacket) with a final temperature of 130°F (instead of 110°F) and find the value of m in $pV^m = C$, and the work. What does $-\int V\,dp$ represent in this system? Compare works.

Ans. (a) −129,000 ft-lb/min, 3.64 lb/min of H_2O, $-\int V\,dp = -165.8$ Btu/min, (b) 1577, −216 Btu/min.

1146. There are compressed 50 lb/min of air from 14 psia, 80°F to 45 psia by a centrifugal compressor. Assume a negligible change in kinetic energy and compute the work of a steady-flow process that is (a) an isentropic, (b) a reversible polytropic with $n =$

iabatic where $m =$
thermal.

7 psia, 80°F, 30,000
4.1 psia by a rotary
elocity is 70 fps; the
; mechanical friction,
red to drive the cen-
ien the compression
opic, **(b)** a reversible
1, **(c)** an irreversible
C, **(d)** an isothermal. **(e)**
(d), what are $\Delta H, \Delta U,$

(a) 2550 hp, **(c)** 3014 hp.

COMPUTER PROGRAM

1148. Write this computer program. The effect of the polytropic exponent n on the conventional volumetric efficiency of a given compressor is under study. Select a specific percentage clearance c and an anticipated pressure ratio p_2/p_1 and calculate the volumetric efficiencies letting n vary in the range of 1–1.4 (say for air).

1149–1150. These numbers may be used for other problems.

15

GAS TURBINE
AND JET
PROPULSION

Note: Show energy diagrams wherever the problem is concerned with energy flux. Allow for the mass of fuel in the products if the amount is specified. When using Items B 8 and B 9, let the molecular weight of the products be 28.90 unless otherwise specified. Most answers are for gas-table solutions.

BRAYTON CYCLE, CLOSED

1151. Sketch the Brayton cycle on the pV and Ts planes; number the corners clockwise and consecutively starting with point 1 at the beginning of the isentropic compression. (a) Show that the efficiency of the cycle is given by $e = 1 - 1/r_k^{(k-1)} = 1 - T_1/T_2 = 1 - T_4/T_3$. (b) Prove that the optimum intermediate temperature for maximum work is $T_2 = (T_1 T_3)^{1/2}$ where T_1 and T_3 are fixed.

1152. An ideal gas-turbine unit (Brayton cycle) operating on a closed cycle is to deliver 5968 kW and receive heat from a nuclear reactor. Different gases are to be studied. Let the gas be argon: $p_1 = 482.64$ kPaa, $t_1 = 43.3°C$. The argon enters the turbine at 1093.3°C and the cycle should be such as to deliver maximum work for these constraints. Use Item B 1. (a) At what rate should the argon circulate? (b) Let $\eta_t = 86\%$, $\eta_c = 84\%$ and compute the argon flow rate for 5968 kW fluid work.

Ans. (a) $T_2 = 657.3$ K, 1867 kg/min, (b) 3378 kg/min.

1153. There are required 2238 kW net from a gas turbine unit for the pumping of crude oil from the North Alaskan Slope. Air enters the compressor section at 99.975 kPaa, 278 K; the pressure ratio is $r_p = 10$. The turbine

section receives the hot gases at 1 Assume the closed Brayton cycle, and the required air flow and (b) the t efficiency. (c) For maximum work, what be the temperature of the air leaving th pressor section?

1154. Neon is used as a working fl nuclear reactor/gas turbine system op on a closed cycle. At the beginning of co sion, state 1, $p_1 = 620.53$ kPaa, $t_1 = $ $r_p = 4.5$. The neon leaves the reactor and the turbine portion at $t_3 = 1260°C$; the regenerator. These efficiencies apply: $\eta_t = 87\%$, compressor $\eta_c = 84\%$. For output of 5968 kW, compute the rate of neon and the mean effective pressu Item B 1.

1155. A blast furnace needs a suppl gas pressurized to 30 psia for its operati gas is furnished by the exhaust from turbine which delivers no power exce required to furnish the gas. For the turb state 1, $p_1 = 15$ psia, $t_1 = 60°F$; the turbi temperature is 1500°F; both efficienci bine and compressor, are 100%. Find th sure ratio r_p for the compressor. Use Iter

1156. A simple gas turbine unit Brayton cycle) has an air flow of 200 lb/ point 1, $p_1 = 14.7$ psia, $t_1 = 100°F$; Respective efficiencies are $\eta_c = 83\%$

85%. The maximum cycle temperature is 1500°F. Sketch the *Ts* diagram (use Item B 2) and find (**a**) the net horsepower, (**b**) the thermal efficiency.

1157. A gas-turbine unit consists of two turbines *A* and *B* (see figure), two combustors, and a single compressor *C*; turbine *A* drives compressor *C* to furnish all air required while turbine *B* delivers 2000 hp, the net output. Turbine and compressor efficiencies are each 83%. At state 1, $p_1 = 15$ psia, $t_1 = 100$°F; $r_p = 5$. The inlet condition for each turbine is 75 psia, 1300°F; both turbines exhaust at 15 psia. Determine (**a**) the heats Q_1 and Q_2, (**b**) the thermal efficiency for the unit, and (**c**) p_m.

Ans. (**a**) 341,700, 135,600 Btu/min, (**b**) 17.75%.

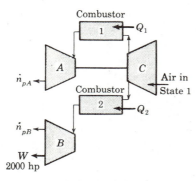

Problem 1157

1158. Hydrogen is being studied as a fluid for the closed Brayton cycle of a nuclear reactor/gas turbine combination. See problem 1152. Hydrogen enters the compressor section at 20 psia, 540°R and leaves at 150 psia, 1040°R to enter the reactor heat source. At the turbine section, the hydrogen is at 2000°R; after expansion it leaves at 1280°R. For a net work output of 10,000 hp and using Item B 5, find (**a**) compressor efficiency η_c, (**b**) turbine efficiency η_t, (**c**) hydrogen flow, lb/sec. Do not interpolate in table for minor differences.

Ans. (**a**) 84%, (**b**) 84.1%, (**c**) 8.54 lb/sec.

1159. The study of the nuclear reactor/gas turbine closed system continues using a gas whose properties are similar to those given in Item B 9; see problem 1152. The gas enters the compressor at 500°R and leaves at 1020°R; the pressure ratio is $r_p = 10$. The gas leaves the compressor, passes through the reactor, and

enters the turbine element at 2040°F to expand to 1300°R and then pass through a heat exchanger; it then reenters the compressor. Sketch the *TS* diagram showing actual and ideal points and find (**a**) the compressor efficiency, (**b**) the turbine (element) efficiency, (**c**) the mass flow of fluid for a power of 5000 hp, mole/sec, (**d**) the thermal efficiency.

1160. A closed-cycle gas turbine has argon as the working substance, and circulation in steady flow at the rate of 100 lb/min. The argon enters the compressor at 600°R and 70 psia and is compressed adiabatically to 1160°R and 280 psia. With negligible pressure drop, it is heated to 2500°R, and then expands to 1600°R and virtually to 70 psia through the turbine. For the actual cycle as defined, determine (**a**) the compressor efficiency, (**b**) the turbine efficiency, (**c**) the power delivered, and the thermal efficiency.

Ans. (**a**) 79.3%, (**b**) 84.6%, (**c**) 74.4 kW, 25.4%.

BRAYTON CYCLE, AIR STANDARD

1161. It is desired to obtain maximum work in a gas turbine operating on the air-standard Brayton cycle between the temperature limits of 37.8°C and 704.4°C; $p_1 = 103.42$ kPaa. Using air properties found in Item B 1, calculate (**a**) the temperature at the end of compression, (**b**) the compression ratio r_k, (**c**) the pressure ratio r_p, and (**d**) the thermal efficiency.

Ans. (Item B 1) (**a**) 278°C, (**b**) 4.18, (**c**) 7.4, (**d**) 43.6%.

1162. The turbine section of a Brayton cycle gas turbine receives the hot compressed air at 150 psia, 2100°R, expands it to 15 psia and develops a gross output of 15,000 hp. Air enters the compressor section at 15 psia, 500°R. All events are ideal. Use Item B 2 and find (**a**) mass of air required, lb/sec, (**b**) compressor power required, (**c**) net power output, (**d**) cycle efficiency. (**e**) For maximum power, what should be the value of the intermediate temperature T_2 (compressor exit)?

Ans. (**a**) 42.2 lb/sec, (**b**) 6660 hp, (**c**) 8340 hp, (**d**) 46.4%, (**e**) 1025°R.

1163. The "heat" received by an air standard gas turbine is 25,953 kJ/s for fluid work of 5000 kW; the turbine efficiency is $\eta_t = 84\%$. In the corresponding ideal cycle, $p_1 = 1$ atm, $t_1 = $

26.7°C, $W_c = 201.13$ kJ/kg, $W_t = 414.01$ kJ/kg; the maximum cycle temperature is $t_3 = 732.2$°C. Compute (a) the compressor efficiency, (b) the rate of air flow, (c) the cycle efficiency, (d) the part of Q_A which is unavailable, (e) that part of the heat rejected which is available, (f) the change of availability for each process; $t_0 = t_1 = 26.7$°C.

Ans. (a) 80.2%, (b) 51.7 kg/s, (c) 19.3%, (d) 198.87, (e) 146.90, (f) $\Delta \mathscr{A}_{1-2'} = +222.30$, $\Delta \mathscr{A}_{2'-3} = +302.63$, $\Delta \mathscr{A}_{3-4'} = -378.02$, $\Delta \mathscr{A}_{4'-1} = -146.90$ kJ/kg.

1164. The pumping of natural gas across the country is accomplished by an air-standard Brayton cycle turbine producing 5000 hp. Air at 14.7 psia, 100°F (point 1) is drawn into the compressor section; the pressure ratio is $r_p = 10$. At the turbine section inlet (point 3), the temperature is 1540°F; $\eta_c = 85\%$, $\eta_t = 85\%$. Use Item B 2 and compute (a) the air flow required, (b) the compressor work, hp, (c) the thermal efficiency.

Ans. (a) 62.33 lb/sec, (b) 12,920 hp, (c) 25.30%.

1165. A gas turbine unit receives 70 lb/sec of air at 80°F (also sink temperature t_0) and 1 atm. The pressure ratio in the compressor is 6; lower heating value of the fuel is 18,500 Btu/lb. There are two turbines; one (HP) just large enough to drive the compressor, the other (LP) delivers the net power. Between the turbines additional fuel is burned. The inlet temperature for each turbine is 1440°F. The LP turbine exhausts through a regenerator. Ignore pressure drops in the computations, neglect the mass of fuel. For the equivalent air-standard cycle and all ideal processes, compute (a) the thermal efficiency, (b) the net power, (c) specific fuel consumption, lb/hp-hr, (d) heat rate, (e) and the irreversibility of the heat rejection process. If there were no irreversibility *here*, what would be the percentage increase in the work done?

Ans. (Item B 2) (a) 58.4%, (b) 12,050, (c) 0.236, (d) 4360, (e) 1410 Btu/sec, 16.5%.

1166. Answer the questions for problem 1165 if the departures from the ideal are defined by the following parameters: compressor $\eta_c = 83\%$, each turbine $\eta_t = 85\%$, combustion $\eta_b = 96\%$, regeneration $\varepsilon_r = 50\%$.

Ans. (a) 26.7%, (b) 7240, (c) 0.515, (d) 9520, (e) 99%.

1167. In standard atmosphere, 14.7 psia and 60°F, a British DeHavilland jet engine develops a static thrust of 5000 lb while it receives 88 lb/sec of air. The specific fuel consumption is 1.06 lb/hr-lb thrust. Compute for the air standard. (a) If the approach velocity to the jet nozzle is 1050 fps, estimate the pressure drop across the jet nozzle if the products temperature at exit is 1230°F. (b) If the products enter the turbine wheel at 40 psig and 1450°F with a velocity of 500 fps and leave the wheel at 7.5 psig with a velocity of 1050 fps, approximate the horsepower developed by the turbine wheel. The products pass through the exit nozzle ($e_n = 95\%$) of the engine to the atmosphere.

1168. A 100-hp, air-standard, Brayton-cycle turbine is to be designed for maximum work. At state 1, $p_1 = 14$ psia, $t_1 = 80$°F; $r_p = 5.5$. Determine (a) the temperature t_3 from the combustor, (b) e, (c) the required air flow, (d) p_m.

Ans. (a) 960°F, (b) 37.6%, (c) 81.8 lb/min, (d) 14.35 psi.

1169. In an air-standard gas-turbine cycle at state 1, $p_1 = 14.5$ psia, $t_1 = 60$°F; $r_p = 6$; The maximum cycle temperature is $t_3 = 1440$°F. Efficiencies are: turbine $\eta_t = 82\%$, compressor $\eta_c = 82\%$. What decrease in turbine efficiency will have the same effect on the cycle thermal efficiency as does a decrease in compressor efficiency to $\eta_c = 75\%$, other values remaining unchanged?

1170. A gas-turbine system operating on the air-standard Brayton cycle with friction is to produce 7500 hp. Air at 14.7 psia, 80°F (point 1) is drawn in by the compressor ($\eta_c = 85\%$). The pressure ratio is 8. At the turbine ($\eta_t = 82\%$) inlet (point 3), the gas temperature is 1520°F. Sketch the Ts diagram and find (a) air required lb/min, (b) compressor work, hp, (c) thermal efficiency. Solve using Item B 1 and then using Item B 2. Compare answers.

1171. The compressor of a Brayton-cycle gas turbine draws in 45,000 cfm of air at 15 psia and 60°F. The pressure ratio is 9.5, and the turbine inlet temperature is 1420°F. Use Item B 2. (a) For the ideal cycle, determine the net horsepower output, the thermal efficiency, the mep, and the availability of the exhaust air with respect to a sink at $p_0 = 15$ psia and $t_0 = 40$°F. (b) For a turbine efficiency of 84% and a compressor efficiency of 82%, compute the net output, the thermal efficiency, and the percentage reduction of power as a result of fluid friction.

OPEN CYCLE, PRODUCTS TABLE

1172. A gas turbine receives 40,000 cfm of air at 14 psia, 60°F and compresses it to 98 psia. Liquid octane fuel at 70°F is injected into the combustors at a rate of $r_{f/a} = 0.01635$ lb fuel/lb air; see equation (13.7, *Text*). Combustion is complete with a release of $E_c = 19,300$ Btu/lb of fuel (corrected to 0°R) and the resulting products are similar to "400% air" (Item B 8). For ideal processes, determine (a) the air temperature at compressor exit, (b) the gas temperature at turbine discharge, (c) the net horsepower delivered, (d) the cycle efficiency, (e) p_m, (f) the unavailable part of Q_A (1 lb of air and $t_0 = 60°F$) and the available part of Q_R.

Ans. (a) 903°R, (b) 1247°R, (c) 8630 hp, (d) 39.8%.

1173. A gas turbine receives 40,000 cfm of air at 14 psia and 60°F, compresses the air to 98 psia. Octane fuel at 70°F is injected into the combustors in the ratio $r_{f/a} = 0.01655$. Assume the combustor efficiency is 100% and a fuel heating value of 19,300 Btu/lb at 0°R. The products from the combustor are for "400% theoretical air" with $M_p = 28.9$ molecular mass. The turbine expansion is to the original pressure. Neglect pressure drop between compressor and turbine. Determine (a) the net power and the thermal efficiency, (b) the pounds of fuel required per minute and per hp-hr, (c) the heat rate. (d) For a sink at 60°F, determine the steady flow availability of the exhaust (at 4) and the irreversibility of the $p = C$ process of the cooling of the exhaust (4'-sink).

Ans. [Items B 2, B 8] (a) 8740 hp, 39.9%, (b) 48.2, 0.331, (c) 6390 Btu/hp-hr, (d) 201,500 Btu/min.

1174. The data are the same as given in problem 1173, but efficiencies as follows are to be accounted for : compressor $\eta_c = 83\%$, turbine $\eta_t = 85\%$, combustors $\eta_b = 100\%$. Continue to ignore the pressure drops between compressor and turbine and solve (a), (b), (c), (d), in problem 1173.

Ans. [Items B 2, B 8] (a) 5250 hp, 23.9%, (b) 0.552 lb/hp-hr, (c) 10,650 Btu/hp-hr, (d) 264,000 Btu/min.

1175. Compressed air is to be delivered by a simple gas turbine with an over-size compressor that supplies both the compressed air and the air required for the turbine; all turbine work is used to drive the compressor. At state

1, $p_1 = 14.7$ psia, $t_1 = 60°F$; the pressure ratio is $r_p = 6$; the maximum cycle temperature is 1500°F; the fuel energy release is 18,500 Btu/lb fuel (corrected to 0°R) and the products are similar to those of "400% air," Item B 8; $t_{fuel} = 60°F$. These efficiencies apply: compressor $\eta_c = 82\%$, turbine $\eta_t = 84\%$. Neglect the mass of fuel and determine (a) the pounds of compressed air delivered per pound of products through the turbine, (b) the air-fuel ratio $r_{a/f}$ for the turbine part of the cycle, (c) the compressed air delivered per pound of fuel burned each second.

Ans. (a) 0.613, (b) 64.6, (c) 39.6 lb/sec.

COMBUSTORS AND REGENERATORS

1176. Air leaves the compressor in a gas turbine and enters the combustor at 482.64 kPaa, 204.4°C, and 45 m/s; gases leave the combustor at 468.85 kPaa, 893.3°C, and 152 m/s. Liquid fuel enters at 15.6°C with a heating value of 42,920 kJ/kg; combustor efficiency $\eta_f = 94\%$. Find the fuel flow per kilogram of entering air. For the products, $M_p = 28.9$, $k = 1.36$. *Ans.* 0.0206 kg fuel/kg air.

1177. A combustor receives air at 480°F and liquid fuel at 80°F [see equation (13.7), *Text*]; $r_{a/f} = 60$; the heating value is 18,450 Btu/lb fuel (0°R basis); combustor efficiency is $\eta_f = 94\%$. The gases enter the turbine at 90 psia, leave at 15 psia; $\eta_t = 85\%$. Find (a) the temperature of the gases leaving the combustor, and (b) their temperature leaving the turbine.

1178. A gas-turbine compressor supplies a regenerator with 82,388 kg/hr of air at 405.75 kPaa, 182.2°C, which leaves the regenerator at 396.86 kPaa, 393.3°C. Hot products from the burning of 832.2 kg/hr of fuel enter the regenerator at 104.53 kPaa, 548.9°C. Determine (a) the effectiveness of the regenerator, and (b) the availability of the products from the regenerator with respect to a sink of $p_0 = 101.70$ kPaa and $t_0 = 21.1°C$. Assume the products to have properties similar to those of air. See Item B 1. *Ans.* (a) 57%, (b) 103.6 kJ/kg.

1179. There are absorbed 11,678,850 kJ/hr by 22.68 kg/s of air passing through a gas-turbine regenerator; the fuel-air ratio is $r_{f/a} = 0.017$; $M_p = 28.8$ kg/mole, $k_p = 1.37$. If the air and products enter the regenerator at

182.2°C and 426.7°C, respectively, compute (a) the regenerator effectiveness and (b) the exit air temperature and the exit products temperature.

REGENERATIVE CYCLES

1180. A regenerator (adiabatic) is added to the gas turbine in problem 1160 cooling the turbine exhaust to 1320°R. Compute the temperature of the air entering the heat exchanger for the heat supplied, the effectiveness of the regenerator, and the thermal efficiency with regeneration.

Ans. 1440°R, 63.7%, 32.1%.

1181. The study of nuclear reactor/gas turbine combination in a closed cycle continues (problem 1152). Helium leaves the compressor ($\eta_c = 100\%$) at 4137 kPaa, 416.7 K; it leaves the reactor at 1088.9 K (ignore pressure drops) entering the turbine; it leaves the turbine ($\eta_t = 100\%$) at 2241 kPaa and passes via a regenerator, thence through another heat exchanger (sink) to the compressor which compresses to 4137 kPaa. From the compressor, it passes through the regenerator (100% effectiveness), whence it enters the reactor and the cycle repeats. For a net power of 16,412 kW, at what rate should the helium flow? Also compute the thermal efficiency. (b) Let the three efficiencies now be $\eta_t = 86\%$, $\eta_c = 83\%$, $\eta_r = 55\%$ and solve for the flow rate and the thermal efficiency.

Ans. (a) 1297 kg/min, 61.8%.

1182. Air enters a stationary gas engine at 500°R and 14.7 psia; $r_p = 7.95$. The actual temperature at discharge from the compressor is 1000°R. The products of combustion enter the turbine at 2000°R and expand to atmospheric pressure. Regeneration with an effectiveness of 60% is used. (No pressure drops.) The actual exhaust temperature is 1320°R. Show all states involved in the solution on a *Ts* diagram. (a) For the ideal Brayton cycle, compute the net work per lb and the thermal efficiency. Compute (b) the compression and turbine efficiencies, (c) the actual net work, (d) the actual heat added and thermal efficiency. What would be the actual thermal efficiency without regeneration? (e) If the output of the actual unit is 5000 hp, what volume of air enters the compressor (cfm at state 1)?

Ans. (a) 124.2 Btu/lb, 43.1%, (b) 79.7%, 82.6%, (c) 61.1, (d) 215 Btu/lb, 28.4%, 23.2%, (e) 43,600 cfm.

1183. A gas turbine exhausts the products at $T_{e'} = 1380°R$; the air leaves the compressor at $T_{2'} = 980°R$ and 98 psia. These streams enter a regenerator whose effectiveness $\varepsilon_r = 65\%$; pressure drops to be neglected. The air flow to the compressor is 3120 lb/min. Include fuel mass in computations. (a) For a first approximation, assume "400%-air" products, $r_{f/a} = 0.01655$, $M_p = 28.9$, and compute the temperature $T_{a'}$ of the air entering the combustors from the regenerator. (b) The temperature of the products leaving the combustor is $T_3 = 2040°R$; the combustor efficiency $\eta_b = 95\%$; heating value on 0°R base is 18,800 Btu/lb f. Make an energy balance on the combustor, and compute the corresponding fuel-air ratio. Let the properties at 3 be for 400% products (will change little for small changes $r_{f/a}$). [*Note:* If more accurate answers are desired, one could iterate with the new value of $r_{f/a}$.] (c) For a cyclic work of 76.7 Btu/lb a, determine the shaft power and the engine thermal efficiency.

Ans. [Items B2, B8] (a) 1253°R, (b) 0.01287, (c) 5650 hp, 31.7%.

1184. A regenerative gas turbine is constructed in two parts, similar to problem 1157 with he addition of a regenerator. One turbine, whose combustor receives 113,600 lb/hr of air and 1150 lb/hr of fuel, drives the compressor. The other turbine, whose combustor receives 68,065 lb/hr of air and 685 lb/hr of fuel, delivers the net power output, 3500-hp capacity. The entire amount of air, 181,665 lb/hr, enters the compressor at 14.49 psia and 60°F and is discharged at 58.85 psia and 363°F to the regenerator. Leaving the regenerator at 57.56 psia and 750°F, the air goes to the respective combustors and leaves each combustor at 56.54 psia and 1500°F, also taken as the throttle state to each turbine. Each turbine exhaust is at 15.16 psia and 1024°F, whence all the products enter the regenerator. Leaving the regenerator, the products are at 14.75 psia and 637°F. For the fuel, $q_l = 18,200$ Btu/lb. Assume no heat losses between the pieces of equipment. Sketch the arrangement of the equipment and find (a) the compressor efficiency, (b) each turbine efficiency, (c) the regenerator effectiveness, and (d) the actual thermal efficiency.

JET PROPULSION

1185. A plane is powered by a jet propulsive system. The fluid jet leaves the nozzle (tail) end of the system with an absolute speed (with respect to the ground) of 853.7 m/s; the plane moves at 1569 km/hr. If the system is developing 7460 kW, find (a) the thrust, (b) the mass flow (neglecting $r_{f/a}$), (c) the propulsive efficiency.

Ans. (a) 17,117 N, (b) 20.05 kg/s, (c) 50.5%.

1186. Atmospheric air at 4 psia, −60°F, enters the diffuser section of a jet plane (v_p = 960 mph) and is brought almost to rest at the compressor entrance of the jet engine. The pressure coefficient is κ_p = 92 percent and the temperature recovery factor is f_T = 94% for the diffuser. Find (a) the air pressure and temperature at the diffuser exit. (b) the propulsive horsepower developed if the absolute exit velocity of the products from the tail section is v_2 = 2500 fps and the air flow is 100 lb/sec; neglect the added mass of fuel. Sketch the *TS* diagram for the diffuser portion of the cycle.

1187. A jet-engine driven plane is expected to travel in dynamic equilibrium at 965.4 km/hr when the net thrust force is 17,793 N and the ratio air-to-fuel is $r_{a/f}$ = 50. The exhaust gases depart the nozzle at 610 m/s (relative to engine). Compute (a) the flow rate of air $\dot{m}_a$ and of fuel $\dot{m}_f$, (b) the power being developed. (c) If the exhaust state temperature is 944.4 K, the sink 277.8 K, determine the availability and the entropy production for the universe and the irreversibility from the exit section of the nozzle to the dead state, per unit mass of air. (Use specific heat of exhaust as c_p = 1.089 kJ/kg-K) (d) Calculate the propulsive efficiency, the TSFC, and the air specific impulse.

Ans. (a) 50.3, 1.006 kg/s, (b) 4772 kW, (c) 515 kJ/kg air, ΔS_p = 1.181 kJ/K-kg air, (d) 61.1%, 0.204 kg$_{fuel}$/N-hr, 353 N-s/kg.

1188. A plane has an air speed of 274.4 m/s where the atmospheric air is at 27.58 kPaa, 222 K. (a) The air is brought virtually to rest relative to the plane in a diffuser. Compute the corresponding stagnation enthalpy, temperature, and pressure. (b) Let the pressure coefficient for the diffuser be κ_p = 96%. Specify the actual state at the diffuser exit when $K_0 \approx 0$. (c) The air from the diffuser is compressed adiabatically through a pressure ratio of

4.5 with $\Delta K = 0$. If the compressor efficiency is 80%, determine the work for unit mass. What power is required for an air flow of 81.63 kg/s? (d) For T_0 = 222 K, compute the overall irreversibility for the event (diffuser and compressor).

1189. A plane has an air speed of 900 fps where the atmospheric air is at 4 psia and −60°F. (a) The air is brought virtually to rest relative to the plane in a diffuser. Compute the corresponding stagnation enthalpy, temperature, and pressure. (b) Let the pressure coefficient for the diffuser be κ_p = 96%. Specify the actual state at the diffuser exit when $K_0 \approx 0$. (c) The air from the diffuser is compressed adiabatically through a pressure ratio of 4.5 with $\Delta K = 0$. If the compressor efficiency is 80%, determine the work for unit mass. What horsepower is required for an air flow of 180 lb/sec? (d) For T_0 = 400°R, compute the overall irreversibility for the event (diffuser and compressor).

1190. A jet engine is operating in an environment at −48°F and 8.88 in. Hg abs; its speed is 630 mph; $r_{f/a}$ = 0.017 lb f/lb a; ram pressure coefficient = 90%; combustion efficiency = 94%; let q_1 = 18,800 Btu/lb f; TSFC = 0.8 lb f/hr-lb thrust; thrust F_t = 3000 lb. Compute (a) mass rate of air flow, (b) propulsive power being developed, (c) jet velocity at the nozzle exit section (relative to engine), (d) propulsive efficiency (e) engine thermal efficiency, (f) cyclic thermal efficiency, (g) the pressure at the exit of the diffuser if the kinetic energy there is negligible, (h) Δh in the nozzle if the entering gases have negligible kinetic energy.

Ans. [Item B 2] (a) 39.2 lb/sec, (b) 5050 hp, (c) 3330 fps, (d) 49.8%, (e) 28.5%, (f) 63.5%, (g) 7.28 psia, (h) −222 Btu/lb a.

1191. The air speed of a turbojet engine is 900 fps in air at 4 psia and −60°F; for the compressor, r_p = 4.5; let $r_{f/a}$ = 0.01635 (virtually "400% air," fuel mass to be accounted for); at 0°R, $−h_{rp}$ = q_1 = 18,500 Btu/lb f; for the products, M_p = 28.9. Consider as negligible the sensible enthalpy of the fuel as it enters the combustor. All processes are ideal. Kinetic energies are negligible as follows: at exit from diffuser, the changes through combustor and turbine. (a) Determine the state (*p*, *T*, and other needed properties) at exit from diffuser, from compressor, from combustors, from the turbine, and from the nozzle. Compute (**b**) the mass flow rate of air to provide a 10,000-lb thrust, (**c**) power developed, (**d**) the propulsive efficiency, (**e**) the engine thermal efficiency, (**f**) the cycle thermal efficiency. [*Note*: $\oint dQ/Q_A$ gives exactly the same number as the definition of e_{cyc} only for a pure substance over the whole cycle. Try it.] (**g**) the TSFC, (**h**) the irreversibility of the exhaust passing to the dead state; $T_0 = 400°R$.

Ans. [Items B 2, B 8] (**a**) $T_3 = 1838°R$, $T_e = 1088°R$, (**b**) 181.2 lb/sec, (**c**) 16,360 hp, (**d**) 50.3%, (**e**) 21.1% (**f**) 42.5%, (**g**) 1.07.

1192. The analysis as asked for in problem 1191 is to be made with basic data therein and with the addition of the following efficiencies: ram pressure coefficient $\kappa_p = 92\%$, compressor efficiency $\eta_c = 82\%$, combustor efficiency $\eta_b = 95\%$, turbine efficiency $\eta_t = 84\%$, nozzle efficiency $\eta_n = 96\%$. The nozzle exhaust pressure $p_c = 4$ psia and the Δp through combustors is to be ignored.

Ans. [Items B 2, B 8] (**a**) $T_3 = 1873°R$, $T_{e'} = 1178°R$, (**b**) 198.5 lb/sec, (**c**) 16,300 hp, (**d**) 53.5%, (**e**) 19.27%, (**f**) 34.9, (**g**) 1.17, (**h**) 306 Btu/lb a.

1193. One of the four jet engines powering a SST plane cruising at 1350 mph scoops in atmospheric air at 1.7 psia, −80°F (50,000 ft altitude) which is brought to rest by the diffuser just ahead of the compressor element. For the diffuser the pressure coefficient is $K_p = 90\%$ and the temperature recovery factor is $f_T = 95\%$. (**a**) Find the pressure and temperature of the air at the compressor element inlet. (**b**) If each engine develops 38,000 lb thrust, find the air flow, lb/sec; the absolute exit velocity of the products from the tail section is $v_2 = 2400$ fps, and the fuel/air ratio is $r_{f/a} = 0.018$; account for the $r_{f/a}$. Show *TS* diagram for the diffuser portion of the cycle.

1194. A ramjet engine is to drive a body at an air speed of 3000 fps at an altitude of 42,000 ft ($p_a = 2.72$ psia, $t_a = −60°F$, approximately NASA standard); let the ram pressure coefficient $\kappa_p = 74\%$, combustion efficiency $\eta_b = 95\%$, nozzle efficiency $\eta_n = 91\%$ with exit pressure $p_{4'} = 2.72$ psia, enthalpy of reaction $−h_{rp} = 18,500$ Btu/lb f. The stagnation temperature of the gases as they enter the nozzle is 4500°R; the power at the specified speed is to be 10,000 hp. For the first approximation, assume that air is the working substance throughout and neglect the effects of the mass

of fuel. Compute (**a**) the stagnation temperature and pressure at exit from the diffuser, (**b**) the relative exit speed of the gases from the nozzle, (**c**) the thrust force and the mass flow for the desired power, (**d**) the work per unit mass, (**e**) the fuel-air ratio and the rate of fuel flow, (**f**) the propulsive efficiency, (**g**) the irreversibility in the nozzle, (**h**) the irreversibility of the exhaust passing to the dead state, (**i**) the efficiency of the diffuser (see § 18.15, *Text*).

Ans. [Item B 2] (**a**) 1138°R, 82.6 psia, (**b**) 5760 fps, (**c**) 1830 lb, 21.4 lb/sec, (**e**) 0.0548, 1.17 lb/sec, (**f**) 68.5%, (**g**) 265 Btu/sec, (**h**) 971 Btu/lb a, (**i**) 88.2%.

1195. A ramjet plane flies with a speed of 2500 fps at an altitude of 50,000 ft for which the environmental conditions are $p = 1.5$ psia, $T = 390°R$. From the viewpoint of an observer located in the ramjet, air approaches the engine at a speed of 2500 fps and is subsequently slowed down to a very small speed in a diffuser that has a ram efficiency of $\eta_r = 94\%$; the air is then led to a combustor wherein its temperature is increased to 2040°F. Finally the heated air (neglect effects of the added fuel mass) expands through a nozzle to a pressure of 1.5 psia; the nozzle efficiency is 92%. Use Item B 2 and determine (**a**) the air temperature and pressure at the diffuser exit, (**b**) the actual velocity at the nozzle exit, (**c**) the developed thrust for a flow rate of 80 lb/sec of air and the fuel required ($q_l = 18,500$ Btu/lb) to support this thrust, (**d**) the thrust developed for a fuel flow of 1 lb/sec.

1196. For approximate comparison purposes, problem 1191 is to be changed to a fan jet engine with basic data as given except that for simplicity the air standard is to be used throughout ($r_{f/a} = 0$). For the fan jet engine, the thrust horsepower will be 16,360 hp, as found in problem 1191, and the bypass ratio (=mass of by-pass air/mass of air through combustors) is 1.5; for the fan $r_{pF} = 2$. Other given data, or data from Item B 2 or the solution of problem 1191 include: $v_p = 900$ fps, $p_i = p_a = 4$ psia, r_p (compressor) = 4.5, $p_0 = 6.92$ psia, $p_2 = 31.14$ psia, $−W_c = 60.42$ Btu/lba, $T_3 = 1840°R$ (rounded off). Let $\dot{m} = $ lb mass of air through gas generator (=compressor and combustors—1.5 $\dot{m}$ = by-pass air). For 1 lb through the gas generator section, compute (**a**) fan work W_F and turbine work W_t, (**b**) condition of air as it leaves the turbine ($K_4 \approx 0$), (**c**) the ideal exit velocity from the primary nozzle and from the by-pass nozzle. Determine (**d**) the mass rate of flow through each nozzle for the given thrust horsepower, (**e**) the thrust force, (**f**) the TSFC and compare with that of problem 1191 (**g**) the horsepower to the fan and to the compressor.

Ans. (**a**) 37.15, 97.57 Btu/lb g, (**b**) 1477°R, (**c**) 2270, 1430 fps, (**d**) 148.6, 222.9 lb/sec, (**f**) 0.875 lb fuel/hr-lb thrust, (**g**) 7790, 12,700 hp.

ROCKET PROPULSION

1197. Show, for a rocket nozzle or any nozzle, for an ideal gas with properties k, M that the specific impulse for isentropic flow is given by

$$I_s = \left\{ \frac{2k\bar{R}T_1}{(k-1)M} \left[1 - \left(\frac{p_2}{p_1}\right)^{(k-1)/k} \right] \right\}^{1/2}$$

where T_1, p_1 give the stagnation initial state, and p_2 is the static pressure at the exit section.

1198. A research rocket delivers a thrust of 17,793 N for a period of 30 sec when steadily and uniformly consuming its 425.9 kg of propellants (red fuming nitric acid and aniline furfuryl). (**a**) With what constant speed do the products leave the nozzle? (**b**) Estimate the temperature in the combustion chamber if the pressure there is 2206.3 kPaa and the expansion (ideal gas, $k = 1.2$) through the nozzle is to 103.4 kPaa, 1560°C.

Ans. (**a**) 1253 m/s, (**b**) 3056 K.

1199. (**a**) The vertical travel of a rocket in a vacuum may be expressed mathematically as $dv = g\,d\tau - v_r\,dm/m$, where v is the rocket speed, g is the local gravity acceleration, $d\tau$ is the interval of burning time for the propellant, v_r is the exit gas velocity relative to the rocket, and m is the combined mass of the rocket and propellant at any given instant. If a rocket is required to escape the earth's gravitational field, determine how much of the total rocket is propellant if the time required to burn the propellant is negligible and if the relative gas velocity $v_r = 8500$ fps is constant during burning. The escape velocity is 25,000 mph; also, let g be constant. (**b**) Four tons of propellant are placed in a 2-ton rocket engine to form a complete 6-ton rocket. It is estimated that the relative jet velocity will be 7500 fps, and that the propellant will burn for 40 sec during flight. Estimate the maximum speed attained by the rocket. Let $g = g_0 = $ constant.

1200. A rocket motor generates combustion gases at 320 psia, 5200°R at entrance to the nozzle where the gas velocity is low (relative to nozzle). The nozzle is designed to expand the gases to the ambient pressure of 5 psia; ambient temperature is 400°R. The expanding gases (considered ideal) have the characteristics $k = 1.2$, $M_g = 15.45$ lb/mole. For a mass flow of 325 lb/sec and a vehicular speed of 4000 mph, determine (**a**) the relative exit gas speed from the nozzle for steady flow through it, (**b**) the thrust force, the specific impulse, (**c**) the momentary power developed, and (**d**) the propulsive efficiency. (**e**) What is the Mach number of the vehicle speed?

Ans. (**a**) 10,050 fps, (**b**) 101,300 lb, 312 lb-sec/lb, (**c**) 1,080,000 hp, (**d**) 87%, (**e**) 5.98.

1201. It is possible that hydrogen heated via a nuclear reactor may be used as a rocket propellant in the upper stage. Assume that during the reactor heating of the H_2 from $T_2 = 150$°R to $T_3 = 4500$°R, the pressure drops from $p_2 = 1000$ psia to $p_3 = 400$ psia. The H_2 then enters the nozzle with negligible kinetic energy and expands isentropically to an exit pressure of 2 psia; the surroundings are also at virtually the same pressure and 380°R. The thrust is to be 10^5 lb. Compute (**a**) the exit speed of the H_2, (**b**) specific impulse, (**c**) the mass flow rate for the desired thrust. (**d**) When the propulsive efficiency of the rocket is 88%, what is its Mach number?

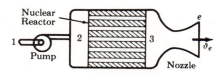

Problem 1201

1202. It is desired that a nozzle used for attitude control in a space ship exert a force of 1 lb. Hydrogen is to expand from a stagnation state of 300 psia and 1180°R; the exit section of the nozzle is designed for a pressure of 3 psia; nozzle efficiency $\eta_n = 93\%$. Neglect the effect of the difference between the exit pressure and the surroundings pressure. (**a**) What mass of H_2 should be in storage for the equivalent of 10 hr of use? Compute (**b**) the specific impulse, (**c**) the throat diameter for an isentropic flow if the pressure there is $p^* = 158$ psia.

Ans. (**a**) 98.5 lb, (**b**) 365 sec, (**c**) 0.0534 in.

1203. A rocket motor generates combusution gases at 360 psia and 5000°R at the nozzle entrance, where the gas relative velocity is low. The nozzle is designed to expand the gases, considered as ideal with $k = 1.2$ and $M = 15.45$, to an ambient pressure of 3 psia, process 1–2. Ambient air temperature is −67°F; vehicle air speed is 3600 mph; gas flow $\dot{m} = 300$ lb/sec; steady flow. Determine (a) the relative exit speed from the nozzle, (b) the thrust force, (c) the specific impulse, (d) the momentary power developed, (e) the propulsive efficiency, (f) the Mach number for the vehicle speed. (g) Let nozzle section be convergent-divergent with the pressure at the throat of $p^* = 204$ psia, other data unchanged. Calculate the throat area for 300 lb/sec isentropic steady flow.

MISCELLANEOUS

1204. A constant volume combustion turbine (explosion type) operates on a cycle composed of the following processes: isentropic compression 1–2; constant volume heating 2–3; isentropic expansion 3–4; constant pressure closure 4–1. This cycle is referred to as the Holzwarth cycle. Sketch the pV and TS diagrams. Let the conditions in each piece of equipment be steady flow, and write equations for compressor work, turbine work, and thermal efficiency.

1205. The same as problem 1204 except that the following data are known: $r_k = 1.4$, combustion pressure ratio $p_3/p_2 = 3$, $p_1 = 15$ psia, $t_1 = 80°F$. For 1 lb of air, determine (a) W_c, (b) W_t, (c) W, and (d) e. (e) What is the net horsepower for 75,000 cfm of air measured at the intake state to the compressor?

Ans. (a) 18.62, (b) 164.08, (c) 145.46 Btu/lb, (d) 62.9%, (e) 19,300 hp.

1206. A gas turbine operating on the air standard Brayton cycle is being analyzed. The effect of the intermediate temperature T_2 on the maximum work is being studied. The cycle operates between the minimum temperature $T_1 = 300$ K and maximum temperature $T_3 = 1400$ K. Write a computer program for this study.

1207. The effect of regeneration on the efficiency of a gas turbine is under study. Let the turbine unit operate on the air standard Brayton cycle and then impose regeneration thereon from its minimum effect to the maximum effect at which point the exit air temperature from the regenerator is equivalent to the entering gas temperature from the turbine elements. Write the program.

1208–1210. These numbers may be used for other problems.

16

INTERNAL COMBUSTION ENGINES

Note: Diagrams on the pV and Ts planes plus mass and energy diagrams should be used freely. When gas tables are used, extrapolation may be necessary and is acceptable for pedagogical purposes.

OTTO CYCLE, AIR STANDARD

1211. An Otto cycle with a compression ratio of 7.5 operates from the suction conditions of 97.91 kPaa, 29.4°C. Find the pressure and temperature at the end of compression **(a)** if cold air ($k = 1.4$) is the working substance, **(b)** if hot air ($k = 1.32$) is the working substance. Compare answers. **(c)** Solve for the ideal thermal efficiency based upon the conditions given in **(a)** and **(b)**.
Ans. **(a)** 1644 kPaa, 404°C, **(b)** 1400 kPaa, 303.3°C, **(c)** 55.35%, 47.5%.

1212. At the beginning of compression in an air standard Otto cycle, the state is 13.8 psia, 120°F; the compression ratio is $r_k = 9.2$. **(a)** Find the clearance c. Find p and T at the end of compression **(b)** if cold air ($k = 1.4$) is the working fluid, **(c)** if hot air ($k = 1.31$) is the working fluid, **(d)** using Item B 2. **(e)** Solve for the ideal thermal efficiency based upon conditions in **(b)** and **(c)**.

1213. For an ideal Otto engine with 17% clearance and an initial pressure of 93.08 kPaa, determine the pressure at the end of compression using air-standard properties from Item B 1. If the pressure at the end of the constant volume heating is 3447.4 kPaa, what is the mep is psi? *Ans.* 1385 kPaa, 471 kPa.

1214. Sketch an Otto cycle on the pV and Ts planes with point 1 being at the beginning of the isentropic compression process. These data apply for the air standard cycle: $p_1 = 101.4$ kPaa, $T_1 = 333.3$ K, $V_1 = 283\ \ell$, $r_k = 5$, $T_3 = 2000$ K. Solve for **(a)** m_1, **(b)** p_2, V_2, T_2, **(c)** p_3, **(d)** p_4, T_4, **(e)** Q_A, **(f)** Q_R, **(g)** e, **(h)** percent clearance c, and **(i)** that portion of Q_A which is unavailable ($T_0 = T_1 = 333.3$ K.)

1215. An ideal Otto cycle engine with 15% clearance operates on 0.5 lb/sec of air; intake state is 14.4 psia, 100°F. The energy released during combustion is 525 Btu/sec. Using air-table values, compute **(a)** r_k, **(b)** V_D, **(c)** p and t at each corner, **(d)** e, **(e)** the percentage of available energy utilized for a sink temperature of 100°F.
Ans. **(a)** 7.67, **(b)** 6.26 cu ft/sec, **(c)** 243 psia, 773°F, 1161 psia, 5434°F, 83.6 psia, 2795°F, **(d)** 47.9%, **(e)** 58.7%.

1216. For an ideal Otto engine operating on the air standard (Item B 2), the temperature at the end of isentropic compression is 840°F and at the end of expansion is 2540°F. The compression ratio is $r_k = 7.5$. Find the work and the efficiency.
Ans. 441.29 Btu/lb air, 47.7%.

1217. An equivalent air-standard Otto cycle rejects heat in a nonflow isometric process from $T_4 = 2100$°R and 54 psia to $T_1 = 560$°R and 14.4 psia. The cycle work is 340 Btu/lb. The surroundings are at 14.4 psia and 60°F. **(a)** If the heat were rejected reversibly, how much work would be done? What percentage of the work is this? Determine **(b)** the irreversibility of process 4–1, **(c)** the unavailable portion of the heat (as it leaves the system).

Ans. [Item B 2] **(a)** 165.4, **(c)** 127.7 Btu/lb.

1218. The fuel/air ratio for an ideal Otto engine with 12% clearance is $r_{f/a} = 0.06$ lb fuel/lb air where the lower heating value is $q_l = 18,800$ Btu/lb fuel. The engine operates on 25 lb/min of air, initially at 14 psia, 110°F. Using the air table (air standard) and neglecting the diluting effect of the mass of fuel, determine **(a)** V_D, **(b)** p and T at each corner of the cycle, **(c)** W and e, **(d)** mep, **(e)** the available energy not utilized for a sink temperature of 110°F.

Ans. **(a)** 336.6 cfm, **(b)** 307 psia, 1344°R, 1440 psia, 6305°R, 80.7 psia, 3298°R, **(c)** 573.9 Btu/lb air, 50.7%, **(d)** 230 psi, **(e)** 360.3 Btu/lb air.

1219. The air in an ideal Otto engine is initially at 14.5 psia, 100°F. At the end of isentropic compression, the pressure is $p_2 = 352$ psia; at the end of combustion, the pressure is $p_2 = 1100$ psia. Based upon air-table values, find **(a)** r_k, **(b)** the percentage clearance, **(c)** t_3, **(d)** e. **(e)** If the sink temperature is 100°F, what percentage of the available part of the heat added was utilized?

Ans. **(a)** 10, **(b)** 11.11%, **(c)** 3790°F, **(d)** 53.7%, **(e)** 68.7%.

1220. Compression in an ideal Otto cycle starts at point 1, 14 psia, 140°F; $r_k = 9$, $T_3 = 5900$°R. **(a)** Determine p, T at each corner of the diagram and the thermal efficiency by the air standard. **(b)** If the closing process 4–1 were reversible internally and externally, how much work could be obtained during it when the sink temperature is 520°R? Compare with W.

OTTO ENGINE PERFORMANCE

1221. Intake air into an Otto engine is at 14.7 psia and 530°R with an air-fuel ratio of 15. The heating value of the fuel is 18,900 Btu/lb fuel. The corresponding ideal cycle efficiency is 50%. The actual engine has a volumetric efficiency of 75% and a brake engine efficiency of 55%. Use an over-all value of $k = 1.33$. Compute the brake mean effective pressure and the compression ratio of the engine. *Ans.* 105.5 psi, 8.18.

1222. A two-stroke, Otto-type, 23.5 × 23.5-cm engine develops 29.85 kW at 200 rpm while using natural gas whose lower heating value is 37,252 kJ/m³ at intake of $p_1 = 1$ atm and $t_1 = 15.6$°C. The heat rate is 14,142 kJ/kW-hr; compression ratio is 6, mechanical efficiency is 81%. Use the air standard with $k = 1.33$ and compute the brake and indicated thermal efficiencies, engine efficiencies, and mep.

Ans. $e_i = 31.4\%$, $\eta_b = 57.1\%$, $p_{mb} = 878$ kPa.

1223. During a 1.45-min test on a 7.785 × 8.731-cm, eight-cylinder automotive engine, it used 454 g of fuel ($q_l = 43,734$ kJ/kg) and developed a torque of 237.3 N-m with a mechanical efficiency of 78%. The engine shaft turned a total of 3520 revolutions. Calculate **(a)** e_b, e_i, **(b)** η_b, η_i, for an ideal cycle efficiency of $e = 53.3\%$, and **(c)** p_{mi}.

Ans. **(a)** $e_b = 26.4\%$, **(b)** $\eta_i = 63.6\%$, **(c)** 1150 kPa.

1224. The 3.4-ℓ British Jaguar XK four-stroke-cycle automotive engine has 6 cylinders in line, 8.306 × 10.592-cm size, a compression ratio of 8, and develops 156.7 kW at 5500 rpm. For the ideal cycle, the condition at the beginning of compression is 101.35 kPaa, 54.4°C. At 5500 rpm the brake thermal efficiency and the volumetric efficiency are 30% and 78% respectively. The condition at the inlet to the engine is 103.42 kPaa, 26.7°C. Solve for **(a)** percentage clearance, **(b)** p, T at the end of ideal compression, **(c)** η_b using $k = 1.4$, **(d)** mass of air used, **(e)** torque, **(f)** p_{mb}, **(g)** friction power where the mechanical efficiency is $\eta_m = 71\%$, **(h)** $r_{a/f}$ with $q_l = 44,432$ kJ/kg.

1225. An Otto-type engine has a clearance of 12% and a volume in the cylinder at the beginning of compression of 0.004 ft³. The heat added is 0.34 Btu/cycle. When the ideal thermal efficiency is 52%, the brake engine efficiency is 50%. Determine r_k, e_b, and the brake mep.

1226. One of the newer lean-burn Otto cycle engines has a compression ratio of $r_k = 10$; the maximum temperature in the cycle is 2870°C. If the pressure and temperature at the beginning of compression are 103 kPaa, 27°C, and if $k = 1.4$, find the mean effective pressure p_m. *Ans.* 1372 kPa.

1227. The Ford Comet engine has 6 cylinders in line, 8.89 × 6.35-cm, a compression ratio of 8.7, displacement of 2365 cm³, and develops 67.1 kW at 4200 rpm. While operating at 4200 rpm, it is noted that the brake thermal efficiency is 31%, the volumetric efficiency is 72%, and the mechanical efficiency is 70%. For the ideal cycle, the condition at the beginning of compression (point 1) is 101.35 kPaa, 60°C. At 4200 rpm, find **(a)** the percentage clearance, **(b)** p, T at the end of ideal compression, $k = 1.4$, **(c)** brake engine efficiency, **(d)** mass of air used, kg/min, **(e)** torque, **(f)** p_{mi}, **(g)** fhp. **(h)** $r_{a/f}$ where $q_l = 44{,}548$ kJ/kg fuel.

1228. There are developed 157 kW by an Otto type engine that burns 26.3 kg/hr of fuel ($q_l = 44{,}199$ kJ/kg) in 395 kg/hr of air. The air and liquid fuel enter at 43.3°C. For the purposes of this problem, use the enthalpy of the products as that of air, The exhaust gases leave at 676.7°C; $\Delta K = 0$. Sketch the energy diagram and find **(a)** the heat rejected (kJ/min) and **(b)** the thermal efficiency.

1229. A 6-cylinder, 3.75×3.5-in. automotive engine, with $r_k = 7.4$, develops 117 bhp at 3600 rpm. Data are: barometer 29.95 in. Hg; room temperature, 80°F; dynamometer brake arm, 21 in.; fuel consumption, 0.48 lb/bhp-hr ($q_l = 18{,}750$ Btu/lb). Calculate **(a)** the brake mep, **(b)** the brake torque, **(c)** the brake thermal efficiency, **(d)** the brake engine efficiency based on the hot-air standard with $k = 1.335$, and **(e)** the air/fuel ratio for a volumetric efficiency of 84%.

Ans. **(c)** 28.3%, **(d)** 57.85% **(e)** 16.

1230. A 4-stroke cycle natural-gas engine, operating on the Otto cycle, has a clearance of 20%. At the end of the suction stroke the charge is 1.24 ft³ of air and 0.10 ft³ of natural gas, each measured at intake $p_1 = 14.2$ psia and $t_1 = 110$°F. Assume the charge to have the properties of hot air with an over-all $k = 1.33$. The lower heating value of the fuel is $q_l = 932$ Btu/ft³ at 14.7 psia and 60°F. Find **(a)** the mass of the mixture in the cylinder ($R = 53.35$), **(b)** the heating value of the mixture in Btu/ft³ at state 1, **(c)** Q_R and ideal e, **(d)** the ideal mep. **(e)** If the actual engine operates at 200 rpm and $\eta_b = 62\%$, what is the bhp?

Ans. **(a)** 0.0902 lb, **(b)** 61.25 Btu/ft³, **(c)** 45.5 Btu, 44.6%, **(d)** 177 psi, **(e)** 53.5.

1231. These data apply to an industrial engine: size, 4.0×4.5 in. $= D \times L$; 10 cylinders with 4-stroke cycle; $n = 3600$ rpm; volumetric efficiency $\eta_v = 80\%$; brake engine efficiency $\eta_b = 60\%$; heating value of fuel $-u_{rp} = q_l = 18{,}600$ Btu/lb f; compression ratio $r_k \doteq 8.5$;

$p_1 = 13.8$ psia; $t_1 = 100$°F. Compute **(a)** the percentage clearance, **(b)** the displacement and the mass $\dot{m}_1$ "in the cylinder," **(c)** the brake power and thermal efficiency, **(d)** the brake mep, **(e)** the pounds of fuel per bhp-hr, the brake heat rate, and the air-fuel ratio, assuming that combustion is complete.

1232. The Chevrolet Corvair rear mounted air-cooled engine has 6 cylinders, horizontally opposed, 3.375×2.60 in., a compression ratio of 8, and develops 80 bhp at 4400 rpm. Operating at 4400 rpm, it is noted that the brake thermal efficiency is 26%, the volumetric efficiency is 74%, and the mechanical efficiency is 71%. For the ideal cycle, the condition at the beginning of compression is 14.7 psia, 140°F. At 4400 rpm find **(a)** percentage clearance, **(b)** p, T at end of ideal compression with $k = 1.4$, **(c)** brake engine efficiency η_b, $k = 1.4$, **(d)** mass of air breathed lb/min, **(e)** torque, **(f)** p_{mi}, **(g)** friction horsepower, **(h)** $r_{a/f}$ with $q_l = 19{,}100$ Btu/lb fuel.

OTTO ENGINE, OPEN CYCLE

1233. There are developed 175 hp by an Otto type engine that burns 61 lb/hr of fuel ($q_1 = 19{,}000$ Btu/lb) in 885 lb/hr of air. The air and liquid fuel enter at 100°F. For purposes of this problem, use the enthalpy of the fuel as given by equation (13.7), *Text*, the enthalpy of the products as that of air. The exhaust gases leave at 1220°F; $\Delta K = 0$. Sketch the energy diagram and find **(a)** the heat rejected (Btu/min) and **(b)** the thermal efficiency.

1234. The following data apply to a spark-ignition engine that is completing 12,000 cpm: $e_b = 31\%$, $r_{a/f} = 15.2$, $m_f = 0.00015$ lb/cycle with $q_l = 18{,}800$ Btu/lb; incoming temperature air/fuel is 100°F; exhaust temperature is 1260°F; $\Delta K = 0$. Sketch the energy diagram, use Item B 2 and determine **(a)** W_B, **(b)** the air mass flow, **(c)** Q, assuming that all energy losses leave the system sooner or later as heat.

Ans. **(a)** 247.5 hp, **(b)** 1640 lb/hr, **(c)** 14,780 Btu/min.

1235. Data (converted to 1 lb of fuel basis) from a test of an automotive engine are: $t_0 = 80$°F (sink), $r_{a/f} = 15.65$, $q_l = 18{,}970$ Btu/lb fuel, indicated work $W_I = 6000$ Btu/lb fuel, brake work $W_B = 4750$ Btu/lb fuel, exhaust gas temperature $t_g = 1275$°F. At state 1 in the Otto cycle, $p_1 = 14.4$ psia, $t_1 = 140$°F, $r_k = 10$.

For the cooling water circulated, temperature in is 70°F, out is 120°F, and the flow rate is 50 lb water/lb fuel. Using Item B 2 investigate the major changes in available energy.

1236. A gasoline engine (practical proto type of the Otto cycle) has a clearance of 12%. (a) Find its compression ratio r_k. (b) For each 10 gal of gasoline burned in this engine, how many gallons are used effectively if the actual engine is half as efficient as the ideal? (c) If the engine consumes these 10 gal of gasoline (assume to be C_8H_{18}, 6.5 lb/gal) while developing a constant work output of 100 bhp, how long (hr) will the engine run? (d) If the engine is producing a brake torque of 175 lb-ft while developing the 100 bhp, what is its rpm?

Ans. (a) 9.33, (b) 2.96 gal, (c) 1.44 hr, (d) 3001 rpm.

OTTO ENGINE, DESIGN

1237. There are required 90 bhp with a torque of 143 lb-ft from a 6-cylinder, 4-stroke cycle, single-acting, spark-ignition engine with a compression ratio of 9.5. Under the conditions, the mechanical efficiency is 78% and the brake mep is 80 psi. For the ideal cycle, $p_1 = 14.7$ psia, $t_1 = 95°F$, and the hot-air standard $k = 1.32$. If $D/L = 1.1$ and the fuel rate is $m_{fi} = 0.58$ lb/ihp-hr ($q_l = 18,900$ Btu/lb), determine (a) the bore and stroke, (b) the indicated thermal efficiency, (c) the brake engine efficiency, and (d) the percentage clearance.

Ans. (a) 3.98 × 3.62 in., (b) 23.2%, (c) 34.4%, (d) 11.77%.

1238. A twin-tandem (2 cylinders placed end-to-end with a common piston rod, and 2 more placed beside these, each set being connected to a common crankshaft), 4-stroke cycle, double-acting blast-furnace gas engine is to develop 3600 bhp at 90 rpm. Expected operating data are: bmep = 65 psi; $\eta_m = 83\%$; $\eta_b = 65\%$; average $k = 1.32$; and $q_l = 85$ Btu/ft³; $L/D = 1.35$; $r_k = 7.1$. Find (a) the cylinder dimensions and (b) the probable fuel consumption, ft³/hr.

Ans. (a) 38.6 × 52.1 in., (b) 35,600 ft³/hr.

1239. An engine designer desires to use a fuel tank that will hold a minimum fuel supply for 1 hr operation for a 6-cylinder 9.21 × 8.89-cm, automotive-type gasoline engine which at maximum output develops a brake torque of 268 N-m at 3000 rpm. The corresponding ideal engine showed a thermal efficiency of 56.5%; the brake engine efficiency is expected to be 53%. For the fuel, $q_l = 43,269$ kJ/kg and its specific gravity is 0.715. Find the smallest tank that will satisfy.

1240. A 6-cylinder, 4-stroke cycle, single-acting, spark-ignition engine with a compression ratio of 9.5 is required to develop 67.14 kW with a torque of 194 N-m. Under the conditions, the mechanical efficiency is 78% and the brake mep is 552 kPa. For the ideal cycle, $p_1 = 101.35$ kPaa, $t_1 = 35°C$, and the hot-air standard $k = 1.32$. If $D/L = 1.1$ and the fuel rate is $m_{fi} = 0.353$ kg/kW-hr ($q_l = 43,967$ kJ/kg), determine (a) the bore and stroke, (b) the indicated thermal efficiency, (c) the brake engine efficiency, and (d) the percentage clearance.

Ans. (a) 10.11 × 9.19-cm, (b) 23.2%, (c) 34.4%, (d) 11.77%.

1241. There is developed a torque of 193 lb-ft by a 6-cylinder, 4-stroke-cycle, single-acting engine having an indicated mep of 118 psi when operating at 3000 rpm. Performance curves suggest a mechanical efficiency of 78%, and a brake thermal efficiency of 23% at this speed. For the engine let the clearance $c = 15.5\%$; the ratio $L/D = 1.0$. At the point of compression, $p_1 = 14.4$ psia and $t_1 = 170°F$; $k = 1.31$. Sketch the pV and TS diagrams and compute (a) the bhp, (b) the bore and stroke, (c) the compression ratio, (d) the indicated engine efficiency, (e) the fuel used, lb/hr at this speed if $q_l = 18,900$ Btu/lb.

Ans. (b) 4.06 × 4.06 in., (d) 63.7%, (e) 64.5 lb/hr.

1242. There is required a vertical, 4-cylinder, 4-stroke-cycle, single-acting gas engine to develop 180 bhp at 275 rpm. The probable brake mep is 58 psi, (a) Let $L/D = 1.25$, and find the bore and stroke. (b) The suction pressure is 14.4 psia, and r_k is 5.75. If the over-all k is 1.32 and the pressure at the end of the combustion process is 460 psia, compute e_b and η_b. (c) If the fuel is natural gas with a lower heating value of 908 Btu/ft³, what will be the fuel consumption in ft³/hr?

Ans. (a) 13.16 × 16.44 in., (b) $\eta_b = 65.3\%$, (c) 1803 ft³/hr.

DIESEL CYCLE, AIR STANDARD

1243. An ideal Diesel engine operates on 1 ft³ (measured at state 1) of air. Let $p_1 = 14.4$

psia, $t_1 = 140°F$, $r_k = 14$, and let the cutoff be at 6.2% of the stroke. Draw the pV and TS diagrams, use the air table, and find (a) t_2, p_2, V_2, t_3, V_3, p_4 and t_4; (b) Q_A and Q_R; (c) W and e; and (d) p_m.

Ans. (a) $t_2 = 1167.2°F$, $p_2 = 550$ psia, $t_3 = 2478°F$, $p_4 = 36.4$ psia, $t_4 = 1049°F$; (b) $Q_A = 24$ Btu; (c) 13.2 Btu, (d) 76.8 psi.

1244. There are supplied 27 Btu/cycle to an ideal 2-stroke, single-cylinder Diesel engine, operating at 280 rpm. At the beginning of compression, $p_1 = 14.7$ psia, $t_1 = 90°F$, and $V_1 = 1.50$ ft³. At the end of compression $p_2 = 500$ psia. For the air standard of Item B 2, compute (a) p, V, and T at each corner of the cycle; (b) W amd p_m; and (c) hp and e.

1245. An ideal Diesel engine operates on 1 lb of air with a suction state at 14.1 psia and 110°F. The pressure at the end of compression is 470 psia and the cutoff is at 6% of the stroke from head-end dead-center position. Using air properties, Item B 2, determine (a) the compression ratio, (b) the percentage clearance, (c) the heat supplied, (d) the heat rejected, (e) the thermal efficiency, and (f) the mep.

Ans. (a) 12.68, (b) 8.57%, (c) 238.1 Btu, (d) −110.0 Btu, (e) 53.7%, (f) 50.2 psi.

1246. The mep of an ideal Diesel cycle is 758.4 kPa. If $p_1 = 93.08$ kPaa, $r_k = 12.5$, and the over-all value of $k = 1.34$, find r_c.

Ans. 2.6.

1247. For an ideal Diesel cycle with the over-all value of $k = 1.33$, $r_k = 15$, $r_c = 2.1$, $p_1 = 97.9$ kPaa, find p_2 and p_m.

Ans. 3596 kPaa, 603 kPa.

1248. The charge in a Diesel engine consists of 18.34 g of fuel, with a lower heating value of 42,571 kJ/kg, and 409 g of air and products of combustion. At the beginning of compression, $t_1 = 60°C$. Let $r_k = 14$. For constant $c_p = 1.110$ kJ/kg-K, what should be the cutoff ratio in the corresponding ideal cycle?

Ans. $r_c = 2.96$.

1249. There are supplied 317 kJ/cycle to an ideal Diesel engine operating on 227 g air; $p_1 = 97.91$ kPaa, $t_1 = 48.9°C$. At the end of compression, $p_2 = 3930$ kPaa. Assume that the air and the products within the cycle have air properties. Determine (a) r_k, (b) the percentage clearance, (c) r_c, (d) W, (e) e, (f) p_m.

1250. Compression in a Diesel engine begins at 14 psia and 140°F; $r_k = 13.5$; for a lightly loaded engine, fuel cutoff occurs at 6% of stroke. Computations are to be made for an ideal hot-air standard with an assumed constant $k = 1.34$. For unit mass, find (a) p and T at states 2, 3, 4 (Fig. 16/6, *Text*), (b) heats added and rejected, (c) the thermal efficiency and the mep. (d) If the actual engine has a brake engine efficiency of 60%, determine the brake work, brake thermal efficiency, brake specific fuel consumption, and the brake heat rate; the heating value $q_l = 18,300$ Btu/lb f. (If you would like to see how the use of variable specific heats varies in detail from the assumption of constant k, solve the major parts of the ideal cycle by Item B 2.)

Ans. (a) $T_3 = 2540°R$, $p_4 = 29.6$ psia, (b) 294, −132 Btu/lb, (c) 55.2%, 59.4 psia, (d) $e_b = 33.1\%$, $m_{fb} = 0.42$ lb f/bhp-hr.

1251. There are developed 1063 kW at 267 rpm by an 8-cylinder, 2-stroke-cycle, 40.64 × 50.80-cm Diesel engine that uses 4.94 kg/min of fuel with a lower heating value of 42,571 kJ/kg. The average indicated mep is 562 kPa. Determine (a) e_b, (b) e_i, (c) η_m.

Ans. (a) 30.3%, (b) 37.6%, (c) 80.7%.

1252. A Diesel engine with a compression ratio of $r_k = 14.5$ takes in air at 13 psia; at the beginning of compression, $t_1 = 160°F$. Liquid fuel at 100°F in the amount of 0.0333 lb f/lb a (consider products to be for "200% air") is injected; its heating value at the same base as the gas tables is 18,600 Btu/lb f; for products, $M_p = 28.85$ lb/mole. Consider the gases before combustion to be all air, allow for the mass and sensible enthalpy of fuel, and use the "convenient approximation" for r_c in footnote in in § 16.9, *Text*. For all ideal processes, find (a) p and T at the corners of the cycle (Fig. 16/6, *Text*), (b) the thermal efficiency, (c) the mep, (d) the change of availability as the exhaust cools nonflow 4 to 1 for $T_0 = 620°R$.

Ans. [Items B 2, B 9] (a) $T_3 = 3552°R$, $p_2 = 513$, $p_4 = 44.5$ psia, (b) 50%, (c) 101.8 psi, (d) 4230 Btu/pmole.

1253. A 6-cylinder, 28 × 36-in. single-acting, 2-stroke-cycle Diesel engine develops 3000 bhp at 128 rpm; also, $r_k = 13$, $r_c = 2.45$, over-all $k = 1.33$, $p_1 = 14.1$ psia, and $t_1 = 130°F$. The average indicated mep is 90 psi. The fuel consumed during a 30-min test was 630 lb with $q_l = 18,300$ Btu/lb. Calculate (a) e_b, (b) ihp, (c) η_m, and (d) η_b.

1254. The energy released from the combustion of fuel in a 6-cylinder, 4-stroke cycle, 17½ × 25-in. Diesel engine is 603.6 Btu/lb mixture. Other data are as follows: $q_l = 18,500$

Btu/lb at $0°R$, $r_k = 15$, $p_1 = 14.4$ psia, $T_1 = 560°R$, temperature of fuel at injection is $80°F$ [see equation (13.7, *Text*)], $\eta_v = 85\%$,. $\eta_b = 65\%$; engine rpm is $n = 225$. Compute **(a)** the air/fuel ratio, **(b)** the thermal efficiency of the ideal cycle that accounts for the fuel and considers the properties of the products of combustion (assume that 100% ideal air for this fuel is equivalent to 15 lb air/lb fuel), **(c)** the brake horsepower developed, **(d)** the brake fuel rate, and **(e)** the brake mep.

1255. A 6-cylinder, $17\frac{1}{2} \times 25$-in., 4-stroke-cycle, single-acting Diesel engine, operating at 225 rpm, develops 750 bhp. The fuel consumption is 300 lb/hr with a lower heating value of the fuel $q_l = 18,300$ Btu/lb. The mechanical efficiency is 85% and the ideal cycle efficiency is 52.3%. Calculate ihp, m_{fi}, m_{fb}, e_i, η_b, η_i, p_{mi}, p_{mb}.

DIESEL ENGINE, OPEN CYCLE

1256. Air and fuel at $100°F$ and $r_{a/f} = 22.5$ (300% air) are received by a Diesel engine whose average exhaust temperature is $840°F$; $M_p = 28.90$. For the gaseous fuel, $q_l = 19,200$ Btu/lb at $0°R$; use equation (13.7), *Text* for h_f. For the engine, $e_b = 27.5\%$. Based on 1 lb/sec of air received and using Items B 2, B 8 and B 9 where relevant, determine **(a)** W_b, **(b)** Q assuming that all energy losses, sooner or later, leave the system as heat.

1257. A Diesel engine completes 300 cpm when burning 16 lb/hr of fuel at $90°F$; $q_l = 18,500$ Btu/lb at $0°R$; for h_f, use equation (13.7), *Text*. Combustion air at $90°F$ is supplied at the rate of 6 lb/min (300% air); exhaust is at $800°F$; $M_p = 28.90$. The developed shaft work is numerically equal to the heat losses from the engine. Use Items B 2, B 8, and B 9 and determine **(a)** the enthalpy of the exhaust, **(b)** W_B, **(c)** e_b.

1258. A Diesel engine using 29.90 lb air/lb fuel (200% air—Item B 9) yields these operating data: Indicated work $W_I = 7300$ Btu/lb fuel; brake work $W_B = 5500$ Btu/lb fuel; temperature of cooling water in is $86°F$, out is $140°F$; water flow is 80 lb water/lb fuel. For state point 1, $p_1 = 14.3$ psia, $t_1 = 160°F$, $r_k = 15$; sink temperature $t_0 = 100°F$; exhaust gas temperature $t_g = 700°F$; molecular weight of exhaust gas is $M_p = 28.90$; $q_l = 18,550$ Btu/lb fuel. Use Items B 2 and B 9 where

relevant and investigate the major changes in available energy.

DUAL COMBUSTION CYCLE

1259. An ideal dual combustion cycle operates on 454 g of air. At the beginning of compression, the air is at 96.53 kPaa, $43.3°C$. Let $r_p = 1.5$, $r_c = 1.6$, and $r_k = 11$. Using the air properties in Item B 1, determine **(a)** the percentage clearance, **(b)** the pressure, volume, and temperature at each corner of the cycle, **(c)** Q_A, Q_R, and W, **(d)** the thermal efficiency, **(e)** the mep.
Ans. **(a)** 10%, **(c)** $W = 277$ kJ, **(d)** 58.5%, **(e)** 713 kPa.

1260. At the beginning of compression in an ideal dual combustion cycle, the working fluid is 1 lb of air at 14.1 psia and $80°F$. The compression ratio is 9, the pressure at the end of the constant volume addition of heat is 470 psia, and there are added 100 Btu during the constant pressure expansion. Using Item B 2, find **(a)** r_p, **(b)** r_c, **(c)** the percentage clearance, **(d)** the thermal efficiency, and **(e)** the mep.
Ans. **(a)** 1.58, **(b)** 1.187, **(c)** 12.5%, **(d)** 54.4%, **(e)** 57.4 psi.

1261. State 1 for a dual combustion engine is $p_1 = 1$ atm and $t_1 = 140°F$; $r_k = 18$; at the end of the constant volume combustion process, $p_3 = 1120$ psia; $r_c = 1.5$. Use Item B 2 for the compression process and Item B 9 for all other processes in the cycle. Base answers on 1 lb/cycle and determine **(a)** the percentage clearance, **(b)** the p, V, and T at each corner point on the cycle, **(c)** W, **(d)** e, **(e)** p_m.

MISCELLANEOUS

1262. The Stirling cycle engine is being studied as a replacement for the conventional open-cycle automotive engine in view of reducing air pollution. An analysis of this cycle follows. Air is made to pass through this cycle, which consists of two isothermal processes and two regenerative isometric processes. At the beginning of the isothermal expansion (point 1), $p_1 = 724$ kPaa, $V_1 = 56.6$ ℓ, $t_1 = 315.6°C$. The isothermal expansion ratio is $r_e = V_2/V_1 = 1.5$; the minimum cycle temperature is $t_3 = 26.7°C$. Sketch the pV and Ts diagrams and for the cycle find (**a**) ΔS for each isothermal process, (**b**) Q_A, (**c**) Q_R, (**d**) W, (**e**) e, (**f**) p_m.

Ans. (**a**) 0.0282 kJ/K, (**b**) 16.62 kJ, (**c**) -8.45 kJ, (**d**) 8.17 kJ, (**e**) 49.15%, (**f**) 288 kPa.

1263. The study of the Stirling engine in problem 1262 continues. Full-load performance data taken from road tests conducted on a 6-cylinder automotive-type Stirling engine follow: cylinder size 3.47×2.37 in., indicated power developed 240 hp, speed 2500 rpm, mechanical efficiency 75%, p_{mb} 317 psi, brake fuel rate 0.418 lb/bhp-hr, q_l 18,200 Btu/lb fuel. Comparable open-cycle automotive engines when tested gave these data: Gasoline Otto type (242 bhp, 4600 rpm, 0.468 lb/bhp-hr, $q_l = 18,900$ Btu/lb fuel, 0.65 bhp/in.^{3} displacement); Diesel type (181 bhp, 2100 rpm, 0.41 lb/bhp-hr, $q_l = 18,200$ Btu/lb fuel, 0.49 bhp/in.^{3} displacement). Analyze the performance of the Stirling engine and compare with those of the other two engines where relevant.

COMPUTER PROGRAMS

1264. Write the program for this problem. The trend of increasing compression ratio in Otto cycle type engines and its effect on both percentage clearance and thermal efficiency is being reviewed. Let the compression ratio r_k vary from 4 (circa 1920) to a current value of 11 and plot curves of clearance c and efficiency e versus compression ratio r_k. Base calculations on cold-air standard.

1265. Let the parameter cut-off ratio r_c in a Diesel type engine vary from 1 to 4 and find the effects of this variation on cycle efficiency and mean effective pressure. Select a particular Diesel cycle (make known the initial state p_1, T_1, V_1, the compression ratio r_k, and use cold-air $k = 1.4$) and write a program for this problem.

1266–1270. These numbers may be used for other problems.

17

REVERSED CYCLES

Note: The answers given for the vapor compression problems were obtained by using the small *ph*-charts located in the appendix; hence, the answers may have inherent differences of varying magnitudes. Always show a *Ts*-diagram; include *ph*-diagrams where appropriate.

REVERSED CARNOT CYCLE

1271. A refrigeration system operating on the reversed Carnot cycle rejects 5800 kJ/min. The minimum and maximum temperatures are 250 K and 345 K, respectively. Sketch the *Ts* diagram and find **(a)** the power input required, **(b)** the refrigeration tonnage developed (211 kJ/min-ton), **(c)** the available part of the heat rejected for a sink temperature of 5°C.

1272. A reversed Carnot cycle has a refrigerating COP of $\gamma = 4$. **(a)** What is the ratio T_{max}/T_{min}? **(b)** If the work input is 6 kW, what will be the maximum refrigeration effect, kJ/min and tons (1 ton = 211 kJ/min)? **(c)** What are the COP and the delivered heat if this cycle is used for heating?

Ans. **(a)** 1.25, **(b)** 1440 kJ/min, **(c)** COP = 5.

1273. There are removed 528 kJ/min of heat from a body by a refrigerator operating between the limits of 244.5 K and 305.5 K. If its coefficient of performance is three fourths of that of a Carnot refrigerator working between the same temperature limits, find **(a)** the heat rejected and **(b)** the work input, kW. **(c)** What are the COP and the heat if this device is used to deliver heat?

1274. The power requirement of a Carnot refrigerator in maintaining a low temperature region at 238.9 K is 1.1 kW per ton. Find **(a)** COP, **(b)** T_2, and **(c)** the heat rejected. **(d)** When this device is used to deliver heat, what is its COP? *Ans.* **(a)** 3.2, **(b)** 313.3 K, **(d)** 4.2.

1275. A Carnot refrigerating system picks up heat at 272 K and requires a power input of 1.75 kW/ton. Find **(a)** the COP and **(b)** the temperature at which heat is discharged. **(c)** If the upper temperature in **(b)** is changed to 311 K, what will be the power input, kW/ton?

1276. A manufacturer of Carnot refrigerators has the choice of varying either the evaporator temperature $T_1 = 250$ K or the condenser temperature $T_2 = 500$ K by ±25 K; no restrictions are placed on the operating temperatures. In the best interest of economy, what would you recommend to this manufacturer?

1277. A reversed Carnot cycle, acting as a heat pump, is to supply 16,500 Btu/min to heat rooms of a building to 75°F when the outside temperature is 60°F. **(a)** Since the processes are externally reversible, compute the heat obtained from the atmospheric air and the power required to operate the cycle. **(b)** If the heating is done directly by an electric coil, what amount of electricity expressed in horse-power is consumed?

Ans. **(a)** 16,037 Btu/min, 10.92 hp, **(b)** 389.

VAPOR COMPRESSION, COOLING

1278. Assume 50 lb/min of F12 refrigerant vapor are compressed adiabatically from 15 psia to 300 psia; liquid refrigerant enters the expansion valve saturated at 300 psia. There are 7.10 tons of refrigeration developed with a power input of 33.9 hp. Sketch the *ph* diagram and find (**a**) the compressor suction temperature, (**b**) the compressor discharge temperature, (**c**) the compressor efficiency.
Ans. (**a**) from *ph* chart, $t_1 = -10°F$, (**b**) from *ph* chart, $t_{2'} = 230°F$, (**c**) $\eta_c = 84.3\%$.

1279. A 20-ton refrigeration compressor receives saturated ammonia vapor at $-20°F$ and compresses it to 200 psia, 340°F; the throttling valve receives the liquid at 90°F. Sketch the *ph* and *Ts* diagrams and find (**a**) the ammonia circulated, lb/min, (**b**) the compression efficiency, (**c**) COP, (**d**) rating, hp/ton.
Ans. (**a**) 8.60 lb/min, (**b**) 87.4%, (**c**) 2.54, (**d**) 1.858 hp/ton.

1280. In a vapor-compression refrigerating system using SO_2, saturated vapor at 20°F (state 1) is received by the compressor, and the actual state at discharge is 100 psia and 260°F (state 2'). The liquid SO_2 enters the expansion valve at 100°F (state 3). For both the ideal and actual cycles, sketch the *Ts* and *ph* diagrams and find (**a**) the required hp/ton, (**b**) the COP, (**c**) the compression efficiency η_c and (**d**) the mass flow of SO_2 required for a 20-ton capacity. See Item B 36.
Ans. (**a**) 1.012, 1.214, (**b**) 4.66, 3.89, (**c**) 83.4%, (**d**) 28.6 lb/min.

1281. An oxygen cryogenic refrigeration system circulates 10 kg/min of O_2. The compressor receives saturated oxygen vapor at 4 atm and discharges it at 60 atm, 256 K. Pressurized boiling nitrogen reduces the temperature of the oxygen to 155 K in the condenser; the oxygen is then throttled to the evaporator pressure of 4 atm. Sketch the *Ts* diagram, use Item B 27, and find (**a**) the ton (211 kJ/min-ton) rating of the oxygen system, (**b**) the COP, (**c**) the compressor efficiency, (**d**) the compressor displacement, ℓ/min.

1282. Air is used in the basic system of a cryogenic refrigeration system. Saturated air vapor enters the ideal compressor at 3 atm and leaves at 50 atm to enter the constant pressure condenser. Pressurized boiling nitrogen condenses the air to 124 K at which point it is throttled to the evaporator pressure of 3 atm.

Sketch the *Ts* diagram, use Item B 26, and for a 5-ton (211 kJ/min-ton) capacity find (**a**) the mass of air circulated, kg/min, (**b**) COP, (**c**) heat absorbed by the boiling nitrogen, kJ/min.
Ans. (**a**) 9.51 kg/min, (**b**) 1.13, (**c**) 1991 kJ/min.

1283. Assume that there is a planet where the average environmental temperature is 82°C and where the evaporator temperature of 30°C may be utilized for cooling. A vapor-compression system is to be designed using water as the refrigerant, with saturated vapor at 100°C leaving the compressor and with liquid at 95°C ($h_f = 395.5$ kJ/kg) entering the expansion valve. For a cooling capacity of 10 tons (211 kJ/min-ton) in an ideal cycle, find (**a**) the mass of refrigerant circulated, (**b**) the required power, and (**c**) the COP. On the basis of the actual cycle with a compression efficiency of 78% and a volumetric efficiency of 75%, find (**d**) kW/ton, (**e**) V_D, and (**f**) the temperature of the vapor from the compressor. See Item B 16(SI).

1284. An automobile engine idling at 1700 rpm drives the Freon 12 compressor of its air conditioner. Saturated vapor enters the compressor at 20 psia and is compressed to 300 psia; no subcooling occurs in the condenser. For the 4.5-ton *ideal* unit, sketch the *TS* and *ph* diagrams and find (**a**) Freon circulated, lb/min, (**b**) work, hp, (**c**) COP, (**d**) heat removed by the condenser, Btu/min. (**e**) In the actual case the compressor efficiency is 80%; find the temperature of the Freon at compressor discharge.

1285. A 12-ton refrigeration system operates on Freon 12. The vapor at compressor suction is saturated at $-20°F$; at compressor discharge the state is at 180 psia, 170°F. Liquid refrigerant at 120°F enters the expansion valve. Sketch the *ph* and *Ts* diagrams and find (**a**) the mass rate of refrigerant circulated, lb/min, (**b**) COP, (**c**) the compressor efficiency.
Ans. (**a**) 61.6 lb/min., (**b**) 1.695, (**c**) 84.7%.

1286. Consider 50 lb/min of Freon F12 refrigerant vapor at 15 psia $-10°F$ that are drawn into a compressor (point 1) and discharged adiabatically at 300 psia, 230°F. The liquid refrigerant leaves the condenser and enters the expansion valve saturated at 300 psia. Sketch the *TS* and *ph* diagrams for the cycle, use Item B 25, and find (**a**) ton rating of the system, (**b**) COP, (**c**) compressor efficiency, (**d**) power, hp.

1287. Sulfur dioxide is used as a refrigerant in a 25-ton vapor compression refrigeration system. Vapor at 13 psia, 20°F enters the compressor and leaves at 300 psia, 500°F; the subcooled liquid refrigerant enters the expansion valve at 180°F. Sketch the *ph* and *Ts* diagrams and find (a) the refrigerant required, lb/min, (b) the compressor efficiency, (c) the COP.

Ans. (a) 45.1 lb/min, (b) 85.2%, (c) 1.5.

1288. In an ammonia refrigeration cycle, 100 lb/min of refrigerant are circulated. The compressor suction receives the ammonia as saturated vapor at 19.7 psia; the compressor discharge is at 200 psia, 320°F. The liquid ammonia leaves the condenser at 90°F. Sketch the *ph* and *TS* diagrams and find (a) capacity, tons, (b) work, hp, (c) the compressor efficiency. See Item B 33.

1289. Saturated F12 vapor at −10°F enters the compressor of a refrigeration system; discharge from the compressor is at 200 psia, 170°F. The liquid leaves the condenser and enters the expansion valve saturated at 200 psia. Sketch the *ph* and *Ts* diagrams for this cycle and find: (a) ton rating based upon a flow of 50 lb/min of F12 refrigerant, (b) COP, (c) compression efficiency η_c, (d) horsepower input for 50 lb/min.

Ans. (a) 9.33 tons, (b) 1.79, (c) 86%, (d) 24.5 hp.

1290. In a vapor-compression refrigerating system using Freon 12, saturated vapor at 12°F enters the compressor and its actual state at discharge is defined by 160 psia and 150°F. Liquid F12 at 100°F enters the expansion valve. The double-acting compressor turns at 300 rpm, and has a volumetric efficiency of 80%. Sketch the *ph* and *Ts* diagrams. (a) For both the ideal and actual cycles, find the coefficients of performance and the hp/ton. Determine (a) the compressor efficiency, (c) the mass rate of flow of Freon 12 for a 50-ton capacity, (d) the required bore D and stroke L of the compressor if $L = D$. (e) Compute the change of steady flow availability through the compressor for a sink temperature of 500°R.

Ans. (a) 1.62 hp/ton (actual), (b) 79.8%, (c) 211 lb/min, (d) 11 × 11 in., (e) 13.3 Btu/lb.

VAPOR COMPRESSION, HEATING

1291. Prove (demonstrate) that the COP(γ_h) of a reversed cycle used for heating, is equivalent to its COP(γ_c), when used for refrigeration, plus one; that is, $\gamma_h = \gamma_c + 1$.

1292. An ammonia compressor is used in a heating cycle. The suction pressure is 30 psia. The discharge pressure is 200 psia. Saturated liquid ammonia enters the throttle valve. The refrigerating effect is 470 Btu/lb of ammonia. Find the coefficient of performance as a heating cycle. *Ans.* 4.76.

1293. A reversed vapor-compression cycle is to be used for heating. The maximum demand is expected to be 600 cfm of 40°F outside air heated to 85°F. Let the temperature in the evaporator be 25°F and the condenser pressure be 300 psia. For the ideal cycle using NH₃ and with saturated vapor entering the compressor, find (a) the pounds of refrigerant to be circulated per minute if the liquid is not subcooled, (b) the ideal horsepower input to the cycle, (c) the COP, (d) the cost of the heating at 5¢/kW-hr, (i) when the heat is obtained from the reversed cycle and (ii) when the heat is obtained from an electrical heating element.

Ans. (a) 0.94 lb/min, (b) 2.35 hp, (c) 4.925, (d) 8.76 ¢/hr, 45.3 ¢/hr.

1294. In a reversed vapor-compression heating cycle using Freon 12, the maximum demand is expected to be 1000 cfm of 40°F outside air heated to 86°F. Let the evaporator temperature be 20°F and the condenser pressure be 140 psia. Saturated vapor enters the compressor and there is no subcooling at the expansion valve. For the ideal cycle, sketch the *ph* and *Ts* diagrams and find (a) the mass flow of refrigerant, lb/min, (b) the horsepower input, (c) the COP, (d) the cost of heating at 5 ¢/kW-hr. (e) What is the heating cost when an electrical heating element is used? (f) The cost of heating with fuel oil at 36¢/gal where the $q_h = 135,000$ Btu/gal and the efficiency of the heater is 80%?

Ans. (a) 15.20, (b) 3.74 hp, (c) 5.54, (d) 14¢/hr, (e) 77.1¢/hr, (f) 17.6¢/hr.

1295. (a) What is the heating capacity of a 9 × 9-in., twin-cylinder, single-acting compressor that turns at 380 rpm and has a volumetric efficiency of 85% when saturated liquid ammonia from the condenser enters the expansion valve at 85°F and saturated vapor at 10°F enters the compressor to leave at 180 psia? (b) Find the isentropic compressor power. (c) Compute each COP based on both heating and cooling.

Ans. (a) 16,800 Btu/min, (b) 67 hp, (c) 5.92, 4.92.

1296. A 25-ton F12 (Item B 35) vapor-compression refrigeration system is to be used for heating. Saturated F12 vapor at 19 psia enters the compressor; discharge is at 200 psia, 180°F. Liquid F12 at 129°F expands through the throttling valve to 19 psia for the heating effect to follow. Sketch the *ph* and *TS* diagrams for this cycle and find (a) mass of F12 circulated, lb/min, (b) COP (heating), (c) the compressor efficiency, (d) the heating available, Btu/min.

VAPOR COMPRESSION, COOLING-HEATING

1297. Sulfur dioxide vapor (see Item B 36) at 15 psia, 20°F enters a refrigeration compressor and is compressed to 300 psia, 500°F. Liquid SO_2 enters the expansion (throttling) valve at 180°F. If the system has a refrigeration capacity of 5 tons, sketch the *ph* and *TS* diagrams and find (a) mass of SO_2 circulated, lb/min, (b) commpressor efficiency, (c) COP for both cooling and heating, (d) the heating effect, Btu/min.

1298. It is desired to replace an existing oil heating system rated at 90,000 Btu/hr (input) with an NH_3 reversed cycle in order to benefit from the refrigeration; the existing system is 80% efficient. For the NH_3 cycle, the evaporator pressure is 37.7 psia and the condenser pressure is 300 psia; the refrigerating effect is 431.7 Btu/lb NH_3 and there is no subcooling at the condenser outlet. The NH_3 leaves the compressor at 340°F; the compressor displacement is 18.63 cfm. Assume no change in the heating requirements and determine (a) the NH_3 circulation requirement, based upon the rated output of the existing heating system, (b) the compressor efficiency, (c) the tons of refrigeration for the same cycle, (d) the volumetric efficiency, (e) COP heating, (f) COP cooling.

Ans. (a) 2 lb/min, (b) 81.5%, (c) 4.137 tons, (d) 80%, (e) 3.57, (f) 2.57.

1299. Freon 12 at 0°F and 100% quality enters the suction side of a compressor and is discharged at 120 psia. Liquid refrigerant at 80°F enters the expansion valve. For a flow of 20 lb/min in an ideal cycle, find (a) the tons of refrigeration, (b) the horsepower input, (c) the

COP, (d) the compressor cylinder size if there are twin cylinders with $L/D = 1$, $\eta_v = 80\%$, and a shaft speed of 450 rpm. (e) From the viewpoint of a heating cycle, find the capacity (same compressor) and COP.

Ans. (a) 5.09 tons, (b) 5.78 hp, (c) 4.15, (d) 4.6×4.6-in., (e) 1264 Btu/min, 5.15.

1300. There are circulated 65 lb/min Freon 12 in a vapor-compression refrigeration system. At the compressor suction (point 1) the vapor is saturated at 0°F; at exit the Freon is at 400 psia, 240°F. Liquid refrigerant enters the expansion valve at 100°F. Sketch the *Ts* diagram and find (a) the capacity tons, (b) the compression efficiency, (c) COP, (d) the heating available, Btu/min.

1301. There are developed 15 tons of refrigeration by a system circulating Freon 12. Saturated vapor at 0°F enters the compressor; discharge is at 400 psia, 240°F; the volumetric efficiency is 80%. No subcooling obtains from the condenser. Sketch the *Ts* diagram showing all pertinent state points and find (a) the mass of refrigerant circulated, lb/min, (b) the compressor efficiency, (c) the COP for both heating and cooling, (d) the displacement volume, cfm, (e) the required horsepower.

1302. In a reversed cycle for both heating and cooling, saturated ammonia vapor at −25°F enters the compressor to be discharged at 210 psia, 380°F; the liquid NH_3 leaves the condenser at 90°F. Sketch the flow diagram (equipment diagram—label each piece), the *ph* and *TS* diagrams, and for a 15-ton capacity find (a) the mass rate of NH_3, lb/min, (b) the compressor efficiency, (c) the COP as a refrigeration system, (d) the COP for heating, and (e) the heating available, Btu/min. (f) What is the anticipated speed (rpm) of the 8×8-in., twin-cylinder, single-acting compressor whose volumetric efficiency is $\eta_v = 85\%$?

VACUUM REFRIGERATION

1303. Water for drinking and air conditioning purposes is chilled from 25°C ($h_f = 105$ kJ/kg) to 10°C ($h_f = 42$ kJ/kg) by a steam refrigeration unit; the 25°C water is admitted to a chamber in which low pressure is maintained by means of steam jet ejectors. Part of the incoming water flashes to vapor and the rest is chilled to 10°C. Find (a) the pressure maintained in the low pressure chamber, (b) the mass of water vapor flashed per kilogram of entering water. See Item B 16(SI).

1304. There are removed 183.52 m³/min of vapor from the water evaporator of a vacuum refrigeration system; the warm water enters the evaporator at 17.8°C (h_f = 74.6 kJ/kg) and chilled water leaves at 10°C (h_f = 42 kJ/kg, v_g = 106 m³/kg); make-up water enters at 17.8°C. Determine the refrigerating capacity.   *Ans.* 20 tons.

1305. In a 10-ton vacuum refrigerating system, warm water at 56°F enters the evaporator wherein the temperature is 44°F. **(a)** What volume of vapor must be removed from the evaporator if the make-up water enters at 44°F? What volume if make-up water enters the evaporator at 90°F? **(b)** If the steam consumption of the ejector is 35 lb/hr-ton of saturated steam at 100 psia, find the Btu input per Btu of refrigeration.

     Ans. **(a)** 4005 cfm, 4120 cfm, **(b)** 3.465.

1306. The same as problem 1305 except that the entering warm water is at 66°F and the evaporator is at 38°F.

1307. The ejector of a vacuum refrigerating system maintains a pressure of 0.178 psia in the water evaporator. After doing 100 tons of refrigeration, the water returns to the evaporator at 64°F. The mass in the evaporator remains constant during steady operation with the make-up up water entering at 84°F. What volume of vapor must be removed from the evaporator each minute? If the steam consumption of the ejector is 2.75 lb steam/lb vapor, determine the energy consumption and the Btu of refrigeration per Btu into the ejector; the steam enters the nozzle at 100 psia, saturated vapor.

1308. There are removed 6480 cfm of vapor from the water evaporator of a vacuum refrigeration system; the warm water enters the evaporator at 64°F and chilled water leaves at 50°F; make-up water enters at 64°F. Determine the refrigerating capacity.

     Ans. 20 tons.

GAS REFRIGERATING CYCLE

1309. An air-refrigerating system with a 10-ton capacity consists of a centrifugal compressor, an aftercooler, and an air turbine. The turbine is directly connected to the compressor. Both processes, compression and expan-

sion, are irreversible adiabatics. At the compressor inlet, p_1 = 82.74 kPaa, t_1 = 21.1°C; at compressor exit, $t_{2'}$ = 90°C; at the turbine inlet, p_3 = 144.79 kPaa, t_3 = 37.8°C; at turbine exit, $t_{4'}$ = 0°C. Sketch the flow diagram and the *TS* plane; steady flow processes; $\Delta K = 0$. Find **(a)** the compressor efficiency, **(b)** the turbine efficiency, **(c)** the mass flow of air, **(d)** the net power, and **(e)** the COP.

     Ans. **(a)** 74%, **(b)** 82.4%, **(c)** 99.5 kg/min, **(d)** 51.83 kW, **(e)** 0.678.

1310. In an aircraft refrigeration unit using the air cycle, 11 lb/min of air at 103 in. Hg abs and 527°F are bled from the air compressor serving the jet engine of the plane. The air then passes through a heat exchanger, leaving at 100 in. Hg abs and 167°F, at which point it is expanded through a small turbine to 22 in. Hg abs and 15.8°F. Ultimately, the air leaves the plane at 90°F. See figure. Find **(a)** the tons of cooling (refrigeration) with respect to the 90°F. **(b)** If the compressor receives the air in the stagnant state of 31 in. Hg abs and 209°F, and if the small air turbine drives a centrifugal fan for passing coolant air through the heat exchanger, find the horsepower input. **(c)** What is the COP?

     Ans. **(a)** 0.978 tons, **(b)** 19.8 hp, **(c)** 0.233.

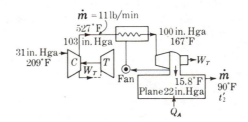

Problems 1310, 1311

1311. For an aircraft refrigerating unit described in problem 1310, the following data are given: bleed air pressure, 166 in. Hg abs; bleed air temperature, 590°F; bleed air flow through heat exchanger and small turbine, 75 lb/min; exit conditions from heat exchanger, 161.5 in. Hg abs, 178°F; small turbine discharge conditions, 30 in. Hg abs, 10°F; ultimate air temperature leaving plane, 90°F; inlet stagnation conditions to the jet engine compressor, 35 in. Hg abs, 145°F. Find **(a)** the tons of cooling with respect to the 90°F, **(b)** the total horsepower input, and **(c)** the COP.

1312. In a "dense-air" refrigerating system, operating on a reversed Brayton cycle, the air enters the compressor from the refrigerator at 345 kPaa, 4.44°C; it is compressed to 1517 kPaa, where the air passes through a heat exchanger and is cooled to 29.44°C. The air then passes through the expander, goes through the refrigerator, and repeats the cycle. Amount of refrigeration desired is 10 tons. (a) Determine the COP and the power required for operation. (b) If the compressor efficiency and expander efficiency is each 78%, compute the COP and power; $\Delta p \approx 0$ in heat exchange processes.

Ans. (**a**) 1.9, 18.5 kW, (**b**) 0.534, 66 kW.

VARIATIONS OF BASIC REFRIGERATING CYCLES

1313. The events of a cascade, split-stage, low-temperature refrigerating cycle are as follows: A Freon 12 vapor-compression system operates between 0°F and 90°F with saturated liquid on the high side of the expansion valve and saturated vapor entering the compressor whose volumetric efficiency is 88%. An NH_3 compression system operates between −63.11°F and 11.66°F with saturated liquid entering the expansion valve and saturated vapor entering the compressor whose volumetric efficiency is 85%. The Freon 12 evaporator serves as the condenser for the NH_3. For the ideal cycle and 1 ton of refrigeration, find (a) the displacement of each compressor, and (b) the total horsepower required for compressor efficiencies of 85%.

1314. A single compressor system using NH_3 serves two evaporators (for two different refrigerating requirements) as shown in the figure. The individual expansion valves A and B allow each evaporator to operate independently of the other, 10 tons in 1 at 40°F and 20 tons in 2 at −20°F. Saturated vapor leaves Evap. 1 and passes through throttling valve D

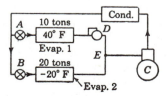

Problem 1314

and then mixes with the saturated vapor from Evap. 2. This mixture of NH_3 enters the compressor C at 18.3 psia and discharges at 240 psia; liquid NH_3 leaves the condenser at 100°F. Sketch the Ts diagram for the ideal cycle, and find (a) the mass of NH_3 handled by the compressor, (b) the work required, (c) COP.

Ans. (**a**) 13.08 lb/min, (**b**) 55.7 hp, (**c**) 2.54.

1315. Ammonia is used to do refrigeration at two different temperatures, at −20°F in evaporator 2 (see figure) and at 37.7°F in evaporator 1. The low pressure compressor C_1 receives saturated vapor, compresses it isentropically, and discharges it at $p_2 = 70$ psia, where the NH_3 enters an intercooler I into which liquid NH_3 flow is regulated by valve D (with negligible pressure drop) at such a rate that the vapor leaving at F is saturated. Saturated vapor from the flash chamber, from evaporator 1, and from the intercooler I combine to enter compressor C_2 at 70 psia. It is then compressed isentropically to 200 psia and then passes through the condenser. All parts are adiabatically lined and the flows are frictionless. The refrigeration to be obtained is 10 tons from evaporator 1 and 20 tons from evaporator 2. Sketch an appropriate Ts diagram and compute (a) the mass of NH_3 through each evaporator, (b) the mass of NH_3 liquid needed in the intercooler, (c) the mass handled by the compressor C_2, all in lb/min, (d) the total ideal horsepower required, (e) the overall COP. (f) If the compressor efficiency for each compressor is 75% what is the actual COP? Also find the irreversibility for each compression process, given $T_0 = 520$°R.

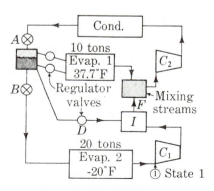

Problem 1315

1316. In an ideal NH_3 refrigerating system, two stages of compression are used with regenerative cooling between stages (see figure). Saturated vapor at −49°F enters the LP compressor C_1 and is discharged at 40 psia into a cooler wherein circulating water cools it to 80°F. There is next a regenerative cooling to state 3, $p_3 = 40$ psia, $t_3 = 30$°F, at which state the NH_3 enters the HP compressor C_2 and is compressed to 180 psia; for regeneration, m lb, including all vapor, is drawn off after passage through the first expansion valve A. Condensation occurs without pressure loss, with saturated liquids entering the expansion valves. For ideal processes, find (a) the mass of NH_3 entering the LP compressor per lb NH_3 through the condenser, (b) the COP, (c) the mass of NH_3 through the condenser for 80 tons refrigeration, (d) the displacement for each compressor for $\eta_v = 65$%. (e) Let the compressor efficiency be 77% for each and find the hp/ton of refrigeration and the actual COP.

Ans. (a) 0.8042 lb, (b) 2.51, (c) 37 lb/min, (d) 1470, 420 cfm, (e) 2.44 hp/ton, 1.932.

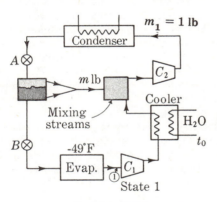

Problem 1316

1317. A refrigeration temperature of about −89°F is needed and regenerative intercooling between the LP and HP compressors is to be investigated for the refrigerant Freon 12. Let the pressure in the condenser be 130 psia. The liquid temperature at the the first expansion valve E_1 is 97°F, where the throttling is to 24 psia in B. At this pressure, all the vapor from the throttling process mixes with the discharge from the LP cylinder to reduce the superheat at entrance to the HP cylinder. All the liquid from the first throttling enters the next expansion valve E_2 and expands to −89°F, after which the desired refrigeration is done. (*Suggestion*: Base computations on 1 lb of

refrigerant in A.) The first stage receives saturated vapor ($h_{g1} = 67.47$, $s_{g1} = 0.1837$, $v_{g1} = 15.315$), compresses it isentropically to 24 psia; after mixing, it enters the second stage. (a) Sketch an appropriate Ts diagram, naming the significant points. Compute (b) the work (Btu/lb) of the first stage of compression, (c) the state of the vapor and the total amount (per pound at A) entering the second stage, (d) the total work and coefficient of performance, (e) the cfm displacement of the LP cylinder for a refrigerating capacity of 6 tons and a volumetric efficiency of 60%.

Ans. (b) 17.07, (c) 1.464 lb/lb at A, (d) $\gamma = 1.56$, (e) 520 cfm.

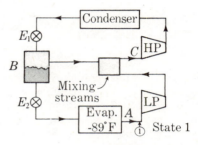

Problems 1317, 1318

1318. (a) Let the actual states in problem 1318 be: at the exit of the LP, 24 psia, 80°F; at the exit of the HP, 130 psia, 200°F. Compute the compressor efficiencies. (Note that state 3 changes.) (b) If there is only one stage of isentropic compression in problem 1318 ($s = C$, no mixing chamber, one throttling), what would be the COP?

Ans. (a) 79.2%, 75.3%, (b) 1.173.

GAS LIQUEFACTION

1319. Liquefied air is produced by the Linde process (see figure). These data apply: $t_1 = t_2 = t_7 = 100$°F; $p_1 = p_4 = p_6 = p_7 = 20$ psia; $p_2 = p_3 = 2500$ psia; $h_1 = 234$, $h_2 = 223$, $h_5 = 50$, $h_6 = 135$, $h_7 = 234$, all Btu/lb of air obtained from an air chart. (a) Determine the amount of air that must be compressed for each pound of liquid air produced. (b) Find the enthalpy of the air entering the separator.

Ans. (a) 16.73 lb, (b) 130 Btu/lb.

1320. There are produced 100 lb/hr of dry ice by a system that throttles saturated liquid

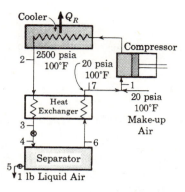

Problem 1319

CO_2 at 600 psia to 15 psia in the collection chamber. See figure. Make-up CO_2 gas is supplied at 15 psia, 75°F. Use Item B 31, Appendix, and determine (a) the amount of CO_2 liquid throttled each hour, (b) the temperature t_1 of the gas at the compressor inlet, (c) the work input if the compressor is single stage and has an adiabatic efficiency of 85%, (d) the work input if the compression is accomplished in two stages, each stage 90% efficient, and with constant pressure intercooling between stages occurring at 150 psia to 50°F.

Ans. (a) 274 lb/hr, (b) −25°F, (c) 13.05 hp.

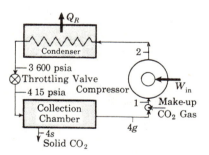

Problem 1320

1321. The Linde process is used to manufacture dry ice (solid CO_2), Item B 31. The CO_2 vapor enters the compressor at 15 psia and 80°F, and after three stages of compression with negligible pressure drops during intercooling, it leaves at 800 psia. Between stages and in the aftercooler, the CO_2 is cooled back to 80°F by cooling water; the compressor efficiency for each stage is 70%. Leaving the aftercooler at 80°F, the CO_2 passes through the regenerative heat exchanger ($\Delta p \approx 0$), throt-

tles 3–4 to 1 atm (Fig. 17/15, *Text*); the solid is removed from the receiver, the vapor returns through the heat exchanger, leaving it at 70°F, state *B*. With makeup and heat, it enters the compressor at 80°F and the cycle repeats; steady state operation, no heat except as mentioned. Compute (a) the fraction of solid CO_2 obtained, (b) the state at entry to the expansion valve (show energy balance), (c) the adiabatic work necessary for 1 lb and for 100 lb/min of solid. Let the works per stage be approximately the same.

Ans. (a) 0.114, (b) $x_3 = 67.7\%$, 63°F, (c) 0.397 kW-hr/lb sol.

1322. In problem 1321, the CO_2 leaving the aftercooler passes through a refrigerator and is cooled to 30°F [see part (b)], its state as it enters the throttling valve. For purposes of this problem, assume that all other data in problem 1321 remain as given. Determine (a) the fraction of solid CO_2 obtained. (b) Let the COP of the refrigeration be $\gamma = 2.8$ and determine the total work for 1 lb of solid.

Ans. (a) 0.4, (b) 0.101 kW-hr/lb solid.

1323. Air is to be liquefied by the Claude process; see Fig. 17/17, *Text*. It is compressed to 50 atm, from 1 atm and 25°C, arriving at *C* from the aftercooler at $t_c = 25°C$; $p_F = 1$ atm. For the first trial, assume that the temperature at the expansion valve is $t_3 = -154°C$, and with help from Item B 26, we assume $t_a = -90°C$, from which it is expected that the expander discharge contains little or no liquid; $t_B = 20°C$; negligible pressure drops in exchangers; steady state, steady flow. (a) For an expansion of unit mass to 1 atm and $\eta_t = 75\%$ for the expander *M*, determine the adiabatic work and the enthalpy and temperature of the exhaust b'. Compute (b) the mass fractions y and m (y = fraction of liquid), (c) the enthalpies and temperatures of the stream at t and r. Make energy balances for systems not used in the foregoing as a check. *Suggestion*: Try an overall energy balance and one for the receiver *F* first. Solve the problem using the units of Item B 26; then convert final answers to desired units.

Ans. (a) 18.7, 48.7 cal/gm, −192°C, (b) 0.152, 0.74, (c) −47.8 cal/gm, −192°C, −139 cal/gm, −139°C.

1324. Omit the expander in problem 1323 and the result is the Linde process. For all other data the same as before, compute the fraction of liquid obtained (Linde).

COMPUTER PROGRAMS

1325. The effect of compressor efficiency on the coefficient of performance of a given vapor-compression refrigeration system is being studied. Select a given refrigerant, specify a particular state at the entrance to the compressor (say saturated vapor at a certain pressure), set the condenser pressure, and then vary the compressor efficiency from the maximum (100%) to a minimum value of 70%. For each compressor efficiency, find the coefficient of performance of the system and plot the curve coefficient of performance vs compressor efficiency. Program this problem.

1326. A refrigeration manufacturer is studying the effect of the evaporator temperature on the coefficient of performance of a Freon 12 vapor-compression system in the range of 20°F to −20°F. Select a set of state conditions (compressor inlet and exit) for an ideal system and use an increment of 10°F for varying the parameter evaporator temperature. Plot the curve coefficient of performance vs evaporator temperature. Write the program for this problem.

1327–1330. These numbers may be used for other problems.

18

NOZZLES, DIFFUSERS, AND FLOWMETERS

Note: Always sketch the Ts and energy diagrams when solving nozzle problems. Be especially mindful of its density when converting a water manometer reading from inches to pressure units; remember that a table of densities for liquid water is available in Item B 13.

BASIC FLOW PRINCIPLES

1331. Show that for a flowing gas stream, the ratio of its stagnation temperature T_0 to its flow temperature T is given by $T_0/T = 1 + M^2(k-1)/2$ where k is the ratio c_p/c_v for the gas and M is its speed expressed as a Mach number.

1332. Derive the Bernoulli equation for frictionless, incompressible flow starting with the steady flow energy equation: $Q = \Delta P + \Delta K + \Delta u + \Delta(pv) + W$. State all assumptions.

1333. The Euler equation for steady flow is expressed as $dp/\rho + v\, dv + g\, dz = 0$. (a) Show that this is a form of the Bernoulli equation. (b) Demonstrate how the Euler equation may be easily converted into the momentum equation. State all assumptions.

1334. Demonstrate that the reaction force F of an incompressible fluid undergoing a reversible flow through a converging nozzle is $F = 2A_t(p_0 - p_t)$, where A_t = throat area, p_0 = stagnation pressure, and p_t = throat pressure.

1335. Water at 40 psig 60°F is contained by a smooth 90° bend in a 6-in. pipe. Find the magnitude and direction of the force on the bend (a) if there is no flow, (b) if the flow is 10 cfs. *Ans.* (a) 1600 lb, (b) 2995 lb.

1336. Oxygen at 172.37 kPaa is flowing in a pipe. The pressure and temperature of the O_2 on the nose of a small stationary object positioned in the stream are 193.05 kPaa and 65.6°C, respectively. Find the velocity.
Ans. 140 m/s.

1337. Two water reservoirs are connected by an underground pipeline; the water surface in one is 10 m above that of the other. For a flow of 0.6 m³/s through the pipe, find the losses in N-m/kg.

1338. A rocket with an exhaust nozzle area of 20 sq in. discharges the products of the propellant reaction at the rate of 10 lb/sec and develops a thrust of 1200 lb in a normal atmosphere at 14.7 psia, 80°F; the products are expanded to 16 psia at the nozzle exit. Determine (a) the velocity of the products at the nozzle exit, (b) the thrust developed in an atmosphere of 2 psia, −67°F, all other quantities being the same, including exit speed from nozzle. *Ans.* (a) 3780 fps, (b) 1454 lb.

1339. Oxygen at 25 psia is flowing in a pipe. The pressure and temperature of the O_2 on the nose of a small stationary object positioned in the stream are 28 psia and 150°F, respectively. Find the velocity. *Ans.* 458 fps.

1340. A stagnation probe made of pure tin is inserted in a high speed air jet whose temperature measured by a thermometer moving with the stream is 100°F. Melting and ablation of the probe occurs. Estimate the least stream velocity. Tin melts at 450°F.

1341. The adiabatic bulk modulus for saturated liquid water at 100°F is $\zeta = 331,000$ psi. (a) Determine the acoustic velocity in this fluid. (b) Estimate the pressure necessary to reduce its volume by 2%.

1342. Extract pertinent data for liquid water at 100°F from both the saturation table (Item B 13) and the compressed liquid table (Table II) obtaining the volume of saturated liquid at 100°F and liquid at 3000 psia, 100°F, and determine the bulk modulus of this fluid. Compare answer with the value given in problem 1341.

1343. Assume 8 ft³ of air at 100 psia, 100°F are compressed isothermally to a volume of $V_2 = 2$ ft³. For each of the end states of the process, find (a) the bulk modulus, (b) the acoustic velocity.

Ans. (a) 100, 400 psi, (b) 1160 fps.

1344. A chemical reaction produces 113.4 kg/s of propellant within a rocket. What minimum effective nozzle exit velocity is required to develop a thrust of 177,930 N?

1345. The speed of a jet-propelled plane is 1125 km/hr. The plane breathes in 75 kg/s air and burns 1.4 kg/s fuel while developing a thrust of 35,585 N. Find the exit speed of the exhaust gas.

1346. A useful parameter for work in fluid mechanics flow is T/T^*, where T is the temperature at any section of the stream and T^* is the temperature at Mach 1. Show that it is equal to

$$\frac{T}{T^*} = \frac{(k+1)/2}{1+M^2(k-1)/2}$$

1347. The same as problem 1346 except that the parameter is p/p^*; to show that

$$\frac{p}{p^*} = \frac{1}{M}\left[\frac{(k+1)/2}{1+M(k-1)/2}\right]^{1/2}$$

GAS NOZZLE

1348. Prove that the change in kinetic energy of a compressible fluid flowing through a frictionless nozzle is given by $\Delta K = -\int v\,dp$, whether or not the nozzle is adiabatic.

1349. Show that the isentropic flow of an ideal gas with k constant through a nozzle across any section of area A_2 is given by

$$\dot{m} = A_2 p_0 \left\{ \frac{2kk}{(k-1)RT_0}\left[\left(\frac{p_2}{p_0}\right)^{2/k} - \left(\frac{p_2}{p_0}\right)^{(k+1)/k}\right]\right\}^{1/2} \text{ lb/sec}$$

1350. Let an ideal gas with k constant flow isentropically through a nozzle; the gas is in uniform states 1 and 2 across any two sections 1 and 2 of the nozzle. Show that the following relations are true [see equation (7-14), *Text*].

(a) $\dfrac{T_1}{T_2} = \dfrac{2+(k-1)M_2^2}{2+(k-1)M_1^2}$

(b) $\dfrac{\rho_1}{\rho_2} = \left[\dfrac{2+(k-1)M_2^2}{2+(k-1)M_1^2}\right]^{1/(k-1)}$

(c) $\dfrac{A_2}{A_1} = \dfrac{M_1^2}{M_2^2}\left[\dfrac{2+(k-1)M_2^2}{2+(k-1)M_1^2}\right]^{(k+1)/[2(k-1)]}$

The foregoing parameters are frequently used with the reference state 1 being at the throat. What is the ratio A_2/A^*?

1351. Show that the velocity and the specific volume of air at the throat of an ideal convergent-divergent nozzle are given respectively by the relations $v_t = 44.7 T_0^{1/2}$ and $v_t = 1.58 v_0$.

1352. Using equation (18-20), § 18.12, *Text*, show that for converging-diverging flow $\dot{m} = 3.79 A_t (p_0/v_0)^{1/2}$ when $k = 1.3$ (suitable for what?).

1353. For a diatomic gas with $k = 1.4$, show that $\dot{m} = 3.88 A_t p_0/(RT_0)^{1/2}$ lb/sec.

1354. Derive the following equation for the mass rate of flow of air expanding isentropically to pressure less than the critical; $\dot{m} = 0.532\, p_0 A_t/T_0^{1/2}$.

1355. Air at 861.85 kPaa and 32.2°C enters a nozzle and expands isentropically to the exit pressure of 172.37 kPaa. Calculate the temperature and the velocity at the exit section (a) when the entrance state is stagnant and (b) when $v_1 = 183$ m/s. (c) What are the stagnation enthalpy and temperature in (b)?

Ans. (a) 193 K, 476 m/s, (b) 510 m/s, (c) $t_0 = 48.9$°C.

1356. An ideal nozzle allows 0.73 kg/s of methane (CH_4) to expand from 690 kPaa and 27°C to 552 kPaa. Determine the temperature, specific volume, velocity, and area at the exit section when (a) the initial kinetic energy is negligible, and (b) the initial speed is 122 m/s.

(c) What are the stagnation properties h_0, t_0, p_0 in (a)? In (b)? (d) Is this nozzle convergent or convergent-divergent?

Ans. (a) 284 K, 7.45 cm^2, (b) 6.75 cm^2, (c) $t_0 = 30.5°C$ in (b).

1357. A convergent-divergent nozzle with a throat area of 0.6 in.^{2} expands helium isentropically from 40 psia and 85°F to atmospheric pressure. What are the pressure, temperature, specific volume, and velocity at the throat (a) when the entrance state is stagnant and (b) when $v_1 = 500$ fps? (c) What mass will be discharged in lb/sec in (a)? In (b)? (d) What are the stagnation properties h_0, t_0, p_0 in (b)? (e) Find the Mach number at the throat and at the exit.

Ans. (a) 19.56 psia, 2910 fps; (b) 20.5 psia, 2915 fps; (c) 2.16 lb/sec $v_1 = 0$); (d) 549°R, 42 psia ($v_1 = 500$); (e) 1.1 (exit).

1358. A nozzle with a minimum area of 6.452 cm^2 and an efficiency of 94% receives air at 76 m/s, 331 kPaa, 682°C, and discharges it at 207 kPaa. (a) Determine the flow rate in kg/hr. (b) What are the stagnation properties h_0 and t_0 at discharge? (c) Sketch the general shape of this nozzle.

1359. In a gas turbine, a nozzle, with a 0.75-in. diameter throat is handling hot gas from a pressure and temperature of 48 psia and 1200°F, respectively, to a pressure of 28 psia with an efficiency of 94%. Assume the gas properties to be those given in Item B 8 ("400% air") with a molecular weight of $M_p = 28.90$. Sketch the nozzle and determine the flow rate in lb/hr, (a) if the initial kinetic energy is negligible, (b) if the initial velocity is 400 fps. (c) Find h_0 in (a) and in (b). (d) What is the nozzle coefficient?

Ans. (a) 933, (b) 958 lb/hr, (c) 423.2 Btu/lb, (d) 97%.

1360. A chemical reaction produces 115 kg/s of propellant within a rocket. What minimum effective nozzle exit velocity is required to develop a thrust of 178 kN.

1361. A stoichiometric mixture of liquid O_2 and H_2 burns and propels a rocket; the products ($R = 85.7$, $k = 1.2$) enter the exhaust nozzle ($e_n = 96\%$) at 250 psia, 4540°F and expand to 14.7 psia. Find (a) the relative jet velocity at nozzle exit, (b) the rate at which the mixture is consumed if the nozzle area is 25 in.^{2}, (c) the developed thrust.

1362. A substance flows isentropically at the rate of 2 lb/sec through a nozzle from a stagnation state of 180 psia and 700°F to 60 psia. Find the temperature, Mach number, and the area at the exit section when the substance is (a) steam, (b) air. (c) If the initial speed of the air is 260 fps, all other properties as given, what is v_2? (d) Compute the force of the fluid on each nozzle [(a) and (b)], ignoring pA forces. (e) For the same initial state, final pressure, and exit area, the nozzle efficiency is 95%. Compute its coefficient of discharge.

Ans. (a) 1.03 in.^{2}, $M_2 = 1.38$, (b) [Item B 1] 0.776 in.^{2}, $M_2 = 1.32$, (c) 1950, (d) 153, 120 lb, (e) 95.7%.

1363. The fuel mixture for a rocket engine is LOX and ammonia NH_3. Combustion pressure and temperature are 600 psia, 5040°F. For the products, the average value of $k = 1.23$; $M_p = 19.8$; $\eta_n = 96\%$ for any part of the expansion. A thrust of 150,000 lb is desired for an expansion to 1 atm at sea level. Compute the diameters at the exit and throat sections, the specific impulse, and the theoretical maximum exit speed for a proper expansion to $p_a = 0$. *Ans.* 3, 1.53 ft, 261 sec, 12,130 fps.

1364. Air at 125 psia and 90°F enters a nozzle and expands isentropically to the exit pressure of 25 psia. Calculate the temperature and the velocity at the exit section (a) when the entrance state is stagnant and (b) when $v_1 = 600$ fps. (c) What are the stagnation enthalpy and temperature in (b)?

Ans. (a) 347°R, 1561 fps, (b) 1673 fps, (c) $t_0 = 120°F$.

1365. A nozzle is designed to pass 2400 lb/hr of air from 45 psia and 100°F to 15 psia. (a) For a nozzle efficiency of 93% and negligible initial kinetic energy, determine the throat area and the exit area. (b) Find the areas if $v_1 = 250$ fps.

Ans. (a) 0.689 in.^{2} throat, 0.765 in^2 exit.

1366. Special nozzles are installed on a steam turbine which drives a centrifugal pump to allow the use of natural gas ($R = 97.6$, $c_p = 0.529$, $k = 1.31$) in lieu of steam. Expansion of the gas occurs through the nozzles ($e_n = 95\%$) from 50 psig and 90°F to 8 psig. The gas exhausts from the turbine at 8 psig and passes through low-pressure mains to a smelting plant. The turbine efficiency is 50%. The output of the pump is 30 bhp; $\eta_m = 90\%$. (a) For the exit section of the nozzles, find $t_{2'}$ and $v_{2'}$ where $K_1 = 0$. (b) Compute the bhp of the turbine and the actual gas consumption in cfm measured at the nozzle inlet. (c) How many nozzles with a throat diameter of 0.5 in. and 96% nozzle efficiency should be installed?

Ans. (**a**) −25°F, 1743 fps, (**b**) 33.3 hp, 268 cfm, (**c**) 4.

EQUILIBRIUM-VAPOR NOZZLE

1367. A frictionless, adiabatic nozzle receives 5 lb/sec of steam at 1300 psia and 800°F and discharges it at 750 psia. For the exit section find t_2, v_2, and A_2 (**a**) where $K_1 = 0$ and (**b**) where $v_1 = 500$ fps. (**c**) Is this nozzle convergent? (**d**) Find the stagnation properties h_0, t_0, s_0, p_0 in (**b**).
   Ans. (**a**) 1789 fps, 0.317 in.^{2}; (**b**) 0.306 in.^{2}; (**d**) $h_0 = 1379.6$ Btu/lb.

1368. The static properties of steam at the entrance of an ideal converging-diverging nozzle are 200 psia, 450°F; the throat pressure is 130.8 psia. For the steam at the nozzle entrance, find (**a**) the velocity, (**b**) the stagnation properties, h_0, p_0, t_0.

1369. A frictionless, adiabatic nozzle receives 2.25 kg/s of steam at 90 bar, 480°C and discharges it at 50 bar. For the exit section find t_2, v_2, and A_2 (**a**) where $K_1 = 0$ and (**b**) where $v_1 = 150$ m/s. (**c**) Is this nozzle convergent? (**d**) Find the stagnation properties h_0, t_0, s_0, p_0 in (**b**). Use Item B 16(SI).
   Ans. (**a**) 590 m/s, 2.097 cm^2.

1370. A nozzle receives 907 kg/hr of steam at 25 bar, 380°C and discharges it at 7 bar. Let the initial kinetic energy be negligible and the nozzle efficiency be 93%. Use $p^* = 0.56\, p_1$ and determine (**a**) the throat area and (**b**) the exit area. Use Item B 16 (SI).

1371. Steam flows isentropically (in equilibrium) through a nozzle from $p_1 = 110$ psia, $y_1 = 10\%$, and $v_1 = 300$ fps to 70 psia. At the 0.5 in.^{2} exit section, find (**a**) the specific volume and temperature, (**b**) the velocity, (**c**) the Mach number, (**d**) the flow, lb/hr, and (**e**) the stagnation enthalpy.
   Ans. (**a**) 5.438 ft^3/lb, (**b**) 1314.8 fps, (**c**) 0.936, (**d**) 3021 lb/hr, (**e**) 1102.5 Btu/lb.

1372. Steam at 180 psia and 500°F enters a nozzle with $v_1 = 400$ fps and expands to 114°F. The throat area is 0.6 in.^{2} For ideal equilibrium conditions and for $p_t = 0.556\, p_1$, find the pressure, volume, Mach number, and mass flow (**a**) at the throat and (**b**) at the exit sections. (**c**) What is the exit area? (**d**) What is the stagnation enthalpy? Compare answers with those in problem 1384.

Ans. (**a**) 100 psia, 1.5 lb/sec, (**d**) 1274.7 Btu/lb.

1373. State 1 for steam at the entrance to a convergent nozzle is: $p_1 = 280$ psia, $t_1 = 500$°F, fluid at rest; at exit, the steam velocity is 1640 fps. For the nozzle, the velocity coefficient is $\eta_v = 92\%$. Find the discharge pressure.

1374. A convergent-divergent nozzle has a throat diameter of 0.30 in. and expands steam from 220 psia and 450°F to 10 psia. For equilibrium flow with negligible entrance kinetic energy and a nozzle efficiency of 96%, compute (**a**) the steam flow, lb/hr; (**b**) the actual quality and area at exit; and (**c**) the change in availability, entrance to throat, where $t_0 = 70$°F.

1375. Steam at 560 psia and 550°F enters a nozzle with a velocity of 250 fps and is discharged at 215 psia. For a flow of 9200 lb/hr, $\eta_n = 0.92$ and $p_c = 0.5358\, p_1$, determine (**a**) the exit velocity, (**b**) the throat area in in.^{2}, (**c**) the actual temperature at discharge, and (**d**) the increase in unavailability for $t_0 = 80$°F.
   Ans. (**a**) 1644 fps, (**b**) 0.346 in.^{2}, (**c**) 424°F, (**d**) 55.5 Btu/lb.

1376. A nozzle receives 907 kg/hr of steam at 25 bar, 380°C and discharges it at 7 bar. Let the initial kinetic energy be negligible and the nozzle efficiency be 93%. Use $p_t = 0.55\, p_1$ and determine (**a**) the throat area and (**b**) the exit area.
   Ans. (**a**) 0.86 cm^2.

1377. Steam expanding adiabatically in a nozzle from an initial pressure of 10 bar is to be dry-saturated at exit where the pressure is 1.7 bar. The nozzle efficiency is 90% and the initial state is that of rest. (**a**) What is the initial quality or degrees superheat? (**b**) If the throat area is 2.58 cm^2, find the exit area.

1378. Steam at 240 psia, 500°F, and 300 fps enters a nozzle and leaves at 190 psia. If the exit area is 0.45 in.^{2} and the nozzle efficiency is 92%, determine (**a**) the flow rate in lb/hr and (**b**) the change of availability for the environmental temperature of 100°F.
   Ans. (**a**) 4413 lb/hr, (**b**) −21.8 Btu/lb.

1379. Steam at 290 psia, 550°F enters a nozzle and expands to 195 psia at the exit; the kinetic energy at the entrance is negligible. The nozzle efficiency is $e_n = 72.5\%$. For a flow of 6000 lb/hr, find the exit area in square inches. Also sketch the shape of the nozzle.

1380. An ideal nozzle receives 2449 kg/hr steam at 19 bar, 260°C and negligible initial velocity and discharges to a pressure which is one half of the initial value. Sketch the shape of the nozzle and determine the discharge section area in square inches.

1381. A convergent nozzle receives 9200 lb/hr of steam at 400 psia, 580°F, 250 fps and discharges it through a 0.50 in.² exit section at 215 psia and 1700 fps. Determine the minimum force necessary to hold the nozzle in position.

SUPERSATURATED-VAPOR NOZZLE

1382. Steam at a virtually stagnation state of 220 psia and 450°F enters a nozzle whose throat area is 2 in.², exit area 3.72 in.²; nozzle efficiency is 95%. Compute the mass rate of flow and the approximate state at the exit section 2, assuming that phase equilibrium never occurs. [If it is desired to make this problem more realistic, assume that a condensation shock occurs at a moisture content of 4.5%, with phase equilibrium thereafter.] (*Suggestion*: Set up equation for $\dot{m}/A_2$ with only p_2 unknown.) Considering the phenomenon of the Wilson line, § 18.2, *Text*, is it likely that supersaturation would continue to the exit state?
Ans. 6 lb/sec, $p_2 \approx 27$ psia, $h_2 \approx 1089$ Btu/lb, $v_2 \approx 12.75$ ft³/lb.

1383. A nozzle expands 2.27 kg/s of steam in ideal supersaturated flow from 11 bar, 193.3°C to a discharge pressure of 4.14 bar. For the throat section, determine the pressure, velocity, specific volume, area, and Mach number (**a**) when the initial state is stagnant and (**b**) when $v_1 = 198$ m/s. (**c**) Find the velocity, volume, and area at the exit section in (a).
Ans. (**a**) 6.01 bar, 479 m/s, 0.29 m³/kg, 13.78 cm², 1.0.

1384. Steam at 180 psia and 500°F expands in supersaturated frictionless flow through a nozzle to 114°F. The throat area is 0.6 in.²; $p_t = 0.556 p_1$; $v_1 = 400$ fps. For the exit section, find (**a**) the volume, (**b**) the velocity, (**c**) the mass flow, (**d**) the Mach number, (**e**) Compare answers with those in problem 1372.

1385. A nozzle expands 5 lb/sec of steam in ideal supersaturated flow from 160 psia and 400°F to a discharge pressure of 60 psia. For the throat section, determine the pressure, velocity, specific volume, area, and Mach number (**a**) when the initial state is stagnant and (**b**)

when $v_1 = 650$ fps. (**c**) Find the velocity, volume, and area at the exit section in (a).
Ans. (**a**) 87.2 psia, 1591 fps, 4.794 ft³/lb, 2.169 in.², 1.0.

1386. An ideal nozzle with a throat area of 0.4 in.² expands steam from 400 psia, 500°F, and an initial velocity of 300 fps to 110 psia. For $p^* = 0.55 p_1$, and considering supersaturation, find (**a**) the specific volume and velocity at the throat and (**b**) the mass rate of flow in lb/sec. (**c**) What is the exit area? Consider equilibrium to exist at the exit. (**d**) Find the stagnation enthalpy at state 1 and the ratio p_t/p_0.
Ans. (**a**) 2.033 ft³/lb, 1660 fps, (**b**) 2.27 lb/sec, (**c**) 0.524 in.², (**d**) 1246.9 Btu/lb.

1387. Steam at 600 psia and 500°F enters a nozzle and leaves at 400 psia. Neglecting initial kinetic energy and considering supersaturation, determine the discharge area for a flow of 23,000 lb/hr and a nozzle coefficient of 96%. What is the nozzle efficiency?
Ans. 0.80 in.², 92.2%.

1388. There are received 1814 kg/hr of steam at 13.8 bar, 215°C, and 76 m/s by a nozzle which expands it to 6.9 bar with a nozzle efficiency of 90%. Let $p^* = 0.55 p_1$. For supersaturated flow compute the throat area in square centimeters. *Ans.* 2.62 cm².

DIFFUSER

1389. Air at 1.037 kPaa, 60°C enters a frictionless diffuser and is decelerated from Mach 3 at entrance to Mach 1 at exit. For a flow of 13.61 kg/s, determine (**a**) the temperature and pressure at exit, (**b**) the inlet area, (**c**) the exit area.

1390. Steam enters a diffuser at 0.07 bar, dry-saturated, and is discharged at 0.40 bar with negligible velocity. (**a**) For an isentropic process, determine the initial velocity in fps. (**b**) The same as (**a**) except that the diffuser efficiency is 85%. What will be the temperature of the steam at discharge?

1391. An airplane powered by a jet engine is moving with an airspeed of 1200 fps (about 820 mph) where the atmospheric pressure is $p_a = 7$ psia and $t_a = 40°F$. (**a**) If the air is brought to rest (relative to the plane) at the exit from the diffuser by an isentropic compression, what are its (stagnation) temperature, enthalpy, and pressure? (**b**) Solve (**a**) with a diffuser efficiency of 82%.

Ans. (**a**) 160°F, 14.85 psia.

1392. Helium enters a diffuser at 10 in. Hg abs, 40°F, and 4200 fps. (**a**) For an isentropic process to 14.7 psia, what are the final velocity and the final temperature? (**b**) If the efficiency of the diffuser is 87%, determine v_2 and $t_{2'}$.

Ans. (**a**) 737 fps, 313°F.

1393. An airplane has an air speed of Mach 0.9 where $p_a = 8$ in. Hg and $t_a = -55°F$, initial condition at the diffuser entrance; at diffuser exit, $K_2 \approx 0$. (**a**) For an isentropic flow, determine the exit temperature and pressure and the pressure ratio. (**b**) Let the pressure coefficient $\kappa_p = 0.76$. Determine $p_{2'}$, $T_{2'}$, and the diffuser efficiency. (**c**) Now let the plane speed increase to Mach 2 causing a standing normal shock wave at diffuser entrance; the pressure and temperature on the downstream side of shock is 17.6 psia, 681°F. Find the pressure and temperature at diffuser exit assuming an isentropic diffusion process from shock wave downstream side to diffuser exit; the exit kinetic energy is negligible. What is the overall pressure ratio?

Ans. (**a**) 471°R, 6.63 psia, (**b**) 5.78 psia, 71.5%, (**c**) 22.1 psia, 727°R.

VENTURI

Note: In sketching the energy diagram, let the system be from entrance to throat.

1394. A 15.25 × 10.15-cm venturi receives air at 344.75 kPaa, 93.3°C. The manometer differential across the venturi is 11.56 cm of water and the discharge coefficient is 0.935 (not including the initial-velocity effect). Environmental conditions are: a barometer of 1 atm and a temperature of 40°C. Find (**a**) the mass of air flowing and (**b**) the equivalent m^3/min of free air.

Ans. (**a**) 43.6 kg/min, (**b**) 40.6 m^3/min.

1395. There are flowing 389 cfm of equivalent free air through a 3 × 2-in. venturi, entering at 20 psig and 170°F. The differential manometer reads 7.55 in. H_2O. The surroundings are at 29.10 in. Hg and 102°F. Determine the discharge coefficient.

Ans. 0.95.

1396. A 20.32 × 15.25-cm venturi is metering oxygen in a steady flow manner. Oxygen enters the venturi at 827.4 kPaa,

4.45°C and the manometer differential, entrance to throat, is 20.3 cm H_2O and located in an atmosphere of 1 atm, 43.3°C. The coefficient of discharge is 0.965. Find the flow of oxygen kg/min accounting for the initial velocity correction.

1397. To measure the air used by an IC engine, a 3 × 1⅜-in. venturi with a coefficient of discharge of 0.97 is placed in the air intake line. At entrance to the venturi, the pressure is atmospheric, barometer 29.45 in. Hg (60°F) and $t = 80°F$ (free air conditions). The pressure drop from the barometer to the throat is 10.25 in. H_2O (60°F). Compute (**a**) the mass and volume of free air flowing (assumed steady flow), (**b**) the stagnation and static temperatures at the throat, (**c**) the velocity pressure and the static pressure in the pipe line (before friction has caused a significant change, but for actual flow).

Ans. (**a**) 0.123 lb/sec, 102 cfm, (**b**) 534.6°R, (**c**) $p_{stat} = 400.7$ in. H_2O.

1398. The velocity through the throat of a carburetor venturi is 150 fps. For the venturi, $\eta_d = 0.80$, $t_1 = 70°F$, and $p_1 = 30$ in. Hg. (**a**) Find the pressure at the throat if the flow is considered incompressible. (**b**) If the diameter of the fuel jet is 0.045 in., find the air/fuel ratio where $\eta_d = 0.75$ for the fuel jet and the fuel weighs 45 lb/ft^3; venturi ID, 0.8 in.

FLOW NOZZLE, ORIFICE

1399. A 5.1-cm flow nozzle is used to measure the flow from a drum of air wherein the pressure is constant at 791 kPaa and the temperature is 32.2°C. The discharge is to the atmosphere, and the coefficient of discharge is 0.97. Find the exit velocity and the mass of air discharged.

Ans. 3.54 kg/s.

1400. A 2-in. flow nozzle is used to measure the flow from a drum of air wherein the pressure is constant at 100 psig and the temperature is 90°F. The discharge is to the atmosphere, and the coefficient of discharge is 0.97%. Find the exit velocity and the mass of air discharged.

Ans. 7.80 lb/sec.

1401. A 5 × 4-in. flow nozzle in a 5-in. ID pipe receives 180.2 lb/min of air at 40 psia and 175°F and causes a manometer differential of 15 in. water. The surroundings are at 88°F and 14.50 psia. Determine the coefficient of discharge.

Ans. 0.92.

1402. A 6-in. (exit section) flow nozzle is used to measure the flow of air in a 10-in. ID pipe. Ahead of the flow nozzle the static pressure is 10 psig and the stagnation temperature is 110°F. The manometer differential across the flow nozzle is 9 in. H_2O. Coefficient of discharge $\eta_d = 0.92$. Atmospheric pressure and temperature are 29.6 in. Hg and 86°F, respectively. Calculate the mass flowing in lb/hr, **(a)** neglecting the correction factor for initial velocity, **(b)** accounting for the initial velocity.

Ans. **(a)** 12,020 lb/hr, **(b)** 12,890 lb/hr.

1403. The fuel consumption of a gas engine is 180.5 kg/min methane gas as metered by a 15.25-cm orifice placed in a 20.3-cm ID flow line. Just ahead of the orifice, the static pressure 552 kPaa and the stagnation temperature is 48.9°C; the manometer differential across the orifice is 55.9 cm H_2O; environmental conditions are 1 atm, 36.7°C. Find the discharge coefficient for the orifice.

1404. A 4-in. thin plate orifice with $\eta_d = 0.615$ (not including correction for initial velocity) is used in an 8-in. ID pipe line to measure the flow of methane (CH_4). Just ahead of the orifice a pressure gage indicates 56 psig and a thermometer indicates 135°F. The manometer differential across the orifice is 47 in. H_2O. The barometer is 29.5 in. Hg, and the room temperature is 94°F. **(a)** What mass is flowing? **(b)** What is the volume, measured at line conditions, in cfm?

Ans. **(a)** 173 lb/min. **(b)** 975 cfm.

1405. There are flowing 3300 cfm of equivalent free air across a 5-in. thin plate orifice installed in a 10-in. ID pipe. Static pressure ahead of the orifice is 40 psia, and the temperature is 110°F. The environmental temperature is 105°F, and the barometer reads 29.55 in. Hg. The discharge coefficient $\eta_d = 0.62$ (does not include the correction for initial velocity). Determine the manometer differential.

Ans. 32 in. H_2O.

1406. Gaseous methane ($R = 96.33$, $k = 1.303$) at 100 psia, 200°F flows in a 10-in. ID pipe and is metered through an 8-in. diameter orifice ($\eta_d = 0.8$) positioned in the pipe. A differential manometer across the orifice reads 30 in. H_2O (at 110°F); the barometer is 14.7 psia. Find the mass flow of gas, lb/min. [*Note*: the value of $\eta_d = 0.8$ does not correct for the approach velocity.]

1407. An 8×6-in. orifice is metering 271 lb/min methane in a steady flow manner. The gas enters the orifice at 80 psia, 140°F; the manometer differential across the orifice is unknown and is located in the environment of 14.7 psia, 104°F. The discharge coefficient is 0.78 and does not account for the initial velocity. Find the reading of the manometer in inches of water. *Ans.* 9 in. wg at 104°F.

PITOT TUBE

1408. Oxygen at atmospheric pressure flows past the entrance of a pitot tube that is directed up stream. For the tube entrance, the oxygen comes to rest at 3 in. H_2O gage static head and 70°F. Atmospheric conditions are 14.7 psia, 70°F. Find the stream velocity.

1409. A pitot tube is used to measure the flow of air in a 10.16-cm ID pipe. The impact (stagnation) temperature is $t_1 = 37.8°C$, the static manometer reads 5.59 cm H_2O gage, and the mean velocity differential is 2.34 cm H_2O. The barometric pressure is 1 atm and the room temperature is 36.7°C. Find **(a)** the mean velocity of the air in the pipe and **(b)** the equivalent volume of free air flowing in m^3/s. **(c)** What is the difference between the stagnation enthalpy of the steam and the flowing enthalpy, Btu/lb? *Ans.* **(a)** 20 m/s, **(b)** 9.74 m^3/min.

1410. A traverse of a 15-in. ID duct with a pitot tube shows a mean velocity differential of 0.75 in. H_2O. The stagnation manometer reading and temperature are 12.5 in. H_2O gage and 105°F, respectively. The barometer reads 29.78 in. Hg and the room temperature is 90°F. Calculate the mean velocity of the air in the duct and the equivalent quantity of free air flowing in cfm. *Ans.* 59 fps, 4344 cfm.

1411. Air at 50 psia, 200°F is flowing in a 20-in. ID duct. A pitot tube traverse indicates an average manometer differential reading of 7.5 in. H_2O. The manometer and duct are located in an environment of 14.7 psia, 80°F. Calculate the mass of air flowing in the duct, lb/hr.

1412. A traverse of a pitot tube across a 10-in. ID pipe section gives an average manometer differential of 1.75 in. H_2O; gaseous oxygen at 100 psia, 240°F is flowing through the pipe. The ambient conditions are 14.7 psia, 110°F. Find the flow of oxygen, lb/min.

COMPUTER PROGRAMS

1413. It is desired to relate the velocity manometer differentials for these three flowmeters that are positioned in a 6-in. ID line in which air is flowing—a pitot tube, a 6×4-in. venturi ($\eta_d = 0.95$), and a 6×4-in. orifice ($\eta_d = 0.62$). Let the air ahead of each meter be at 50 psia, 100°F and let the flow vary from 10 lb/min to 100 lb/min. Compare the three manometer differentials as they vary with air flow. Program this study.

1414. The effect of discharge pressure on the mass rate of a gas through an ideal nozzle is desired. Select an initial state for a given gas, let the minimum cross-sectional area in the nozzle remain constant (discharge and/or throat area), and vary the discharge pressure from that of the initial state to some value well below critical. Write the program for this study.

1415–1420. These numbers may be used for other problems.

19

HEAT TRANSFER

Note: Tables and charts pertinent to this chapter, are to be found in the appendix. In solving these problems, use dimensional equations and think carefully of the need for order in the units.

CONDUCTION, PLANE WALL

1421. Compare the heat fluxes that result from a 15°C temperature difference existing across the respective surfaces of 3-cm layers of aluminum, steel, concrete, and cork.

1422. An 20.32×20.32-cm test panel, 2.54 cm thick, is placed between two plates, and the whole is properly insulated. The insulated surface of one plate is maintained at 79.4°C by an electric energy supply of 50 W; the other plate has an interface surface temperature of 21.1°C. Find k for the test panel.

Ans. 0.528 W/m K.

1423. It is desired that no more than 1892 W/m² be conducted through a 30-cm thick wall whose average thermal conductivity is $k = 0.865$ W/m K; the conducted heat will be controlled by insulating one side. Find the least thickness of insulating material ($k = 0.346$ W/m K) that will assure this heat constraint if the surface temperatures of the composite wall are 1150°C and 40°C. *Ans.* 8.1 cm.

1424. A manufacturer of gas kitchen stoves desires to substitute fiber glass for 85% magnesia, used as the insulation for the oven. With a maximum oven temperature of 600°F, the top outer surface of the oven is not to exceed 120°F. Neglect the metallic resistance to heat flow and determine (**a**) the thickness of 85% magnesia currently used, (**b**) the thickness of the fiber glass to be used.

1425. There are conducted 5000 Btu/hr through a 10-ft² section of a 0.3-in. thick plane copper wall ($k = 2650$) with a 0.15-in. thick air film ($k = 0.25$) and a 0.15-in. thick water film ($k = 4.6$) on the respective surfaces. Find the temperature drop (**a**) across each material and (**b**) across the composite section. (k, Btu-in./ft²-hr-°F).

Ans. (**a**) $\Delta t_a = 300°F, 0.0566°F, 16.3°F.$

1426. (**a**) Find an equation for the heat conducted through a plate of area A, thickness L, having surface temperatures of t_1 and t_2, when the conductivity varies in accordance with $k = k_0(1 + at)$. (**b**) Data for a plane plate glass door are: $A = 1.86$ m², $L = 1.905$ cm, $t_1 = 4.4°C, t_2 = 26.7°C, k_0 = 0.721$ W/m K, $a = 0.031/°C$. Determine the hourly heat flow.

CONDUCTION, CURVED WALL

1427. A cylindrical pipe of length L and radii r_i and r_o is made of material whose conductivity is k. The inner surface temperature is t_i; the outer is t_o. (**a**) Determine the rate of heat flow if k remains constant. (**b**) Determine the rate of heat flow if k varies linearly with temperature and is given as $k = k_0[1 + \alpha t]$ where k_0 and α are constant.

1428. Hot water is flowing through a 11.43-cm OD steel pipe ($k = 45$ W/m K) which is insulated with 5.08 cm of 85%

magnesia ($k = 0.062$ W/m K). Thermocouples embedded in the inner and outer surfaces of the insulation indicate temperatures of 121.1°C and 46.1°C, respectively. Find the hourly heat loss per 61 m of pipe length.

1429. Demonstrate that the heat flowing from a simple pipe of length L, radii r_o and r_i, surfaces temperatures t_o and t_i, and having a thermal conductivity k may be found by using the expression $q = kA_m(t_i - t_o)/(r_o - r_i)$. Here A_m is the logarithmic mean area $A_m = (A_o - A_i)/\ln(A_o/A_i)$. *Hint:* Equate the two heat transfer equations, one for a plane wall with area $A = A_m$ and $\ell = r_o - r_i$, and the other as that obtained from Fourier's equation applied to a cylindrical pipe of length and radii r_o and r_i.

1430. What percentage error would result if for a pipe of length L and radii r_o and r_i, the heat flow q would be calculated using the arithmetic mean area $A_a = \pi L(r_o + r_i)$ instead of the logarithmic mean area A_m as found in problem 1429? Let $r_o/r_i = 2$.
Ans. 3.97% error.

1431. The steel fire tubes of a small boiler have an OD of 2 in. and a thickness of 0.125 in. The boiling water receives 6500 Btu/hr-ft^2 of heating surface when the temperature difference, gas to water, is 1100°F. Find the percentage of the total temperature drop which occurs in the metal. *Ans.* 0.0252%.

1432. Determine the heat flow per unit length of a thick cylindrical pipe of radii $r_i = 12$ cm, $r_o = 24$ cm, surface temperatures of $t_i = 425$°C, $t_o = 95$°C, and with $k = 0.05 + 0.0008t$ where t is in °C and k is in Wm/K. Assume steady state conditions and account for the variation of thermal conductivity with temperature.

1433. A hollow sphere with inner radius r_i, outer radius r_o, inner and outer surface temperatures t_i and t_o, is made of a material whose thermal conductivity is k. Derive the expression for the conducted heat loss, W/m^2, (a) based upon the outer area and (b) based upon the inner area. (c) Let $r_i = 7.62$ cm; $r_o = 12.70$ cm; $k = 46.15$ W/m K; $t_i = 426.7$°C. If the heat from the sphere is 439.6 W, what is t_o?
Ans. 422.7°C.

1434. If a 1-in. layer of 85% magnesia is wrapped on the outside of the sphere in problem 1433 what will be t_o (outside magnesia surface temperature) all other data remaining the same?

1435. A nuclear reactor shell is spherical in shape, has an internal volume of 65.4 ft^3, contains water boiling at 400°F, and is made from stainless steel ($k = 160$) 3 in. thick. The reactor has a 2-in. layer of lead around it with a layer of 85% magnesia in between the two materials; the maximum power level for the reactor is 5 kW. If the maximum heat loss through the shell is not to exceed 5% of the power, compute the needed thickness of 85% magnesia. What will be the outer surface temperature of the lead under maximum heat loss conditions?

HEAT TRANSFER, FLUID TO FLUID

1436. Apply Fourier's equation, account for the two film coefficients h_i and h_o, and find the heat flux q/A for a simple plane wall of thickness ℓ and thermal conductivity k. Let the two fluids be at temperatures t_1 and t_2. Next let the wall be curved, a pipe of length L and with radii r_i and r_o, and solve for q/L. Finally, let the curved wall be a hollow sphere and solve for q/A_o.

1437. A composite plane wall consisting of two layers of materials (1.5-in. steel and 2-in. aluminum) separates a hot gas at $t_i = 200$°F, $h_i = 2$, from a cold gas at $t_o = 80$°F, $h_o = 5$ Btu/hr-ft^2-°F. If the hot fluid is on the aluminum side, find (a) the transmittance U, (b) the resistance R, (c) the interface temperature at the junction of the two metals, and (d) the heat through 100 ft^2 of the surface under steady state conditions.
Ans. (a) 1.416 Btu/hr-ft^2-°F, (b) 0.70615, (c) 115°F, (d) 17,000 Btu/hr.

1438. A boiler tube (OD = 3.5 in., ID = 2.7 in.) contains water boiling at 1250 psia. The water film coefficient is $h_i = 2000$ Btu/hr-ft^2-°F when the heat flux is 52,000 Btu/hr-ft^2 of outside tube surface. Determine (a) the outside tube temperature, (b) the permissible thickness of boiler scale if the metallic temperature is not to exceed 925°F. Thermal conductivities are: for steel, $k = 310$; for scale, $k = 3.5$ Btu-in./hr-ft^2-°F.

1439. Dry saturated steam at 30 psia enters a 50-ft section of steel pipe (OD = 2.375 in., ID = 1.939 in.) and flows at a rate of 10 lb/min; the pipe is covered with 1 in. of 85% magnesia; the film coefficients are: $h_i = 1000$, $h_o = 4$. Determine the quality of the steam as it leaves the section. Neglect pressure loss.

1440. Saturated steam at 180 psia is flowing through a 6-in. steel pipe (6.625-in. OD, 6.065-in. ID). The environmental temperature is 84°F; $h_i = 1500$ and $h_o = 2.8$ Btu/hr-ft²-°F. Determine the thickness of 85% magnesia insulation necessary to reduce the heat loss from the pipe to 12% of that through the bare pipe (same h_o for both cases).

1441. Steam is flowing from a boiler to a small turbine through 200 ft of 3.5-in. steel pipe (4-in. OD, 3.548-in. ID). The steam leaves the boiler saturated at 175 psia and enters the turbine at 173.33 psia and with a moisture content of 1%. The turbine develops 50 bhp with a brake steam rate of 41 lb/bhp-hr. The ambient temperature is 90°F; $h_i = 1000$ and $h_o = 1.9$ Btu/hr-ft²-°F. If the pipe is lagged with a 2.5-in. layer of insulation, compute the value of the thermal conductivity for the insulation.

Ans. $k = 0.542$ Btu-in./hr-ft²-°F.

1442. A hollow steel sphere contains a 100-watt electrical filament, and these data are known; $r_i = 9$ in., $r_o = 12$ in. The film coefficients for the inner and outer surfaces are $h_i = 6$, $h_o = 2$ Btu per hr-ft²-°F; the environmental temperature is 80°F. Assuming steady state, compute the temperature of the inside air. (See problems 1433, 1436.)

Ans. 101.9°F.

1443. The same as problem 1442 except that a 1-in. layer of 85% magnesia is wrapped around the sphere. *Ans. 158.4°F.*

1444. Heat is generated internally within a plane wall that is 8 cm thick and has a thermal conductivity of $k = 17.3$ W/m K. One wall side is perfectly insulated; the other is exposed to a fluid at 95°C for which the convective film coefficient is $h = 570$ W/m² K. If the generated heat is 105 kW and steady state obtains find the temperature at the wall-insulation interface.

LOGARITHMIC MEAN TEMPERATURE DIFFERENCE

1445. Air enters a preheater at 25°C and leaves at 110°C. The hot gas leaves at 130°C. Find the temperature of the hot gas entering when the logarithmic mean temperature difference is 67.4°C and (a) the flow is parallel (b) the flow is counter-current. *Ans. (b) 160°C.*

1446. An economizer receives hot gas ($c_p = 0.27$ Btu/lb-°R) and water in the ratio 1.5 lb gas/lb water. The gas enters at 850°F and leaves at 355°F; the water enters at 120°F. Find the exit temperature of the water and the LMTD **(a)** for parallel flow, **(b)** for counterflow. Assume no energy losses external to the system.

Ans. (a) 320.5°F, LMTD = 228°F.

1447. Water enters a 4850-ft², counterflow economizer at 165°F and leaves at 276°F. There are flowing through the economizer 75,000 lb/hr of flue gases ($c_p = 0.24$ Btu/lb-°F) which decrease in temperature from 580°F to 295°F. Find **(a)** the amount of water heated, lb/hr, **(b)** LMTD, and **(c)** the transmittance U (corresponding to the given area).

1448. The oil ($c_p = 1759$ W-s/kg K) from an oil-cooled electric transformer is cooled from 79.4°C to 29.4°C at the rate of 1360.5 kg/hr. This is done in an oil-water heat exchanger that receives 2948 kg/hr of water at 15.6°C. For the exchanger, $U = 295$ W/m² K. Find the exit water temperature and heating area required **(a)** for counterflow and **(d)** for parallel flow.

1449. Steam at 285 psia enters a convection superheater in a saturated state and leaves at 600°F. The hot gases ($c_p = 0.241$ Btu/lb-°F) leave the superheater at 1150°F. There are 1.6 lb gas/lb steam and the total steam flow is 17,580 lb/hr. If the transmittance is $U = 4$ Btu/hr-ft²-°F, find **(a)** the temperature of gases entering the superheater and **(b)** the amount of superheater surface required.

Ans. (a) 1441°F, (b) 623 ft².

1450. A water cooler uses 50 lb/hr of melting ice to cool running water from 80°F to 42°F. Based on the inside coil area, $U_i = 110$ Btu/hr-ft²-°F. Find **(a)** the LMTD, **(b)** the inside area of the coil, and **(c)** the gpm of water cooled.

Ans. (a) 24.24°F, (b) 2.664 ft², (c) 0.380 gpm.

1451. **(a)** A closed feedwater heater, with a transmittance of $U = 350$ Btu/hr-ft²-°F, uses condensing steam at 20 psia for heating 85,000 lb/hr of water from 60°F to 215°F. What is the transmitting area? **(b)** After some fouling of the tubes, the transmittance decreases to $U = 305$. Find the exit temperature of the feedwater. *Ans. (a) 621 ft², (b) 208°F.*

1452. A single-pass surface condenser with $\frac{5}{8}$-in. OD tubes whose effective length is 18 ft and whose thickness is 0.046 in., receives

112,000 lb/hr of steam at 84°F with an enthalpy of $h = 960$ Btu/lb. The resulting condensate leaves saturated at 84°F with little change of kinetic energy. Circulating water enters the tubes counter-flow at 68°F and leaves at 78°F. If the heat transfer coefficient is $U = 630$ Btu/hr-ft²-°F, find (a) the rate of flow of water, (b) the heating surface, (c) the number of tubes, and (d) the average velocity of the water.

Ans. (a) 10,180,000 lb/hr, (b) 15,850 ft², (c) 5380, (d) 5.44 fps.

1453. In a 10-ton Freon 12 refrigerating system, liquid refrigerant from the condenser is cooled from 80°F to 70°F in a concentric double-pipe heat exchanger. This is done by passing the liquid through the inner pipe and saturated vapor (after the refrigeration is done) from the 20°F evaporator through the annulus. For the heat exchanger, $U = 110$ Btu/hr-ft²-°F; for the vapor, $c_p = 0.15$ Btu/lb-°F. Find the required heating surface for (a) counterflow, and (b) parallel flow.

RADIATION

1454. The value and English units of the Stefan-Boltzmann constant are $\sigma = 0.1713 \times 10^{-8}$ and Btu/hr-ft²-R⁴. What are its value and SI units?

1455. Calculate the rate of energy emission from each square foot of a "black body" at a temperature of (a) −100°F, (b) 0°F, (c) 100°F, and (d) 2000°F. Does the presence of other bodies affect this rate? Explain.

1456. A $12 \times 12 \times 60$-in. billet of steel with oxidized surfaces lies cooling on the floor of a steel mill. The temperature of the surroundings is 110°F. Omitting the surface in contact with the floor, determine the rate of heat radiation when the billet temperature is 1000°F.

1457. A room with a heated floor has a ceiling through which heat can leak. (a) Sketch a radiation network for the system when the walls are insulated and find an expression for the net radiative heat transfer. (b) If all surface temperatures are known, sketch a radiation network and outline a method to find the net radiative heat transfer to each surface.

1458. What surface area must be provided by the filament of a 100-W evacuated light globe where $t = 2482°C$ and $\varepsilon = 0.38$ for the filament? Assume the ambient temperature to be 25.6°C. *Ans.* 0.806 cm².

1459. A manufacturer of electrical roaster ovens decided to change the oven cover from aluminum to a colorful porcelain enamel finish for marketing reasons. These data are known: surface area of the cover is 1807 cm²; when 592 W of power are consumed, the aluminum cover is at 204.4°C; environmental temperature is 22.2°C; respective emissivities, ε (aluminum) $= 0.08$, ε (porcelain cover) $= 0.89$; assume the convection losses to be the same in each case. If the cover temperature of the porcelain cover is 204.4°C, what power is consumed in steady-state operation?

1460. Determine the net heat transferred by radiation from a 9-ft² hot plate to a cold plate of equal size that are parallel to one another, and 20 ft apart, for the following situations: (a) hot plate, oxidized steel at 700°F; cold plate, dull brass at 175°F; (b) hot plate, cleaned stainless steel at 1000°F; cold plate, aluminum foil at 212°F; (c) hot plate, asbestos paper at 300°F; cold plate, glass at 70°F. *Ans.* (a) 2,863 Btu/hr.

1461. A 14-in. steel pipe (15-in. OD), with a 3-in., 85%-magnesia lagging, is concentrically suspended in a 7-ft diam concrete tunnel. For the outer insulation surface, $t = 125°F$, and the film coefficient of free convection, excluding radiation, is 1.8. If the ambient air and concrete surface temperatures are 80°F, find (a) the equivalent film coefficient for radiation and (b) the total heat lost from 500 ft of piping.

Ans. (a) 1.48 Btu/hr-ft²-°F, (b) 406,500 Btu/hr.

1462. What surface area must be provided by the filament of a 100-W evacuated light globe where $t = 4500°F$ and $\varepsilon = 0.38$ for the filament? Assume the ambient temperature to be 78°F. Find the corresponding film coefficient for radiation.

Ans. $h_r = 89.4$ Btu/hr-ft²-°F.

1463. A 30×40-ft room is heated by means of hot water coils laid in the concrete floor. The ceiling is 9 ft high and painted white. The respective surface temperatures are 82°F floor, 60°F ceiling. If the connecting walls are nonconducting but reradiating, find the net exchange of radiant energy between floor and ceiling.

1464. A 20×30-ft furnace floor is lined with refractory brick. The vertical distance from the floor to the water tubes is 22 ft, and the walls are nonconducting but reradiating. For the tube surfaces, $t = 525°F$ and the emissivity is $\varepsilon = 0.93$; the floor surface temperature is 2250°F. Find the amount of radiant energy received by the tubes.

Ans. 26,000,000 Btu/hr.

1465. Dry steam at 600°F is flowing through a 4-in. extra heavy steel pipe (4.5-in. OD, 3.82-in. ID). The pipe is covered with 2 in. of asbestos insulation ($k = 0.86$, Btu-in./hr-ft^2-°F). The surroundings are at 100°F. For the inner pipe surface, $h_i = 98$ Btu/hr-ft^2-°F; for the outer insulation surface, $\varepsilon = 0.88$; and $h_o = 2.5$ Btu/hr-ft^2-°F, which includes radiation and convection. On the basis of outer surface, find (a) the heat per square foot, (b) the equivalent radiation film coefficient, (c) the convection film coefficient.

Ans. (a) 140.8 Btu/hr-ft^2, (b) 1.228 Btu/hr-ft^2-°F, (c) 1.272 Btu/hr-ft^2-°F.

1466. (a) Find the heat loss by radiation only from an 8-in. diameter, polished steel sphere whose outer surface temperature is maintained at 750°F by means of internal electrical heating coils. The sphere is suspended in a large room wherein the environmental temperature is 50°F. (b) What will be the heat loss if the surface is oxidized?

Ans. (b) 3940 Btu/hr.

UNITS AND DIMENSIONAL ANALYSIS

1467. Equation (b) § 19.36, *Text*, is empirical for heat transfer by free convection from vertical plates, that is, $h_c = 0.27 \, \Delta t^{0.25}$ where the units of h_c are Btu/hr-ft^2-°F. If h_c is expressed on the SI basis in W/m^2 K, what should the constant be in place of 0.27 leaving Δt in °F? If Δt is also changed to K?

1468. The flow resistance R per unit area encountered by a fluid moving through a closed duct depends principally upon the fluid properties of density ρ, absolute viscosity μ, and velocity v; also, the duct diameter D. In mathematical form, $R = K\rho^a \mu^b v^c D^d$, where K is a dimensionless proportionality constant and a, b, c, and d are constant exponents. Through dimensional analysis, show that $R = f\rho v^2$ where $f = C\mathbf{R}^{-b}$, a dimensionless quantity called the coefficient of friction; C is a constant and $\mathbf{R}$ the Reynolds number.

1469. The same as problem 1468 except that the velocity of sound a is included for which the assumption is $R = K\rho^a \mu^b v^c D^d a^e$.

Now demonstrate that the coefficient of friction f will depend upon the Mach number $\mathbf{M}$ as well as the Reynolds number $\mathbf{R}$.

1470. The kinetic energy that a body possesses is a function of the mass m and the velocity v of the body; also, of the standard gravity acceleration $\mathbf{k}$. In mathematical parlance, $K = \phi(m^a v^b k^c)$. Through dimensional analysis, determine the values of the exponents, and find an expression for kinetic energy.

1471. The water resistance (drag) R on the submarine Nautilus is a function of its length L, velocity v of the ship, the viscosity μ, and density ρ of the water in which it moves. Determine dimensionless groups that could be used to organize test data.

FORCED CONVECTION

1472. Steam at 30 bar, 240°C flows through a 10.2-cm steel pipe (9.73-cm ID) at 2200 m/min. Calculate the film coefficient for the inside surface of the pipe; for the steel, $k = 45$ W/m K.

1473. The same as problem 1472 except that the steam is at 1000 psia and 900°F, and the velocity is 12,000 fpm through a 10-in. steel pipe (9.75-in. ID).

Ans. 452 Btu/hr-ft^2-°F.

1474. The main trunk duct of an air conditioning system is rectangular in cross section (16×30-in.) and has air at 15 psia and 40°F flowing through it with a velocity of 1400 fpm. Find h_i.

Ans. 3.69 Btu/hr-ft^2-°F.

1475. Air at 15 psia and 200°F is flowing through a 3-in. steel pipe (3.50-in. OD, 3.067-in. ID) which is covered with a 3-in. layer of asbestos. The air velocity is 150 fps, and the film coefficient for the outer surface of the asbestos is $h_o = 8.0$ Btu/hr-ft^2-°F; ambient temperature = 80°F. Find (a) h_i, (b) U_i, U_o, (c) heat for 1-ft length.

Ans. (a) 20, (b) 0.54, 0.174 Btu/hr-ft^2-°F, (c) 52 Btu/hr.

1476. A double-pipe, counterflow heat exchanger contains a 1.5-in. steel pipe (1.90-in. OD, 1.61-in. ID) inside of a 2.5-in. steel pipe (2.88-in. OD, 2.47-in. ID). Hot oil with properties similar to those of oil C, Fig. 19/20, Appendix C, is flowing through the inner pipe with a velocity of 3.5 fps and a bulk temperature of 200°F; also, $c_p = 0.52$ Btu/lb-°R, $k =$

0.96 Btu-in. per hr-ft^2-°F. Cold oil with properties similar to those of oil *B*, Fig. 19/20, is flowing through the annular space with a velocity of 12.5 fps and a bulk temperature of 80°F; also, $c_p = 0.52$ Btu/lb-°R, $k = 0.94$ Btu-in./hr-ft^2-°F. (a) Find the film coefficients for the inner and outer surfaces of the inner pipe. (b) What is *U* for the inner pipe?

1477. The same as problem 1476 except that the bulk temperatures of the hot and cold oils are 160°F and 65°F, respectively.

Ans. (a) 44.2, (b) 157, (c) 51.6 Btu/hr-ft^2-°F.

1478. An oil heater, with No. 16 BWG steel tubes (0.75-in. OD, 0.620-in. ID) and effective length of 12 ft/pass, receives oil *D*, Fig. 19/20, Appendix C, at 70°F. The oil flows through the tubes with an average velocity of 4 fps; condensing saturated steam at 15 psia surrounds the tubes. For the oil, $c_p = 0.5$ Btu/lb-°F. If the heater has two passes with 300 tubes per pass, find (a) the temperature of the oil at the end of first pass, (b) the exit oil temperature, and (c) the amount of steam condensed each hour.

1479. Flue gas at 15 psia and 600°F is flowing across a single tube of an economizer with a velocity of 20 fps. For the tube, OD is 4.5 in. and surface temperature is $t_o = 300$°F. Assume the gas to have thermal properties similar to those of dry air, and find (a) the outer surface film coefficient for convection only, (b) the convected heat for 10 ft of pipe length, and (c) the percentage increase in the film coeffi-

cient if the gas velocity is increased 30 per cent.

Ans. (a) 4.95 Btu/hr-ft^2-°F, (b) 17,550 Btu/hr, (c) 16.55%.

FREE CONVECTION

1480. A single, 10.16-cm steel pipe, whose OD is 11.43 cm, has an outer surface temperature of 149°C. The horizontal pipe is located in a large room where the ambient temperature is 25.6°C and the barometer is standard. Determine the total heat (free convection and radiation) for 10 m of pipe length. *Ans.* 7920 W.

1481. A metal cylinder (2 ft long, 3 in. diameter) initially at 150°F is placed vertically in a tank of 70°F water at rest. Determine the film coefficient and the rate of heat transfer at the time of immersion. Evaluate the film properties at 110°F (average of the two known temperatures).

1482. Atmospheric air at 14.7 psia, 80°F surrounds a 12 × 12-in. metal plate; at a given instant, the plate temperature is 200°F. Find the film coefficient and the heat flux from each side, if the position of the plate is (a) horizontal, (b) vertical.

1483. Water at 100°F is to be heated by immersing in it a 5-ft Calrod electrical heating element (0.5-in. diameter rod) in a horizontal position. What must be the rod temperature when the electrical input (heating rate) is to be 1.5 kW?

Note: There are not 1483 problems in this book (see blank numbers at the end of each chapter); there are well over 1350.

Appendixes

139

CONTENTS OF APPENDIX C

APPENDIX A:
Selected Tables

TABLE I Variable Specific Heats at Low Pressure

All equations derived from spectrographic data: $c_v = c_p - R$; $C_v = C_p - 1.986$. See Item B 1 for values of R.

(a) This value is derived from Spencer and Justice[2.2]; (b) from Spencer and Flannagan[2.3]; (c) from Chipman and Fontana[2.6]; (d) from Sweigert and Beardsley[2.1]; (e) from Spencer.[2.7]

Substance (Temp. range)	M (Mol. mass)	Btu/lb-°R	Btu/pmole-°R
(a) Air (500–2700°R)	28.97	$c_p = 0.219 + 0.342T/10^4 - 0.293T^2/10^8$	$C_p = 6.36 + 9.92T/10^4 - 8.25T^2/10^8$
(b) SO_2, sul. diox. (540–3400°R)	64.07	$c_p = 0.1875 + 0.0944T/10^4 - 1.336 \times 10^4/T^2$	$C_p = 11.89 + 6.05T/10^4 - 85.6 \times 10^4/T^2$
(b) NH_3, ammonia (540–1800°R)	17.03	$c_p = 0.363 + 2.57T/10^4 - 1.319T^2/10^8$	$C_p = 6.19 + 43.8T/10^4 - 22.47T^2/10^8$
(c) H_2, hydrogen (540–4000°R)	2.016	$c_p = 2.857 + 2.867T/10^4 + 9.92/T^{1/2}$	$C_p = 5.76 + 5.78T/10^4 + 20/T^{1/2}$
(d) O_2, oxygen (540–5000°R)	32	$c_p = 0.36 - 5.375/T^{1/2} + 47.8/T$	$C_p = 11.515 - 172/T^{1/2} + 1530/T$
(d) N_2, nitrogen (540–9000°R)	28.016	$c_p = 0.338 - 123.8/T + 4.14 \times 10^4/T^2$	$C_p = 9.47 - 3470/T + 116 \times 10^4/T^2$
(d) CO, carb. mon. (540–9000°R)	28.01	$c_p = 0.338 - 117.5/T + 3.82 \times 10^4/T^2$	$C_p = 9.46 - 3290/T + 107 \times 10^4/T^2$
(d) H_2O, steam (540–5400°R)	18.016	$c_p = 1.102 - 33.1/T^{1/2} + 416/T$	$C_p = 19.86 - 597/T^{1/2} + 7500/T$
(d) CO_2, carb. diox. (540–6300°R)	44.01	$c_p = 0.368 - 148.4/T + 3.2 \times 10^4/T^2$	$C_p = 16.2 - 6530/T + 141 \times 10^4/T^2$
(e) CH_4, methane (540–2700°R) (d) (540–1500°R)	16.04	$c_p = 0.211 + 6.25T/10^4 - 8.28T^2/10^8$ $c_p = 0.282 + 4.598T/10^4$	$C_p = 3.38 + 100.2T/10^4 - 132.7T^2/10^8$ $C_p = 4.52 + 0.00737T$
(b) C_2H_4, ethylene (540–2700°R) (d) (350–1100°R)	28.04	$c_p = 0.0965 + 5.78T/10^4 - 9.97T^2/10^8$ $c_p = 0.151 + 4.2T/10^4$	$C_p = 2.706 + 162T/10^4 - 279.6T^2/10^8$ $C_p = 4.23 + 0.01177T$
(e) C_2H_6, ethane (540–2700°R) (d) (400–1100°R)	30.07	$c_p = 0.0731 + 7.08T/10^4 - 11.3T^2/10^8$ $c_p = 0.1334 + 5.44T/10^4$	$C_p = 2.195 + 212.7T/10^4 - 340T^2/10^8$ $C_p = 4.01 + 0.01636T$
(e) C_4H_{10}, n-butane (540–2700°R)	58.12	$c_p = 0.075 + 6.94T/10^4 - 11.77T^2/10^8$	$C_p = 4.36 + 403T/10^4 - 683T^2/10^8$
(e) C_3H_8, propane (540–2700°R)	44.09	$c_p = 0.0512 + 7.27T/10^4 - 12.32T^2/10^8$	$C_p = 2.258 + 320T/10^4 - 543T^2/10^8$
(b) C_2H_2, acetylene (500–2300°R)	26.04	$c_p = 0.459 + 0.937T/10^4 - 2.89 \times 10^4/T^2$	$C_p = 11.94 + 24.37T/10^4 - 75.2 \times 10^4/T^2$
(d) C_8H_{18}, octane (400–1100°R)	114.22	$c_p = 0.0694 + 5.27T/10^4$	$C_p = 7.92 + 0.0601T$

TABLE II Compressed Water

Extracted with permission from the ASME *Steam Tables*, published by the American Society of Mechanical Engineers. The ASME S.T. contain many more states of compressed liquid. See also Item B 15.

Absolute Pressure (sat. °F)	Temperature:						
	32°F	100°F	200°F	300°F	400°F	500°F	600°F
200 (381.8)							
v =	0.01601	0.01612	0.01663	0.01744			
h =	0.59	68.52	168.51	269.96			
s =	−0.0000	0.1294	0.2938	0.4369			
600 (486.20)							
v =	0.01599	0.01610	0.01660	0.01741	0.0186		
h =	1.8	69.58	169.42	270.70	375.49		
s =	0.0000	0.1292	0.2933	0.4362	0.5657		
1000 (544.58)							
v =	0.01597	0.01608	0.01658	0.01738	0.01855	0.02036	
h =	3.00	70.63	170.33	271.44	375.96	487.79	
s =	0.0001	0.1289	0.2928	0.4355	0.5647	0.6876	
2000 (635.80)							
v =	0.01591	0.01603	0.01653	0.01731	0.01844	0.02014	0.02332
h =	5.99	73.26	172.60	273.32	377.19	487.53	614.48
s =	0.0002	0.1283	0.2916	0.4337	0.5621	0.6834	0.8091
3000 (695.33)							
v =	0.01586	0.01599	0.01648	0.01724	0.01833	0.01995	0.02276
h =	8.95	75.88	174.88	275.22	378.47	487.52	610.08
s =	0.0002	0.1277	0.2904	0.4320	0.5597	0.6796	0.8009

TABLE VII Conductivities

The units of $k*$ are Btu-in./ft^2-hr-°F, at atmospheric pressure; k for a solid changes little with pressures below 200 psi, but significant changes of k for liquids and vapors may accompany pressure changes. The values are from various sources, here selected largely from McAdams[19.1]. Straight-line interpolations are permissible between the temperatures given. Nearby extrapolations may give satisfactory results.

Material	Temp. °F	$k*$	Material	Temp. °F	$k*$
Solids			*Liquids (continued)*		
Aluminum	32	1400	Kerosene	68	1.03
	392	1490		167	0.97
Aluminum piston alloy	0-400	1290*	Petroleum oil,	68	1.0
			average		
Asbestos, 29 lb./ft.^{3}	−200	0.865	Sodium	212	590
				410	550
Asbestos, corrugated, 4	300	0.828	Sulfur dioxide	5	1.53
plies/in.				68	1.33
Bearing metal, white	68	164			
Brickwork, low density	68	5	Water	32	4.1
Cast iron, grey	0-400	360*		200	4.7
Copper, pure	32	2690*		300	4.75
	212	2616		620	3.3
Concrete, 1-4 dry		5.4			
Cork Board	86	0.3	*Gases*		
Glass window		3.6–7.4	Air	−148	0.109
Gold	64	2028		32	0.168
Graphite	32	1165		572	0.312
	392	910	Ammonia	−58	0.107
Gypsum	68	3		32	0.151
Gypsum plaster		3.3		212	0.23
Magnesia (85%)	100–300	0.43*	Carbon dioxide	−58	0.077
Mineral wool (glass and	86	0.27		32	0.101
rock wool)				212	0.154
Monel	68	242	Freon F12	32	0.057
				212	0.096
Plaster on wood lath,		2.5	Hydrogen	32	1.06
$\frac{3}{4}$-in. total thickness				572	2.04
Steel	0-400	312*			
Wallboard, insulating	70	0.34	Nitrogen	32	0.167
Wood, balsa	86	0.32		572	0.306
Oak, maple	59	1.44	Oxygen	32	0.17
White pine	59	1.05		212	0.226
			Steam	212	0.163
Liquids				932	0.394
Ammonia	68	3.13	Sulfur dioxide	32	0.06
	140	3.48		212	0.0827

* Average for temperature range given. Multiply given value by 0.14419 to obtain W/m-K units.

TABLE VIII Conductances and Transmittances

The units of k/L and U are Btu per hr-ft^2-°F. These values are intended as representative, suggesting the order of magnitude in the various situations. They are not to be used in actual design unless it is known that they apply. Since the values of U are not particularized, the reference area is not meaningful. However, if these values are used for problem work, let the reference area be the internal tube or pipe area in such cases. (a) From McAdams[19.1]. (b) From ASHRAE[19.3].

Construction and Materials		$\dfrac{k}{L}$	U
Air space, $\frac{3}{4}$ in. or more in width	(b)	1.10	
Air space $\frac{3}{4}$ in. or more in width, bounded by aluminum foil	(b)	0.46	
Ammonia condenser, 2 × 3-in. double pipe, water inside at $v = 6$ fps, NH$_3$ in annular space, $\Delta t_m = 3.5$°F, clean	(a)		320
Asphalt shingles	(b)	6.50	
Brick wall, 8 in. thick, plaster inside	(b)		0.46
Brick veneer, frame wall with wood sheathing, $\frac{1}{2}$-in. plaster on gypsum lath	(b)		0.27
Brick veneer as above, plus 2-in. mineral wool insulation	(b)		0.097
Concrete blocks, 8 in., hollow gravel aggregate	(b)	1.00	
Feedwater heaters, closed; steam condensers, free convection	(a)		50–200
Feedwater heaters, closed; steam condensers, forced convection	(a)		150–800
Insulating board, $\frac{1}{2}$ in. thick	(b)	0.66	
Heat exchanger, air in tube, condensing steam outside tubes (on outside surface area)	(a)		8
Heat exchanger, cooling oil with water in tubes			50
Steam condensing, to air, free convection	(a)		1–2
Steam condensing, to air, forced convection	(a)		2–10
Steam condensing, to boiling water, free convection	(a)		300–800
Steam condensing, to liquid oil, free convection	(a)		10–30
Steam condensing, to liquid oil, forced convection	(a)		20–60
Superheaters, steam, free convection	(a)		1.6–2
Superheaters, steam, forced convection	(a)		2–6
Water to gas and liquid to gas (hot water radiators, air coolers, economizers, steam boilers), free convection	(a)		1–3
Water to gas and liquid to gas (hot water radiators, air coolers, economizers, steam boilers, forced convection	(a)		2–10
Water to water, free convection	(a)		25–60
Water to water, forced convection	(a)		150–300

TABLE IX Configuration (Space) Factors for Radiation Equation*

Case	Configuration of Surface	Area, A	F_{12}
1	Infinite parallel planes.	Either	1
2	Completely enclosed body 1, small compared with enclosing body 2.	A_1	1
3	Completely enclosed body 1, large compared with enclosing body 2.	A_1	1
4	Concentric spheres or infinite cylinders	A_1	1
5	Element dA and rectangular surface above and parallel to it, with one corner of rectangle contained in normal to dA.	dA	Given in Fig. 19/10.
6	Two parallel circular disks of same diameter with centers on same normal to their planes, or	Either	Given in Fig. 19/11.
7	Two equal rectangles in parallel planes and directly opposite one another.	Either	Given in Fig. 19/12.
8	Two perpendicular rectangles with a common edge.	A_1	Given in Fig. 19/13.

* Hottel[19.9].

TABLE X Total Normal Emittances*

Material		Temperature of Radiating Body, °F (S = Solar rad.)	Emittance
Aluminum, oxidized	(a)	100–1000	0.11–0.18
Aluminum foil	(b)	212	0.087
with 1 coat linseed oil paint	(b)	212	0.561
Aluminum paint			
26% Al, 27% lacquer	(b)	212	0.3
Asbestos paper	(b)	100–700	0.93–0.945
Brass, dull plate	(b)	120–660	0.22
Brick, red	(a)	S	0.70
silica	(a)	2500	0.84
refractory, black and chrome	(a)	200–1000–2000	0.92–0.97–0.98
Chromium, polished	(b)	100–2000	0.08–0.36
Concrete	(a)	2500–S	0.63–0.65
Galvanized sheet iron			
bright	(b)	82	0.23
oxidized	(b)	75	0.28
Glass	(b)	72	0.94
Lampblack, rough deposit	(b)	212–932	0.84–0.78
Paint			
black	(a)	200–600–1000–S	0.92–0.95–0.97–0.90
green	(a)	200–600–1000–S	0.93–0.90–0.80–0.50
white	(a)	200–600–1000–S	0.92–0.84–0.68–0.30
Stainless steel 301, cleaned	(b)	450–1740	0.57–0.55
Steel, oxidized	(a)	100–1000	0.79–0.79
polished	(a)	100–1000–S	0.07–0.14–0.45
rolled sheet	(b)	70	0.66
rough plate	(b)	100–700	0.94–0.97
Water	(b)	32–212	0.95–0.963

* Selected values from (a) Croft[19.27] and (b) McAdams[19.1].

APPENDIX B:
Properties of
Selected Substances

ITEM B 1   Gas Constants; Specific Heats at Low Pressure

For each substance, the specific gas constant was computed from $R = 1545.32/M$ ft-lb/lb-°R. Instantaneous values of C_p at the standard temperature of 77°F were taken from the literature, from which other values were computed as follows: $c_p = C_p/M$, $c_v = c_p - \bar{R}$, $\bar{R} = 1.986$ Btu/pmole-°R, $k = C_p/C_v$, $c_v = c_p - R$.

Notes. A number of values are brought up to date, principally with data in JANAF,[0.22] but in most cases the change is not of engineering significance. (a) Values at 100°F from Keenan and Kaye Gas Tables. (b) Molal specific heat of all monatomic gases is taken as $C_p = 4.97$ Btu/pmole-°R. (c) From Rossini et al.[0.1,0.2] (d) McBride et al.[0.23] (e) JANAF.[0.22] There is a movement under way to change the basis of molecular masses from $O_2 = 32$ exactly to $C = 12$. Most available data are on the old basis. All molecular masses in this book are for $O_2 = 32$.

Gas		M, lb/pmole	c_p, Btu/lb-°R	c_v, Btu/lb-°R	c_p, kJ/kg-K	c_v, kJ/kg-K	$k = c_p/c_v$	R, ft-lb/lb-°R	R, J/kg-K
Argon (A)	(b)	39.950	0.1244	0.0747	0.5215	0.3132	1.666	38.68	208.17
Helium (He)	(b)	4.003	1.241	0.745	5.2028	3.1233	1.666	386.04	2077.67
Mercury (Hg)	(b)	200.61	0.0248	0.0148	0.1039	0.0624	1.666	7.703	41.45
Neon (Ne)	(b)	20.183	0.246	0.1476	1.0313	0.6188	1.666	76.57	412.10
Xenon (Xe)	(b)	131.30	0.0378	0.0227	0.1585	0.0952	1.666	11.77	63.34
Air	(a)	28.970	0.24	0.1714	1.0062	0.7186	1.4	53.342	287.08
Carbon monoxide (CO)		28.01	0.2487	0.1778	1.0426	0.7454	1.399	55.170	296.92
Chlorine (Cl$_2$)		70.914	0.1144	0.0864	0.4796	0.3622	1.324	21.791	117.28
Fluorine (F$_2$)	(d)	38.00	0.197	0.1447	0.8259	0.6066	1.36	40.67	218.88
Hydrogen (H$_2$)		2.016	3.419	2.434	14.3338	10.2043	1.40	766.54	4125.52
Hydroxyl (OH)	(e)	17.008	0.421	0.3031	1.7650	1.2708	1.383	90.858	488.99
Nitric oxide (NO)		30.008	0.2378	0.1716	0.9969	0.7194	1.386	51.497	277.15
Nitrogen (N$_2$)		28.016	0.2484	0.1775	1.0414	0.7442	1.399	55.158	296.86
Oxygen (O$_2$)	(e)	32	0.2194	0.1573	0.9198	0.6595	1.395	48.291	259.90
Carbon dioxide (CO$_2$)		44.010	0.2016	0.1565	0.8452	0.6561	1.288	35.11	188.96
Hydrogen sulfide (H$_2$S)	(e)	34.086	0.2397	0.1799	1.0049	0.7542	1.321	45.33	243.96
Nitrogen dioxide (NO$_2$)	(e)	46.008	0.1921	0.1489	0.8054	0.6242	1.29	33.59	180.78
Nitrous oxide (N$_2$O)	(e)	44.016	0.2097	0.1646	0.8791	0.6901	1.274	35.11	188.96
Ozone (O$_3$)	(e)	48	0.1954	0.154	0.8192	0.6456	1.269	32.194	173.27
Sulfur dioxide (SO$_2$)	(e)	64.07	0.1487	0.1177	0.6234	0.4934	1.263	24.12	129.81
Water vapor (H$_2$O)	(a)	18.016	0.4454	0.3352	1.8673	1.4053	1.329	85.77	461.61
Acetylene (C$_2$H$_2$)	(e)	26.036	0.4048	0.3285	1.6971	1.3772	1.232	59.35	319.42
Ammonia (NH$_3$)	(e)	17.032	0.499	0.382	2.0920	1.6015	1.304	90.73	488.31
n-Butane (C$_4$H$_{10}$)		58.120	0.4007	0.3665	1.6799	1.5365	1.093	26.59	143.11
Cyanogen (C$_2$N$_2$)	(e)	52.038	0.261	0.2228	1.0942	0.9341	1.172	29.7	159.84
Ethane (C$_2$H$_6$)		30.068	0.4186	0.3526	1.7549	1.4782	1.187	51.39	276.58
Ethylene (C$_2$H$_4$)	(e)	28.052	0.3654	0.2946	1.5319	1.2351	1.240	55.09	296.49
Hydrazine (N$_2$H$_4$)	(e)	32.048	0.393	0.33	1.6476	1.3834	1.195	48.22	259.52
Hydrogen peroxide (C$_2$H$_2$)	(e)	34.016	0.303	0.2446	1.2703	1.0225	1.239	45.43	244.50
Methane (CH$_4$)	(e)	16.043	0.5099	0.3861	2.1377	1.6187	1.321	96.33	518.45
Methanol (CH$_4$O)	(c)	32.042	0.336	0.274	1.4086	1.1487	1.226	48.23	259.57
n-Octane (C$_8$H$_{18}$)		114.224	0.3952	0.3778	1.6568	1.5839	1.046	13.53	72.82
Propane (C$_3$H$_8$)		44.094	0.3985	0.3535	1.6707	1.4820	1.127	35.05	188.64

ITEM B 2 Properties of Air at Low Pressures (one pound)

Reproduced from Keenan and Kaye, *Gas Tables*, with permission of authors and publisher, John Wiley

T°R	h Btu/lb	p_r	u Btu/lb	v_r	ϕ Btu/lb-°R	T°R	h Btu/lb	p_r	u Btu/lb	v_r	ϕ Btu/lb-°R
360	85.97	0.3363	61.29	396.6	0.50369	1460	358.63	50.34	258.54	10.743	0.84704
380	90.75	0.4061	64.70	346.6	0.51663	1480	363.89	53.04	262.44	10.336	0.85062
400	95.53	0.4858	68.11	305.0	0.52890	1500	369.17	55.86	266.34	9.948	0.85416
420	100.32	0.5760	71.52	270.1	0.54058	1520	374.47	58.78	270.26	9.578	0.85767
440	105.11	0.6776	74.93	240.6	0.55172	1540	379.77	61.83	274.20	9.226	0.86113
460	109.90	0.7913	78.36	215.33	0.56235	1560	385.08	65.00	278.13	8.890	0.86456
480	114.69	0.9182	81.77	193.65	0.57255	1580	390.40	68.30	282.09	8.569	0.86794
500	119.48	1.0590	85.20	174.90	0.58233	1600	395.74	71.73	286.06	8.263	0.87130
520	124.27	1.2147	88.62	158.58	0.59173	1620	401.09	75.29	290.04	7.971	0.87462
537	128.10	1.3593	91.53	146.34	0.59945	1640	406.45	78.99	294.03	7.691	0.87791
540	129.06	1.3860	92.04	144.32	0.60078						
						1660	411.82	82.83	298.02	7.424	0.88116
560	133.86	1.5742	95.47	131.78	0.60950	1680	417.20	86.82	302.04	7.168	0.88439
580	138.66	1.7800	98.90	120.70	0.61793	1700	422.59	90.95	306.06	6.924	0.88758
600	143.47	2.005	102.34	110.88	0.62607	1720	428.00	95.24	310.09	6.690	0.89074
620	148.28	2.249	105.78	102.12	0.63395	1740	433.41	99.69	314.13	6.465	0.89387
640	153.09	2.514	109.21	94.30	0.64159						
						1760	438.83	104.30	318.18	6.251	0.89697
660	157.92	2.801	112.67	87.27	0.64902	1780	444.26	109.08	322.24	6.045	0.90003
680	162.73	3.111	116.12	80.96	0.65621	1800	449.71	114.03	326.32	5.847	0.90308
700	167.56	3.446	119.58	75.25	0.66321	1820	455.17	119.16	330.40	5.658	0.90609
720	172.39	3.806	123.04	70.07	0.67002	1840	460.63	124.47	334.50	5.476	0.90908
740	177.23	4.193	126.51	65.38	0.67665						
						1860	466.12	129.95	338.61	5.302	0.91203
760	182.08	4.607	129.99	61.10	0.68312	1880	471.60	135.64	342.73	5.134	0.91497
780	186.94	5.051	133.47	57.20	0.68942	1900	477.09	141.51	346.85	4.974	0.91788
800	191.81	5.526	136.97	53.63	0.69558	1920	482.60	147.59	350.98	4.819	0.92076
820	196.69	6.033	140.47	50.35	0.70160	1940	488.12	153.87	355.12	4.670	0.92362
840	201.56	6.573	143.98	47.34	0.70747						
						1960	493.64	160.37	359.28	4.527	0.92645
860	206.46	7.149	147.50	44.57	0.71323	1980	499.17	167.07	363.43	4.390	0.92926
880	211.35	7.761	151.02	42.01	0.71886	2000	504.71	174.00	367.61	4.258	0.93205
900	216.26	8.411	154.57	39.64	0.72438	2020	510.26	181.16	371.79	4.130	0.93481
920	221.18	9.102	158.12	37.44	0.72979	2040	515.82	188.54	375.98	4.008	0.93756
940	226.11	9.834	161.68	35.41	0.73509						
						2060	521.39	196.16	380.18	3.890	0.94026
960	231.06	10.610	165.26	33.52	0.74030	2080	526.97	204.02	384.39	3.777	0.94296
980	236.02	11.430	168.83	31.76	0.74540	2100	532.55	212.1	388.60	3.667	0.94564
1000	240.98	12.298	172.43	30.12	0.75042	2150	546.54	233.5	399.17	3.410	0.95222
1020	245.97	13.215	176.04	28.59	0.75536	2200	560.59	256.6	409.78	3.176	0.95868
1040	250.95	14.182	179.66	27.17	0.76019						
						2250	574.69	281.4	420.46	2.961	0.96501
1060	255.96	15.203	183.29	25.82	0.76496	2300	588.82	308.1	431.16	2.765	0.97123
1080	260.97	16.278	186.93	24.58	0.76964	2350	603.00	336.8	441.91	2.585	0.97732
1100	265.99	17.413	190.58	23.40	0.77426	2400	617.22	367.6	452.70	2.419	0.98331
1120	271.03	18.604	194.25	22.30	0.77880	2450	631.48	400.5	463.54	2.266	0.98919
1140	276.08	19.858	197.94	21.27	0.78326						
						2500	645.78	435.7	474.40	2.125	0.99497
1160	281.14	21.18	201.63	20.293	0.78767	2550	660.12	473.3	485.31	1.9956	1.00064
1180	286.21	22.56	205.33	19.377	0.79201	2600	674.49	513.5	496.26	1.8756	1.00623
1200	291.30	24.01	209.05	18.514	0.79628	2650	688.90	556.3	507.25	1.7646	1.01172
1220	296.41	25.53	212.78	17.700	0.80050	2700	703.35	601.9	518.26	1.6617	1.01712
1240	301.52	27.13	216.53	16.932	0.80466						
						2750	717.83	650.4	529.31	1.5662	1.02244
1260	306.65	28.80	220.28	16.205	0.80876	2800	732.33	702.0	540.40	1.4775	1.02767
1280	311.79	30.55	244.05	15.518	0.81280	2850	746.88	756.7	551.52	1.3951	1.03282
1300	316.94	32.39	227.83	14.868	0.81680	2900	761.45	814.8	562.66	1.3184	1.03788
1320	322.11	34.31	231.63	14.253	0.82075	2950	776.05	876.4	573.84	1.2469	1.04288
1340	327.29	36.31	235.43	13.670	0.82464						
						3000	790.68	941.4	585.04	1.1803	1.04779
1360	332.48	38.41	239.25	13.118	0.82848	3500	938.40	1829.3	698.48	0.7087	1.09332
1380	337.68	40.59	243.08	12.593	0.83229	4000	1088.26	3280	814.06	0.4518	1.13334
1400	342.90	42.88	246.93	12.095	0.83604	4500	1239.86	5521	931.39	0.3019	1.16905
1420	348.14	45.26	250.79	11.622	0.83975	5000	1392.87	8837	1050.12	0.20959	1.20129
1440	353.37	47.75	254.66	11.172	0.84341	6000	1702.29	20120	1291.00	0.11047	1.25769
						6500	1858.44	28974	1412.87	0.08310	1.28268

ITEM B 3 Carbon Dioxide Gas at Low Pressures (per p-mole)

Reproduced from Keenan and Kaye, *Gas Tables*, with permission of authors and publisher, John Wiley.

$T°R$	$\bar{h}$	p_r	$\bar{u}$	v_r	$\bar{\phi}$	$T°R$	$\bar{h}$	p_r	$\bar{u}$	v_r	$\bar{\phi}$
300	2108.2	0.013705	1512.4	234900	46.353	1380	13101.0	21.33	10360.5	694.3	60.949
320	2256.6	0.017440	1621.1	196920	46.832	1400	13344.7	23.30	10564.5	644.8	61.124
340	2407.3	0.02196	1732.1	166170	47.289	1420	13589.1	25.43	10769.2	599.3	61.298
360	2560.5	0.02738	1845.6	141090	47.728	1440	13834.5	27.72	10974.8	557.5	61.469
380	2716.4	0.03385	1961.8	120480	48.148	1460	14080.8	30.19	11181.4	518.9	61.639
400	2874.7	0.04153	2080.4	103360	48.555	1480	14328.0	32.86	11388.9	483.2	61.808
420	3035.7	0.05062	2201.7	89050	48.947	1500	14576.0	35.74	11597.2	450.4	61.974
440	3199.4	0.06131	2325.6	77000	49.329	1520	14824.9	38.83	11806.4	420.0	62.138
460	3365.7	0.07386	2452.2	66830	49.698	1540	15074.7	42.16	12016.5	392.0	62.302
480	3534.7	0.08852	2581.5	58190	50.058	1560	15325.3	45.74	12227.3	365.9	62.464
500	3706.2	0.10560	2713.3	50820	50.408	1580	15576.7	49.58	12439.0	342.0	62.624
520	3880.3	0.12541	2847.7	44500	50.750	1600	15829.0	53.70	12651.6	319 7	62.783
537	4030.2	0.14471	2963.8	39838	51.032	1620	16081.9	58.13	12864.8	299.0	62.939
540	4056.8	0.14833	2984.4	39070	51.082	1640	16335.7	62.87	13078.9	279.9	63.095
560	4235.8	0.17474	3123.7	34390	51.408	1660	16590.2	67.95	13293.7	262.2	63.250
580	4417.2	0.2051	3265.4	30340	51.726	1680	16845.5	73.39	13509.2	245.6	63.403
600	4600.9	0.2399	3409.4	26840	52.038	1700	17101.4	79.20	13725.4	230.3	63.555
620	4786.8	0.2797	3555.6	23780	52.343	1800	18391.5	114.84	14816.9	168.21	64.292
640	4974.9	0.3252	3704.0	21120	52.641	1900	19697.8	163.89	15924.7	124 41	64.999
660	5165.2	0.3769	3854.6	18796	52.934	2000	21018.7	230.5	17046.9	93.08	65.676
680	5357.6	0.4355	4007.2	16756	53.225	2100	22352.7	320.0	18182.4	70.42	66.327
700	5552.0	0.5019	4161.9	14968	53.503	2200	23699.0	438.7	19330.1	53.82	66.953
720	5748.4	0.5769	4318.6	13393	53.780	2300	25056.3	594.5	20488.8	41.52	67.557
740	5946.8	0.6615	4477.3	12004	54.051	2400	26424.0	797.0	21657.9	32.32	68.139
760	6147.0	0.7568	4637.9	10777	54.319	2500	27801.2	1057.9	22836.5	25.36	68.702
780	6349.1	0.8637	4800.1	9692	54.582	2600	29187.1	1391.2	24023.8	20.06	69.245
800	6552.9	0.9837	4964.2	8729	54.839	2700	30581.2	1813.1	25219.4	15.981	69.771
820	6758.3	1.1177	5129.9	7875	55.093	2800	31982.8	2344	26422.4	12.820	70.282
840	6965.7	1.2677	5297.6	7112	55.343	2900	33391.5	3007	27632.5	10.351	70.776
860	7174.7	1.4347	5466.9	6433	55.589	3000	34806.6	3828	28849.0	8.410	71.255
880	7385.3	1.6206	5637.7	5827	55.831	3100	36227.9	4841	30071.7	6.871	71.722
900	7597.6	1.8276	5810.3	5285	56.070	3200	37654.7	6082	31299.9	5.646	72.175
920	7811.4	2.057	5984.4	4799	56.305	3300	39086.7	7593	32533.3	4.664	72.616
940	8026.8	2.311	6160.1	4363	56.536	3400	40523.6	9425	33771.6	3.872	73.045
960	8243.8	2.594	6337.4	3972	56.765	3500	41965.2	11633	35014.7	3.229	73.462
980	8462.2	2.905	6516.1	3620	56.990	3600	43411.0	14282	36261.9	2.705	73.870
1000	8682.1	3.249	6696.2	3303	57.212	3700	44860.6	17445	37512.9	2.276	74.267
1020	8903.4	3.628	6877.8	3017	57.432	3800	46314.0	21200	38767.7	1.9229	74.655
1040	9126.2	4.046	7060.9	2759	57.647	3900	47771.0	25660	40026.1	1.6311	75.033
1060	9350.3	4.505	7245.3	2525	57.861	4000	49231.4	30910	41287.9	1.3887	75.404
1080	9575.8	5.010	7431.1	2313	58.072	4100	50695.1	37080	42553.0	1.1865	75.765
1100	9802.6	5.563	7618.1	2122	58.281	4200	52162.0	44310	43821.4	1.0172	76.119
1120	10030.6	6.170	7806.4	1948.0	58.485	4300	53632.1	52740	45092.9	0.8749	76.464
1140	10260.1	6.834	7996.2	1790.1	58.689	4400	55105.1	62550	46367.3	0.7548	76.803
1160	10490.6	7.560	8187.0	1646.5	58.889	4500	56581.0	73930	47644.6	0.6533	77.135
1180	10722.3	8.353	8379.0	1515.9	59.088	4600	58059.7	87080	48924.7	0.5669	77.460
1200	10955.3	9.219	8572.3	1396.8	59.283	4700	59541.1	102250	50207.5	0.4933	77.779
1220	11189.4	10.163	8766.6	1288.2	59.477	4800	61024.9	119640	51492.7	0.4305	78.091
1240	11424.6	11.188	8962.1	1189.1	59.668	4900	62511.3	139640	52780.5	0.3766	78.398
1260	11661.0	12.307	9158.8	1098.6	59.858	5000	64000.0	162480	54070.6	0.3303	78.698
1280	11898.4	13.525	9356.5	1015.6	60.044	5100	65490.9	188530	55363.0	0.2904	78.994
1300	12136.9	14.846	9555.3	939.9	60.229	5200	66984.0	218100	56657.5	0.2558	79.284
1320	12376.4	16.273	9755.0	870.4	60.412	5300	68479.1	251800	57954.0	0.2258	79.569
1340	12617.0	17.828	9955.9	806.7	60.593	5380	69676.5	281900	58992.5	0.2048	79.793
1360	12858.5	19.509	10157.7	748.1	60.772						

ITEM B 4   Carbon Monoxide at Low Pressures (per p-mole)

Reproduced from Keenan and Kaye, *Gas Tables*, with permission of authors and publisher, John Wiley.

$T°R$	$\bar{h}$	p_r	$\bar{u}$	v_r	$\bar{\phi}$	$T°R$	$\bar{h}$	p_r	$\bar{u}$	v_r	$\bar{\phi}$
300	2081.9	0.2834	1486.1	11357	43.223	1380	9796.6	65.12	7056.1	227.3	54.021
320	2220.9	0.3553	1585.4	9666	43.672	1400	9948.1	68.80	7167.9	218.4	54.129
340	2359.9	0.4393	1684.7	8305	44.093	1420	10100.0	72.64	7280.1	209.8	54.237
360	2498.8	0.5366	1783.9	7200	44.490	1440	10252.2	76.64	7392.6	201.6	54.344
380	2637.9	0.6484	1883.3	6290	44.866	1460	10404.8	80.81	7505.4	193.89	54.448
400	2776.9	0.7760	1982.6	5532	45.223	1480	10557.8	85.16	7618.7	186.48	54.552
420	2916.0	0.9205	2081.9	4897	45.563	1500	10711.1	89.69	7732.3	179.48	54.655
440	3055.0	1.0833	2181.2	4359	45.886	1520	10864.9	94.41	7846.4	172.78	54.757
460	3194.0	1.2657	2280.5	3900	46.194	1540	11019.0	99.32	7960.8	166.40	54.858
480	3333.0	1.4692	2379.8	3506	46.491	1560	11173.4	104.44	8075.4	160.30	54.958
500	3472.1	1.6950	2479.2	3166	46.775	1580	11328.2	109.76	8190.5	154.47	55.056
520	3611.2	1.9440	2578.6	2869	47.048	1600	11483.4	115.28	8306.0	148.92	55.154
537	3729.5	2.177	2663.1	2648	47.272	1620	11638.9	121.03	8421.8	143.66	55.251
540	3750.3	2.220	2677.9	2611	47.310	1640	11794.7	127.00	8537.9	138.57	55.347
560	3889.5	2.521	2777.4	2384	47.563	1660	11950.9	133.20	8654.4	133.72	55.441
580	4028.7	2.851	2876.9	2183	47.807	1680	12107.5	139.64	8771.2	129.12	55.535
600	4168.0	3.211	2976.5	2005	48.044	1700	12264.3	146.33	8888.3	124.68	55.628
620	4307.4	3.603	3076.2	1846.5	48.272	1800	13053.2	183.64	9478.6	105.19	56.078
640	4446.9	4.028	3175.9	1704.8	48.494	1900	13849.8	228.1	10076.6	89.38	56.509
660	4586.5	4.488	3275.8	1577.9	48.709	2000	14653.2	280.7	10681.5	76.45	56.922
680	4726.2	4.986	3375.8	1463.6	48.917	2100	15463.3	342.6	11293.0	65.78	57.317
700	4866.0	5.521	3475.9	1360.7	49.120	2200	16279.4	414.7	11910.5	56.92	57.696
720	5006.1	6.098	3576.3	1267.1	49.317	2300	17101.0	498.5	12533.5	49.51	58.062
740	5146.4	6.717	3676.9	1181.9	49.509	2400	17927.4	595.1	13161.3	43.28	58.414
760	5286.8	7.382	3777.5	1104.8	49.697	2500	18758.8	706.1	13794.1	38.00	58.754
780	5427.4	8.094	3878.4	1034.2	49.880	2600	19594.3	832.8	14431.0	33.50	59.081
800	5568.2	8.854	3979.5	969.6	50.058	2700	20434.0	976.9	15072.2	29.66	59.398
820	5709.4	9.666	4081.0	910.4	50.232	2800	21277.2	1140.1	15716.8	26.35	59.705
840	5850.7	10.532	4182.6	855.9	50.402	2900	22123.8	1324.0	16364.8	23.50	60.002
860	5992 3	11.453	4284.5	805.8	50.569	3000	22973.4	1530.8	17015.8	21.03	60.290
880	6134.2	12.434	4386.6	759.5	50.732	3100	23826.0	1762.1	17669.8	18.878	60.569
900	6276.4	13.476	4489.1	716.7	50.892	3200	24681.2	2020	18326.4	16.994	60.841
920	6419.0	14.582	4592.0	677.0	51.048	3300	25539.0	2308	18985.6	15.344	61.105
940	6561.7	15.755	4695.0	640.3	51.202	3400	26399.3	2626	19647.3	13.895	61.362
960	6704.9	16.998	4798.5	606.1	51.353	3500	27261.8	2979	20311.2	12.608	61.612
980	6848.4	18.312	4902.3	574.3	51.501	3600	28126.6	3368	20977.5	11.469	61.855
1000	6992.2	19.700	5006.3	544.7	51.646	3700	28993.5	3796	21645.8	10.460	62.093
1020	7136.4	21.17	5110.8	517.0	51.788	3800	29862.3	4266	22316.0	9.560	62.325
1040	7281.0	22.72	5215.7	491.2	51.929	3900	30732.9	4780	22988.0	8.756	62.551
1060	7425.9	24.36	5320.9	467.0	52.067	4000	31605.2	5343	23661.7	8.035	62.772
1080	7571.1	26.08	5426.4	444.4	52.203	4100	32479.1	5956	24337.0	7.387	62.988
1100	7716.8	27.90	5532.3	423.2	52.337	4200	33354.4	6623	25013.8	6.804	63.198
1120	7862.9	29.81	5638.7	403.2	52.468	4300	34231.2	7349	25692.0	6.279	63.405
1140	8009.2	31.82	5745.4	384.5	52.598	4400	35109.2	8136	26371.4	5.804	63.607
1160	8156.1	33.93	5852.5	366.9	52.726	4500	35988.6	8987	27052.2	5.374	63.805
1180	8303.3	36.15	5960.0	350.2	52.852	4600	36869.3	9907	27734.3	4.983	63.998
1200	8450.8	38.48	6067.8	334.6	52.976	4700	37751.0	10900	28417.4	4.627	64.188
1220	8598.8	40.93	6176.0	319.9	53.098	4800	38633.9	11970	29101.7	4.303	64.374
1240	8747.2	43.49	6284.7	306.0	53.218	4900	39517.8	13121	29787.0	4.008	64.556
1260	8896.0	46.18	6393.8	292.8	53.337	5000	40402.7	14357	30473.4	3.737	64.735
1280	9045.0	48.99	6503.1	280.4	53.455	5100	41288.6	15683	31160.7	3.490	64.910
1300	9194.6	51.93	6613.0	268.6	53.571	5200	42175.5	17104	31849.0	3.263	65.082
1320	9344.6	55.02	6723.2	257.4	53.685	5300	43063.2	18625	32538.1	3.054	65.252
1340	9494.8	58.24	6833.7	246.9	53.799	5380	43774.1	19914	33090.1	2.899	65.385
1360	9645.5	61.61	6944.7	236.9	53.910						

ITEM B 5 Hydrogen at Low Pressures (per p-mole)

Reproduced from Keenan and Kaye, *Gas Tables*, with permission of authors and publisher, John Wiley.

T°R	$\bar{h}$	p_r	$\bar{u}$	v_r	$\bar{\phi}$	T°R	$\bar{h}$	p_r	$\bar{u}$	v_r	$\bar{\phi}$
300	2063.5	0.9517	1467.7	3383	27.337	1380	9532.6	183.04	6792.1	80.90	37.781
320	2189.4	1.1678	1553.9	2940	27.742	1400	9673.8	192.66	6893.6	77.98	37.883
340	2317.2	1.4195	1642.0	2570	28.130	1420	9815.1	202.6	6995.2	75.21	37.983
360	2446.8	1.7104	1731.9	2259	28.501	1440	9956.5	213.0	7096.8	72.57	38.083
380	2577.8	2.044	1823.2	1994.6	28.856	1460	10098.0	223.7	7198.7	70.05	38.181
400	2710.2	2.426	1915.8	1769.7	29.195	1480	10239.7	234.8	7300.6	67.64	38.277
420	2843.7	2.858	2009.6	1577.2	29.520	1500	10381.5	246.3	7402.7	65.33	38.372
440	2978.1	3.345	2104.3	1411.5	29.833	1520	10523.4	258.3	7504.9	63.15	38.466
460	3113.5	3.892	2200.0	1268.2	30.133	1540	10665.5	270.6	7607.3	61.06	38.559
480	3249.4	4.503	2296.2	1143.9	30.424	1560	10807.6	283.4	7709.6	59.06	38.651
500	3386.1	5.182	2393.2	1035.4	30.703	1580	10950.0	296.7	7812.3	57.14	38.740
520	3523.3	5.936	2490.6	940.1	30.972	1600	11092.5	310.4	7915.1	55.31	38.830
537	3640.3	6.633	2573.9	869.0	31.194	1620	11235.1	324.5	8018.0	53.57	38.919
540	3660.9	6.762	2588.5	857.0	31.232	1640	11378.0	339.2	8121.2	51.89	39.007
560	3798.8	7.673	2686.7	783.2	31.482	1660	11521.0	354.3	8224.5	50.28	39.093
580	3937.1	8.671	2785.3	717.9	31.724	1680	11664.1	370.0	8327.8	48.73	39.179
600	4075.6	9.758	2884.1	659.8	31.959	1700	11807.4	386.1	8431.4	47.26	39.264
620	4214.3	10.942	2983.1	608.0	32.187	1800	12526.8	474.9	8952.2	40.68	39.675
640	4353.1	12.228	3082.1	561.7	32.407	1900	13250.9	578.5	9477.8	35.25	40.067
660	4492.1	13.617	3181.4	520.0	32.621	2000	13980.1	698.2	10008.4	30.73	40.441
680	4631.1	15.116	3280.7	482.7	32.829	2100	14714.5	836.3	10544.2	26.94	40.799
700	4770.2	16.733	3380.1	448.9	33.031	2200	15454.4	994.7	11085.5	23.74	41.143
720	4909.5	18.469	3479.6	418.4	33.226	2300	16199.8	1175.2	11632.3	21.00	41.475
740	5048.8	20.33	3579.2	390.6	33.417	2400	16950.6	1380.6	12184.5	18.656	41.794
760	5188.1	22.33	3678.8	365.3	33.603	2500	17707.3	1613.0	12742.6	16.633	42.104
780	5327.6	24.46	3778.6	342.2	33.784	2600	18469.7	1875.0	13306.4	14.881	42.403
800	5467.1	26.73	3878.4	321.1	33.961	2700	19237.8	2170	13876.0	13.353	42.692
820	5606.7	29.16	3978.3	301.8	34.134	2800	20011.8	2500	14451.4	12.019	42.973
840	5746.3	31.74	4078.2	284.0	34.302	2900	20791.5	2870	15032.5	10.845	43.247
860	5885.9	34.47	4178.0	267.7	34.466	3000	21576.9	3281	15619.3	9.811	43.514
880	6025.6	37.38	4278.0	252.7	34.627	3100	22367.7	3739	16211.5	8.897	43.773
900	6165.3	40.45	4378.0	238.8	34.784	3200	23164.1	4247	16809.3	8.087	44.026
920	6305.1	43.70	4478.1	225.9	34.938	3300	23965.5	4808	17412.1	7.365	44.273
940	6444.9	47.14	4578.1	214.0	35.087	3400	24771.9	5428	18019.9	6.722	44.513
960	6584.7	50.77	4678.3	202.9	35.235	3500	25582.9	6111	18632.4	6.148	44.748
980	6724.6	54.59	4778.4	192.64	35.379	3600	26398.5	6860	19249.4	5.633	44.978
1000	6864.5	58.62	4878.6	183.06	35.520	3700	27218.5	7682	19870.8	5.170	45.203
1020	7004.4	62.87	4978.8	174.09	35.659	3800	28042.8	8582	20496.5	4.753	45.423
1040	7144.4	67.32	5079.1	165.78	35.795	3900	28871.1	9562	21126.2	4.377	45.638
1060	7284.4	71.99	5179.4	158.02	35.928	4000	29703.5	10632	21760.0	4.037	45.849
1080	7424.5	76.90	5279.8	150.72	36.059	4100	30539.8	11799	22397.7	3.729	46.056
1100	7564.6	82.02	5380.1	143.89	36.188	4200	31379.8	13066	23039.2	3.449	46.257
1120	7704.7	87.42	5480.6	137.51	36.314	4300	32223.5	14438	23684.3	3.196	46.456
1140	7844.9	93.05	5581.0	131.47	36.438	4400	33070.9	15926	24333.1	2.965	46.651
1160	7985.2	98.95	5681.6	125.81	36.560	4500	33921.6	17537	24985.2	2.754	46.842
1180	8125.5	105.11	5782.2	120.46	36.681	4600	34775.7	19275	25640.7	2.561	47.030
1200	8265.8	111.54	5882.8	115.44	36.798	4700	35633.0	21150	26299.4	2.384	47.215
1220	8406.2	118.26	5983.4	110.71	36.913	4800	36493.4	23170	26961.2	2.223	47.396
1240	8546.7	125.25	6084.2	106.24	37.028	4900	37356.9	25340	27626.1	2.075	47.574
1260	8687.3	132.55	6185.1	102.00	37.140	5000	38223.3	27680	28294.0	1.9383	47.749
1280	8828.0	140.16	6286.1	98.00	37.251	5100	39092.8	30190	28964.9	1.8130	47.921
1300	8968.7	148.07	6387.1	94.21	37.360	5200	39965.1	32870	29638.6	1.6973	48.090
1320	9109.5	156.31	6488.2	90.62	37.468	5300	40840.2	35750	30315.1	1.5907	48.257
1340	9250.4	164.89	6589.4	87.20	37.574	5380	41542.1	38200	30858.1	1.5113	48.388
1360	9391.5	173.78	6690.7	83.97	37.678						

ITEM B 6 Nitrogen at Low Pressures (per p-mole)

Reproduced from Keenan and Kaye, *Gas Tables*, with permission of authors and publisher, John Wiley.

$T°R$	$\bar{h}$	p_r	$\bar{u}$	v_r	$\bar{\phi}$	$T°R$	$\bar{h}$	p_r	$\bar{u}$	v_r	$\bar{\phi}$
300	2082.0	0.13130	1486.2	24520	41.695	1380	9747.5	29.45	7007.0	502.8	52.444
320	2221.0	0.16458	1585.5	20870	42.143	1400	9896.9	31.09	7116.7	483.2	52.551
340	2360.0	0.2035	1684.8	17931	42.564	1420	10046.6	32.80	7226.7	464.6	52.658
360	2498.9	0.2485	1784.0	15543	42.962	1440	10196.6	34.57	7337.0	446.9	52.763
380	2638.0	0.3003	1883.4	13579	43.337	1460	10347.0	36.43	7447.6	430.1	52.867
400	2777.0	0.3594	1982.6	11943	43.694	1480	10497.8	38.36	7558.7	414.1	52.969
420	2916.1	0.4263	2082.0	10572	44.034	1500	10648.9	40.38	7670.1	398.8	53.071
440	3055.1	0.5017	2181.3	9410	44.357	1520	10800.4	42.46	7781.9	384.1	53.171
460	3194.1	0.5862	2280.6	8420	44.665	1540	10952.2	44.64	7893.9	370.2	53.271
480	3333.1	0.6805	2379.9	7570	44.962	1560	11104.3	46.90	8006.4	356.9	53.369
500	3472.2	0.7852	2479.3	6835	45.246	1580	11256.9	49.25	8119.2	344.2	53.465
520	3611.3	0.9003	2578.6	6198	45.519	1600	11409.7	51.70	8232.3	332.1	53.561
537	3729.5	1.0083	2663.1	5717	45.743	1620	11562.8	54.23	8345.7	320.5	53.656
540	3750.3	1.0281	2678.0	5637	45.781	1640	11716.4	56.87	8459.6	309.5	53.751
560	3889.5	1.1676	2777.4	5147	46.034	1660	11870.2	59.60	8573.6	298.8	53.844
580	4028.7	1.3200	2876.9	4715	46.278	1680	12024.3	62.44	8688.1	288.8	53.936
600	4167.9	1.4868	2976.4	4331	46.514	1700	12178.9	65.38	8802.9	279.1	54.028
620	4307.1	1.6679	3075.9	3989	46.742	1720	12333.7	68.43	8918.0	269.7	54.118
640	4446.4	1.8645	3175.5	3684	46.964	1740	12488.8	71.59	9033.4	260.8	54.208
660	4585.8	2.077	3275.2	3410	47.178	1760	12644.3	74.87	9149.2	252.3	54.297
680	4725.3	2.307	3374.9	3163	47.386	1780	12800.2	78.26	9265.3	244.1	54.385
700	4864.9	2.554	3474.8	2941	47.588	1800	12956.3	81.77	9381.7	236.2	54.472
720	5004.5	2.820	3574.7	2740	47.785	1820	13112.7	85.41	9498.4	228.7	54.559
740	5144.3	3.106	3674.7	2557	47.977	1840	13269.5	89.17	9615.5	221.4	54.645
760	5284.1	3.411	3774.9	2391	48.164	1860	13426.5	93.07	9732.8	214.4	54.729
780	5424.2	3.738	3875.2	2239	48.345	1880	13583.9	97.11	9850.5	207.8	54.813
800	5564.4	4.088	3975.7	2100	48.522	1900	13741.6	101.29	9968.4	201.3	54.896
820	5704.7	4.461	4076.3	1972.8	48.696	1920	13899.5	105.58	10086.7	195.16	54.979
840	5845.3	4.858	4177.1	1855.6	48.865	1940	14057.8	110.02	10205.2	189.19	55.061
860	5985.9	5.281	4278.1	1747.8	49.031	1960	14216.4	114.61	10324.0	183.48	55.143
880	6126.9	5.729	4379.4	1648.3	49.193	1980	14375.2	119.37	10443.2	178.00	55.223
900	6268.1	6.206	4480.8	1556.4	49.352	2000	14534.4	124.28	10562.6	172.69	55.303
920	6409.6	6.711	4582.6	1471.2	49.507	2100	15334.0	151.27	11163.7	148.97	55.694
940	6551.2	7.246	4684.5	1392.2	49.659	2200	16139.8	182.70	11770.9	129.22	56.068
960	6693.1	7.812	4786.7	1318.7	49.808	2300	16951.2	219.1	12383.7	112.66	56.429
980	6835.4	8.410	4889.3	1250.4	49.955	2400	17767.9	261.0	13001.8	98.68	56.777
1000	6977.9	9.043	4992.0	1186.7	50.099	2500	18589.5	309.0	13624.9	86.82	57.112
1020	7120.7	9.712	5095.1	1127.2	50.241	2600	19415.8	363.8	14252.5	76.69	57.436
1040	7263.8	10.414	5198.5	1071.6	50.380	2700	20246.4	426.0	14884.5	68.02	57.750
1060	7407.2	11.155	5302.2	1019.8	50.516	2800	21081.1	496.4	15520.6	60.54	58.053
1080	7551.0	11.939	5406.2	971.0	50.651	2900	21919.5	575.6	16160.5	54.07	58.348
1100	7695.0	12.759	5510.5	925.2	50.783	3000	22761.5	664.6	16803.9	48.44	58.632
1120	7839.3	13.622	5615.2	882.4	50.912	3100	23606.8	764.0	17450.6	43.53	58.910
1140	7984.0	14.527	5720.1	842.1	51.040	3200	24455.0	875.3	18100.2	39.24	59.179
1160	8129.0	15.479	5825.4	804.1	51.167	3300	25306.0	998.5	18752.7	35.46	59.442
1180	8274.4	16.481	5931.0	768.4	51.291	3400	26159.7	1135.3	19407.7	32.14	59.697
1200	8420.0	17.530	6037.0	734.6	51.413	3500	27015.9	1286.5	20065.3	29.19	59.944
1220	8566.1	18.629	6143.4	702.8	51.534	3600	27874.4	1453.0	20725.3	26.59	60.186
1240	8712.6	19.774	6250.1	672.8	51.653	3700	28735.1	1636.4	21387.4	24.27	60.422
1260	8859.3	20.98	6357.2	644.5	51.771	3800	29597.9	1837.3	22051.6	22.19	60.562
1280	9006.4	22.24	6464.5	617.5	51.887	3900	30462.8	2057	22717.9	20.34	60.877
1300	9153.9	23.56	6572.3	592.0	52.001	4000	31329.4	2298	23386.0	18.681	61.097
1320	9301.8	24.94	6680.4	568.0	52.114	4500	35687.8	3853	26751.4	12.533	62.123
1340	9450.0	26.38	6788.9	545.1	52.225	5000	40079.8	6141	30150.5	8.738	63.049
1360	9598.6	27.88	6897.8	523.4	52.335	5300	42728.3	7956	32203.2	7.148	63.563
						5380	43436.0	8504	32752.1	6.789	63.695

ITEM B 7 Oxygen at Low Pressures (per p-mole)

Reproduced from Keenan and Kaye, *Gas Tables*, with permission of authors and publisher, John Wiley.

$T°R$	$\bar{h}$	p_r	$\bar{u}$	v_r	$\bar{\phi}$	$T°R$	$\bar{h}$	p_r	$\bar{u}$	v_r	$\bar{\phi}$
300	2073.5	0.6684	1477.8	4816	44.927	1480	10855.1	232.5	7916.0	68.32	56.547
320	2212.6	0.8379	1577.1	4099	45.375	1500	11017.1	245.5	8038.3	65.56	56.656
340	2351.7	1.0360	1676.5	3522	45.797	1520	11179.6	259.2	8161.1	62.94	56.763
360	2490.8	1.2658	1775.9	3052	46.195	1540	11342.4	273.4	8284.2	60.43	56.869
380	2630.0	1.5295	1875.3	2666	46.571	1560	11505.4	288.3	8407.4	58.04	56.975
400	2769.1	1.8305	1974.8	2345	46.927	1580	11668.8	303.8	8531.1	55.80	57.079
420	2908.3	2.172	2074.3	2075	47.267	1600	11832.5	320.0	8655.1	53.65	57.182
440	3047.5	2.556	2173.8	1847.1	47.591	1620	11996.6	336.9	8779.5	51.61	57.284
460	3186.9	2.988	2273.4	1652.2	47.900	1640	12160.9	354.4	8904.1	49.65	57.385
480	3326.5	3.470	2373.3	1484.7	48.198	1660	12325.5	372.6	9029.0	47.81	57.484
500	3466.2	4.005	2473.2	1339.7	48.483	1680	12490.4	391.6	9154.1	46.03	57.582
520	3606.1	4.598	2573.4	1213.8	48.757	1700	12655.6	411.4	9279.6	44.34	57.680
537	3725.1	5.151	2658.7	1119.0	48.982	1720	12821.1	431.9	9405.4	42.73	57.777
540	3746.2	5.253	2673.8	1103.2	49.021	1740	12986.9	453.3	9531.5	41.19	57.873
560	3886.6	5.973	2774.5	1006.2	49.276	1760	13153.0	475.5	9657.9	39.72	57.968
580	4027.3	6.764	2875.5	920.2	49.522	1780	13319.2	498.5	9784.4	38.32	58.062
600	4168.3	7.629	2976.8	844.0	49.762	1800	13485.8	522.4	9911.2	36.98	58.155
620	4309.7	8.572	3078.4	776.3	49.993	1820	13652.5	547.2	10038.2	35.69	58.247
640	4451.4	9.600	3180.4	715.3	50.218	1840	13819.6	572.9	10165.6	34.46	58.339
660	4593.5	10.718	3282.9	660.7	50.437	1860	13986.8	599.5	10293.1	33.29	58.428
680	4736.2	11.930	3385.8	611.6	50.650	1880	14154.4	627.2	10421.0	32.16	58.518
700	4879.3	13.244	3489.2	567.1	50.858	1900	14322.1	656.0	10549.0	31.08	58.607
720	5022.9	14.662	3593.1	526.9	51.059	1920	14490.1	685.6	10677.2	30.05	58.695
740	5167.0	16.194	3697.4	490.4	51.257	1940	14658.2	716.4	10805.6	29.06	58.782
760	5311.4	17.843	3802.2	457.1	51.450	1960	14826.6	748.2	10934.3	28.11	58.868
780	5456.4	19.619	3907.5	426.6	51.638	1980	14995.2	781.1	11063.2	27.20	58.954
800	5602.0	21.53	4013.3	398.8	51.821	2000	15164.0	815.1	11192.3	26.33	59.039
820	5748.1	23.57	4119.7	373.3	52.002	2100	16010.9	1003.8	11840.6	22.45	59.451
840	5894.8	25.77	4226.6	349.8	52.179	2200	16862.6	1225.2	12493.7	19.269	59.848
860	6041.9	28.11	4334.1	328.3	52.352	2300	17718.8	1483.9	13151.3	16.632	60.228
880	6189.6	30.62	4442.0	308.4	52.522	2400	18579.2	1784.4	13813.1	14.434	60.594
900	6337.9	33.30	4550.6	290.0	52.688	2500	19443.4	2131	14478.7	12.589	60.946
920	6486.7	36.16	4659.7	273.1	52.852	2600	20311.4	2530	15148.1	11.030	61.287
940	6636.1	39.20	4769.4	257.3	53.012	2700	21182.9	2985	15821.0	9.707	61.616
960	6786.0	42.44	4879.5	242.7	53.170	2800	22057.8	3504	16497.4	8.576	61.934
980	6936.4	45.89	4990.3	229.2	53.326	2900	22936.1	4092	17177.1	7.605	62.242
1000	7087.5	49.55	5101.6	216.6	53.477	3000	23817.7	4756	17860.1	6.770	62.540
1020	7238.9	53.44	5213.3	204.8	53.628	3100	24702.5	5503	18546.3	6.044	62.831
1040	7391.0	57.56	5325.7	193.86	53.775	3200	25590.5	6344	19235.7	5.413	63.113
1060	7543.6	61.94	5438.6	183.67	53.921	3300	26481.6	7282	19928.2	4.863	63.386
1080	7696.8	66.56	5552.1	174.14	54.064	3400	27375.9	8330	20623.9	4.380	63.654
1100	7850.4	71.46	5665.9	165.20	54.204	3500	28273.3	9495	21322.8	3.956	63.914
1120	8004.5	76.63	5780.3	156.85	54.343	3600	29173.9	10788	22024.8	3.581	64.168
1140	8159.1	82.09	5895.2	149.02	54.480	3700	30077.5	12221	22729.8	3.249	64.415
1160	8314.2	87.86	6010.6	141.68	54.614	3800	30984.1	13802	23437.8	2.954	64.657
1180	8469.8	93.94	6126.5	134.79	54.748	3900	31893.6	15545	24148.7	2.692	64.893
1200	8625.8	100.36	6242.8	128.32	54.879	4000	32806.1	17463	24862.6	2.458	65.123
1220	8782.4	107.10	6359.6	122.23	55.008	4100	33721.6	19569	25579.5	2.248	65.350
1240	8939.4	114.19	6476.9	116.52	55.136	4200	34639.9	21870	26299.2	2.060	65.571
1260	9096.7	121.68	6594.5	111.11	55.262	4300	35561.1	24400	27021.9	1.8916	65.788
1280	9254.6	129.55	6712.7	106.04	55.386	4400	36485.0	27150	27747.2	1.7392	66.000
1300	9412.9	137.80	6831.3	101.25	55.508	4500	37411.8	30150	28475.4	1.6016	66.208
1320	9571.6	146.46	6950.2	96.71	55.630	4600	38341.4	33420	29206.4	1.4773	66.413
1340	9730.7	155.54	7069.6	92.44	55.750	4700	39273.6	36960	29940.0	1.3643	66.613
1360	9890.2	165.07	7189.4	88.40	55.867	4800	40208.6	40820	30676.4	1.2621	66.809
1380	10050.1	175.08	7309.6	84.58	55.984	4900	41146.1	44990	31415.3	1.1689	67.003
1400	10210.4	185.54	7430.1	80.98	56.099	5000	42086.3	49500	32157.0	1.0838	67.193
1420	10371.0	196.50	7551.1	77.56	56.213	5100	43029.1	54380	32901.2	1.0064	67.380
1440	10532.0	208.0	7672.4	74.32	56.326	5200	43974.3	59640	33647.9	0.9355	67.562
1460	10693.3	219.9	7793.9	71.25	56.437	5300	44922.2	65320	34397.1	0.8708	67.743
						5380	45682.1	70170	34998.1	0.8227	67.885

ITEM B 8 Products—400 % Stoichiometric Air (per p-mole)

Reproduced from Keenan and Kaye, *Gas Tables*, with permission of authors and publisher, John Wiley.

$T°R$	$\bar{h}$	p_r	$\bar{u}$	v_r	$\bar{\phi}$	$T°R$	$\bar{h}$	p_r	$\bar{u}$	v_r	$\bar{\phi}$
380	2644.9	0.3967	1890.3	10280	43.890	1460	10562.4	53.75	7663.0	291.5	53.639
400	2784.7	0.4754	1990.3	9030	44.249	1480	10718.7	56.71	7779.6	280.1	53.745
420	2925.0	0.5646	2090.9	7982	44.591	1500	10875.6	59.80	7896.8	269.2	53.851
440	3065.2	0.6654	2191.4	7096	44.917	1520	11033.1	63.01	8014.6	258.8	53.955
460	3205.7	0.7785	2292.2	6341	45.229	1540	11190.7	66.37	8132.5	249.0	54.057
480	3346.2	0.9050	2393.0	5692	45.528	1560	11348.6	69.86	8250.7	239.6	54.160
500	3486.7	1.0457	2493.8	5131	45.815	1580	11506.8	73.51	8369.1	230.6	54.260
520	3627.4	1.2017	2594.7	4644	46.091	1600	11665.6	77.30	8488.2	222.1	54.360
537	3746.8	1.3469	2680.4	4279	46.318	1620	11824.6	81.24	8607.5	214.0	54.459
540	3768.0	1.3738	2695.6	4218	46.357	1640	11984.1	85.35	8727.3	206.2	54.557
560	3909.2	1.5632	2797.1	3845	46.613	1660	12143.8	89.61	8847.2	198.80	54.654
580	4050.4	1.7709	2898.6	3514	46.861	1680	12303.9	94.05	8967.6	191.71	54.750
600	4191.9	1.998	3000.4	3223	47.101	1700	12464.3	98.64	9088.3	184.93	54.844
620	4333.5	2.246	3102.3	2963	47.333	1720	12625.3	103.43	9209.6	178.46	54.939
640	4475.2	2.515	3204.2	2731	47.558	1740	12786.4	108.40	9331.0	172.25	55.032
660	4617.5	2.807	3306.8	2522	47.777	1760	12947.8	113.55	9452.7	166.33	55.124
680	4759.3	3.124	3408.9	2336	47.989	1780	13109.4	118.90	9574.5	160.66	55.215
700	4901.7	3.467	3511.6	2167.0	48.195	1800	13271.7	124.45	9697.1	155.21	55.306
720	5044.2	3.836	3614.4	2014.4	48.396	1820	13434.3	130.21	9820.0	150.00	55.396
740	5187.0	4.233	3717.5	1876.0	48.591	1840	13597.0	136.18	9943.0	145.01	55.485
760	5330.2	4.660	3820.9	1750.2	48.783	1860	13760.3	142.35	10066.6	140.22	55.573
780	5473.8	5.118	3924.8	1635.4	48.968	1880	13923.6	148.76	10190.2	135.62	55.660
800	5617.5	5.609	4028.8	1530.6	49.150	1900	14087.2	155.39	10314.1	131.22	55.747
820	5761.7	6.134	4133.3	1434.6	49.329	1920	14251.3	162.26	10438.4	126.98	55.833
840	5905.7	6.695	4237.6	1346.3	49.502	1940	14415.7	169.37	10563.1	122.91	55.918
860	6050.5	7.294	4342.6	1265.3	49.672	1960	14580.3	176.73	10688.0	119.01	56.002
880	6195.2	7.932	4447.6	1190.6	49.839	1980	14745.3	184.33	10813.3	115.27	56.086
900	6340.3	8.611	4553.0	1121.6	50.002	2000	14910.3	192.21	10938.6	111.66	56.169
920	6485.9	9.334	4658.9	1057.8	50.162	2020	15075.8	200.35	11064.3	108.20	56.252
940	6631.7	10.101	4765.0	998.9	50.319	2040	15241.6	208.76	11190.4	104.87	56.333
960	6778.3	10.916	4871.9	943.7	50.473	2060	15407.6	217.45	11316.7	101.66	56.414
980	6925.1	11.779	4978.9	892.8	50.624	2080	15574.0	226.42	11443.4	98.58	56.494
1000	7072.1	12.694	5086.2	845.3	50.773	2100	15740.5	235.7	11570.2	95.61	56.574
1020	7219.7	13.662	5194.1	801.1	50.919	2150	16157.9	260.2	11888.3	88.66	56.771
1040	7367.2	14.685	5301.9	760.1	51.062	2200	16577.1	286.7	12208.2	82.33	56.964
1060	7515.6	15.768	5410.6	721.2	51.203	2250	16998.0	315.3	12529.8	76.56	57.152
1080	7664.1	16.909	5519.4	685.5	51.342	2300	17419.8	346.2	12852.3	71.28	57.338
1100	7812.9	18.116	5628.4	651.6	51.479	2350	17843.2	379.5	13176.4	66.46	57.520
1120	7962.3	19.385	5738.1	620.0	51.613	2400	18268.0	415.3	13501.9	62.02	57.699
1140	8112.0	20.723	5848.1	590.5	51.746	2450	18694.1	453.7	13828.7	57.94	57.875
1160	8262.1	22.14	5958.5	562.5	51.877	2500	19121.4	494.9	14156.8	54.20	58.048
1180	8412.5	23.61	6069.2	536.3	52.006	2550	19550.1	539.1	14486.1	50.76	58.217
1200	8563.4	25.17	6180.4	511.6	52.132	2600	19979.7	586.4	14816.5	47.58	58.384
1220	8715.0	26.80	6292.2	488.4	52.257	2650	20410.6	636.9	15148.0	44.65	58.548
1240	8866.6	28.52	6404.1	466.6	52.380	2700	20842.8	690.9	15481.0	41.94	58.710
1260	9018.8	30.32	6516.6	445.9	52.502	2750	21276.0	748.5	15814.8	39.43	58.869
1280	9171.3	32.21	6629.4	426.4	52.622	2800	21709.8	809.9	16149.4	37.10	59.026
1300	9324.1	34.20	6742.5	407.9	52.741	2850	22145.3	875.2	16485.5	34.94	59.180
1320	9477.6	36.28	6856.3	390.5	52.858	2900	22581.4	944.7	16822.4	32.94	59.331
1340	9631.4	38.45	6970.3	374.0	52.973	2950	23018.5	1018.6	17160.2	31.08	59.481
1360	9785.5	40.73	7084.7	358.4	53.088	3000	23456.6	1096.8	17499.0	29.35	59.628
1380	9939.9	43.10	7199.4	343.6	53.201	3100	24335.5	1268.3	18179.3	26.23	59.916
1400	10095.0	45.60	7314.8	329.5	53.312	3200	25217.8	1460.4	18863.1	23.51	60.196
1420	10250.6	48.19	7430.7	316.2	53.422	3300	26102.9	1675.3	19549.5	21.14	60.469
1440	10406.2	50.91	7546.5	303.6	53.531	3400	26991.4	1914.6	20239.6	19.06	60.734

ITEM B 9 Products—200 % Stoichiometric Air (per p-mole)

Reproduced from Keenan and Kaye, *Gas Tables*, with permission of authors and publisher, John Wiley.

$T°R$	$\bar{h}$	p_r	$\bar{u}$	v_r	$\bar{\phi}$	$T°R$	$\bar{h}$	p_r	$\bar{u}$	v_r	$\bar{\phi}$
380	2660.3	0.3878	1905.7	10516	43.845	1460	10729.3	57.26	7829.9	273.6	53.764
400	2801.4	0.4655	2007.0	9222	44.208	1480	10889.5	60.49	7950.4	262.5	53.874
420	2943.0	0.5539	2108.9	8138	44.553	1500	11050.2	63.88	8071.4	252.0	53.981
440	3084.8	0.6539	2211.0	7223	44.883	1520	11211.4	67.40	8192.9	242.0	54.088
460	3226.8	0.7663	2313.3	6441	45.198	1540	11372.8	71.08	8314.6	232.5	54.194
480	3368.9	0.8925	2415.7	5772	45.500	1560	11534.7	74.91	8436.7	223.5	54.298
500	3511.2	1.0330	2518.3	5194	45.791	1580	11696.8	78.92	8559.1	214.8	54.401
520	3653.7	1.1893	2621.0	4692	46.070	1600	11859.6	83.10	8682.2	206.63	54.504
537	3774.9	1.3350	2708.5	4317	46.300	1620	12022.7	87.44	8805.6	198.81	54.605
540	3796.3	1.3620	2723.9	4255	46.340	1640	12186.2	91.97	8929.4	191.35	54.705
560	3939.4	1.5526	2827.3	3871	46.600	1660	12350.0	96.69	9053.5	184.25	54.805
580	4082.7	1.7621	2930.9	3532	46.851	1680	12514.2	101.60	9177.9	177.46	54.903
600	4226.3	1.992	3034.8	3233	47.094	1700	12678.6	106.70	9302.6	170.97	55.000
620	4370.1	2.243	3138.9	2967	47.330	1720	12843.8	112.01	9428.1	164.79	55.097
640	4514.0	2.516	3243.0	2730	47.558	1740	13009.0	117.53	9553.6	158.88	55.192
660	4658.6	2.814	3347.9	2517	47.781	1760	13174.6	123.27	9679.5	153.22	55.287
680	4802.8	3.136	3452.4	2326	47.996	1780	13340.3	129.23	9805.5	147.80	55.380
700	4947.7	3.487	3557.6	2154.5	48.207	1800	13507.0	135.43	9932.4	142.63	55.473
720	5092.6	3.864	3662.8	1999.3	48.411	1820	13673.8	141.86	10059.5	137.68	55.566
740	5237.9	4.273	3768.4	1858.7	48.610	1840	13840.5	148.54	10186.5	132.94	55.657
760	5383.7	4.711	3874.4	1731.1	48.804	1860	14008.4	155.46	10314.7	128.40	55.748
780	5529.9	5.183	3980.9	1614.9	48.994	1880	14176.1	162.55	10442.7	124.03	55.837
800	5676.3	5.690	4087.6	1508.7	49.179	1900	14344.1	170.09	10571.0	119.87	55.926
820	5823.1	6.234	4194.7	1411.7	49.360	1920	14512.5	177.82	10699.6	115.87	56.015
840	5969.9	6.815	4301.8	1322.6	49.537	1940	14681.4	185.82	10828.8	112.04	56.102
860	6117.5	7.437	4409.6	1241.0	49.711	1960	14850.4	194.13	10958.1	108.35	56.189
880	6264.9	8.101	4517.3	1165.8	49.881	1980	15019.8	202.71	11087.8	104.82	56.275
900	6413.0	8.808	4625.7	1096.4	50.047	2000	15189.3	211.6	11217.6	101.43	56.360
920	6561.5	9.564	4734.5	1032.4	50.210	2020	15359.3	220.8	11347.9	98.16	56.444
940	6710.4	10.366	4843.7	973.3	50.370	2040	15529.7	230.4	11478.5	95.04	56.529
960	6859.8	11.221	4953.4	918.2	50.528	2060	15700.3	240.2	11609.4	92.03	56.612
980	7009.7	12.126	5063.6	867.2	50.682	2080	15871.3	250.4	11740.7	89.15	56.694
1000	7159.8	13.089	5173.9	819.8	50.833	2100	16042.4	260.9	11872.1	86.36	56.777
1020	7310.5	14.109	5284.9	775.8	50.983	2150	16471.5	288.9	12201.9	79.86	56.978
1040	7461.1	15.189	5395.8	734.9	51.128	2200	16902.5	319.2	12533.6	73.96	57.177
1060	7612.7	16.333	5507.7	696.2	51.273	2250	17335.3	352.0	12867.1	68.57	57.377
1080	7764.3	17.542	5619.6	660.8	51.415	2300	17769.3	387.5	13201.8	63.68	57.562
1100	7916.4	18.822	5731.9	627.1	51.555	2350	18204.9	425.9	13538.1	59.21	57.749
1120	8069.0	20.170	5844.8	595.9	51.692	2400	18642.1	467.4	13876.0	55.12	57.933
1140	8222.1	21.595	5958.2	566.6	51.828	2450	19080.7	511.9	14215.3	51.36	58.114
1160	8375.5	23.10	6071.9	539.0	51.961	2500	19520.7	559.8	14556.0	47.91	58.292
1180	8529.2	24.68	6185.9	513.2	52.093	2550	19962.0	611.3	14898.0	44.76	58.467
1200	8683.6	26.34	6300.6	488.9	52.222	2600	20404.6	666.6	15241.3	41.85	58.639
1220	8838.6	28.09	6415.8	466.0	52.351	2650	20848.4	725.9	15585.8	39.18	58.808
1240	8993.7	29.94	6531.2	444.5	52.477	2700	21293.8	789.4	15932.0	36.71	58.974
1260	9149.3	31.87	6647.1	424.2	52.601	2750	21740.3	857.2	16279.2	34.42	59.138
1280	9305.3	33.90	6763.4	405.1	52.724	2800	22187.5	929.8	16627.1	32.31	59.300
1300	9461.7	36.05	6880.1	387.0	52.845	2850	22636.3	1007.2	16976.6	30.36	59.459
1320	9618.8	38.29	6997.4	370.0	52.965	2900	23086.0	1089.8	17327.0	28.56	59.615
1340	9776.2	40.64	7115.1	353.9	53.084	2950	23536.7	1177.9	17678.4	26.88	59.769
1360	9933.8	43.10	7233.0	338.6	53.200	3000	23988.5	1271.2	18030.9	25.321	59.921
1380	10091.9	45.68	7351.4	324.2	53.316	3100	24895.3	1476.8	18739.1	22.528	60.218
1400	10250.7	48.38	7470.5	310.5	53.430	3200	25805.6	1708.2	19450.8	20.103	60.507
1420	10410.0	51.21	7590.1	297.6	53.543	3400	27636.4	2259.1	20884.4	16.152	61.063
1440	10569.3	54.17	7709.7	285.3	53.654	3600	29479.9	2946	22330.8	13.114	61.590
						3900	32266.2	4284	24521.3	9.770	62.333

ITEM B 10 Water Vapor at Low Pressures (per p-mole)

Reproduced from Keenan and Kaye, *Gas Tables*, with permission of authors and publisher, John Wiley.

$T°R$	$\bar{h}$	p_r	$\bar{u}$	v_r	$\bar{\phi}$	$T°R$	$\bar{h}$	p_r	$\bar{u}$	v_r	$\bar{\phi}$
300	2367.6	0.06975	1771.8	46150	40.439	1380	11441.4	39.68	8700.9	373.2	53.037
320	2526.8	0.09033	1891.3	38010	40.952	1400	11624.8	42.41	8844.6	354.3	53.168
340	2686.0	0.11515	2010.8	31690	41.435	1420	11808.8	45.29	8988.9	336.4	53.299
360	2845.1	0.14479	2130.2	26690	41.889	1440	11993.4	48.34	9133.8	319.7	53.428
380	3004.4	0.17982	2249.8	22680	42.320	1460	12178.8	51.55	9279.4	304.0	53.556
400	3163.8	0.2209	2369.4	19436	42.728	1480	12364.8	54.94	9425.7	289.1	53.682
420	3323.2	0.2686	2489.1	16780	43.117	1500	12551.4	58.53	9572.7	275.1	53.808
440	3482.7	0.3237	2608.9	14585	43.487	1520	12738.8	62.30	9720.3	261.8	53.932
460	3642.3	0.3870	2728.8	12756	43.841	1540	12926.8	66.28	9868.6	249.4	54.055
480	3802.0	0.4592	2848.8	11217	44.182	1560	13115.6	70.47	10017.6	237.6	54.177
500	3962.0	0.5412	2969.1	9914	44.508	1580	13305.0	74.90	10167.3	226.4	54.298
520	4122.0	0.6337	3089.4	8805	44.821	1600	13494.9	79.53	10317.6	215.9	54.418
537	4258.0	0.7217	3191.9	7987	45.079	1620	13685.7	84.43	10468.6	205.9	54.535
540	4282.4	0.7381	3210.0	7851	45.124	1640	13877.0	89.58	10620.2	196.47	54.653
560	4442.8	0.8548	3330.7	7029	45.415	1660	14069.2	94.99	10772.7	187.53	54.770
580	4603.7	0.9853	3451.9	6317	45.696	1680	14261.9	100.69	10925.6	179.04	54.886
600	4764.7	1.1305	3573.2	5696	45.970	1700	14455.4	106.67	11079.4	171.03	54.999
620	4926.1	1.2914	3694.9	5153	46.235	1720	14649.5	112.93	11233.8	163.45	55.113
640	5087.8	1.4696	3816.8	4672	46.492	1740	14844.3	119.54	11388.9	156.20	55.226
660	5250.0	1.6662	3939.3	4250	46.741	1760	15039.8	126.45	11544.7	149.36	55.339
680	5412.5	1.8825	4062.1	3876	46.984	1780	15236.1	133.73	11701.2	142.83	55.449
700	5575.4	2.120	4185.3	3543	47.219	1800	15433.0	141.35	11858.4	136.66	55.559
720	5738.8	2.380	4309.0	3246	47.450	1820	15630.6	149.33	12016.3	130.78	55.668
740	5902.6	2.665	4433.1	2979	47.673	1840	15828.7	157.71	12174.7	125.20	55.777
760	6066.9	2.976	4557.6	2741	47.893	1860	16027.6	166.51	12333.9	119.89	55.884
780	6231.7	3.314	4682.7	2526	48.106	1880	16227.2	175.72	12493.8	114.83	55.991
800	6396.9	3.683	4808.2	2331	48.316	1900	16427.5	185.36	12654.4	110.01	56.097
820	6562.6	4.082	4934.2	2156	48.520	1920	16628.5	195.43	12815.6	105.43	56.203
840	6728.9	4.515	5060.8	1996.3	48.721	1940	16830.0	206.0	12977.4	101.06	56.307
860	6895.6	4.984	5187.8	1851.7	48.916	1960	17032.4	217.1	13140.1	96 89	56.411
880	7062.9	5.491	5315.3	1719.8	49.109	1980	17235.3	228.6	13303.3	92.93	56.514
900	7230.9	6.038	5443.6	1599.4	49.298	2000	17439.0	240.8	13467.3	89.15	56.617
920	7399.4	6.627	5572.4	1489.6	49.483	2100	18466.9	310.0	14296.6	72.69	57.119
940	7568.4	7.263	5701.7	1389.0	49.665	2200	19510.8	396.0	15141.9	59.61	57.605
960	7738.0	7.945	5831.6	1296.6	49.843	2300	20570.6	502.2	16003.1	49.15	58.077
980	7908.2	8.680	5962.0	1211.6	50.019	2400	21645.7	632.4	16879.6	40.73	58.535
1000	8078.9	9.469	6093.0	1133.3	50.191	2500	22735.4	791.5	17770.7	33.89	58.980
1020	8250.4	10.313	6224.8	1061.4	50.360	2600	23839.5	984.8	18676.2	28.33	59.414
1040	8422.4	11.219	6357.1	994.8	50.528	2700	24957.2	1218.4	19595.4	23.78	59.837
1060	8595.0	12.187	6490.0	933.4	50.693	2800	26088.0	1499.4	20527.6	20.04	60.248
1080	8768.2	13.220	6623.5	876.7	50.854	2900	27231.2	1835.6	21472.2	16.953	60.650
1100	8942.0	14.327	6757.5	823.8	51.013	3000	28386.3	2237	22428.7	14.394	61.043
1120	9116.4	15.507	6892.2	775.1	51.171	3100	29552.8	2713	23396.6	12.263	61.426
1140	9291.4	16.766	7027.5	729.6	51.325	3200	30730.2	3270	24375.4	10.481	61.801
1160	9467.1	18.106	7163.5	687.6	51.478	3300	31918.2	3940	25364.8	8.988	62.167
1180	9643.4	19.536	7300.1	648.1	51.630	3400	33116.0	4720	26364.0	7.730	62.526
1200	9820.4	21.05	7437.4	611.7	51.777	3500	34323.5	5633	27373.0	6.668	62.876
1220	9998.0	22.67	7575.2	577.7	51.925	3600	35540.1	6697	28391.0	5.770	63.221
1240	10176.1	24.39	7713.6	545.7	52.070	3700	36765.4	7935	29417.7	5.004	63.557
1260	10354.9	26.21	7852.7	516.0	52.212	3800	37998.9	9368	30452.6	4.353	63.887
1280	10534.4	28.14	7992.5	488.2	52.354	3900	39240.2	11025	31495.3	3.796	64.210
1300	10714.5	30.19	8132.9	462.1	52.494	4000	40489.1	12934	32545.6	3.319	64.528
1320	10895.3	32.37	8274.0	437.7	52.631	4500	46835.9	27530	37899.5	1.7543	66.028
1340	11076.6	34.67	8415.5	414.9	52.768	5000	53327.4	54970	43398.0	0.9760	67.401
1360	11258.7	37.10	8557.9	393.3	52 903	5380	58338.7	89600	47654.7	0.6443	68.371

ITEM B 11 Enthalpy and Gibbs Function of Formation; Absolute Entropy

See also Table III, p. 152, for additional entropy values. The original data of this table were from Rossini,[0.1,0.2] many of which have been slightly up-dated from JANAF,[0.22] also the source of the new additions; designated by—J. Δh_f° Btu/pmole = enthalpy of formation (§ 13.29), $\Delta \bar{G}_f^\circ$ Btu/pmole = Gibbs function of formation (§ 13.33), $\bar{s}^\circ$ Btu/pmole-°R = the absolute entropy, each at the standard state of 1 atm and 77°F; $\bar{h}_{fg}^\circ$ Btu/pmole = the enthalpy of vaporization at 77°F.

Substance	Mol. mass, M	$\Delta \bar{h}_f^\circ$	$\Delta \bar{G}_f^\circ$	$\bar{h}_{fg}^\circ$	$\bar{s}^\circ$
Acetylene, C_2H_2(g)—J	26.036	+97,542	+89,987		48.004
Ammonia, NH_3(g)—J	17.032	−19,746	−7,047	8,545	46.03
Benzene, C_6H_6(g)	78.108	+35,676	+55,780		64.34
C_6H_6(l)—J		+20,934	+52,920		29.756
n-Butane, C_4H_{10}(g)	58.120	−54,270	−7,380	9,063	74.12
Carbon (graphite), C(s)—J	12.01	0	0		1.359
Carbon (diamond)—J		+0.453	+0.685		0.583
Carbon dioxide, CO_2(g)	44.010	−169,293	−169,668		51.061
Carbon monoxide, CO(g)—J	28.01	−47,560	−59,010		47.21
Cyanogen, C_2N_2(g)—J	52.038	+132,480	+127,458		57.86
Electron gas—J	0.0005488	0	0		4.988
Ethane, C_2H_6(g)	30.068	−36,425	−14,148		54.85
Ethanol, C_2H_6O(g)—J	46.068	−101,232	−72,540	18,216	67.4
C_2H_6O(l)—J		−119,448	−75,186		38.4
Ethene, C_2H_4(g)	28.052	+22,572	+29,408		52.396
n-Heptane, C_7H_{16}(g)—J	100.198	−80,802	+3,762	15,728	101.64
C_7H_{16}(l)—J		−96,530	+756		77.92
Hydrazine, N_2H_4(g)—J	32.048	+41,022	+68,476		57.03
Hydrogen (Mono), H(g)—J	1.008	+93,780	+87,453		27.392
Hydrogen peroxide,					
$\quad H_2O_2$(g)—J	34.016	−58,554	−45,374	22,158	55.66
$\quad H_2O_2$(l)		−80,712	−49,032		21.2
Hydrogen sulfide, H_2S(g)—J	34.086	−8,784	−14,391		49.15
Hydroxyl, OH(g)—J	17.008	+16,978	+14,953		43.88
Methane, CH_4(g)—J	16.042	−32,210	−21,862		44.48
Methanol, CH_4O(g)	32.042	−86,544	−69,642	16,096	56.8
CH_4O(l)—J		−102,640	−71,514		30.3
Methyl chloride, CH_3Cl(g)—J	50.49	−37,190	−27,083		55.99
Nitrogen, N_2(g)	28.016	0	0		45.767
Nitrogen oxide, NO(g)	30.008	+38,880	+37,294		50.339
Nitrogen dioxide, NO_2(g)—J	48.008	+14,238	+22,045		57.343
n-Octane, C_8H_{18}(g)	114.224	−89,676	+7,452	17,856	111.82
C_8H_{18}(l)—J		−107,532	+3,186		85.50
Nonane, C_9H_{20}(g)		−98,432	+10,728	19,940	120.86
Oxygen (Mono), O(g)—J	16	+107,206	+99,711		38.468
Oxygen, O_2(g)	32	0	0		49.004
Ozone, O_3(g)—J	48	+61,380	+70,195		57.080
Propane, C_3H_8(g)	44.094	−44,676	−10,105	6,489	64.51
Sulfur dioxide, SO_2(g)—J	64.07	−127,705	−129,134	9,370	59.298
Water, H_2O(g)	18.016	−104,036	−98,344		45.106
Water (l)	18.016	−122,971	−102,042		16.716

ITEM B 12   Enthalpy of Reaction, Typical Fuels

Heating values are for a reference state at 77°F, or essentially so, with combustion in air or oxygen to stable species. The values for the hydrocarbons were taken from reference [0.1], given to more significant figures than are warranted by the accuracy of the individual values in order to retain the significance of small differences between liquid and gaseous states. Miscellaneous values are from references [13.3] and [13.7]. Values marked with an asterisk * are for academic use only, since the compositions and heating values vary markedly. Because of different sources or basic data, some values in this table may not be consistent with some of those in Item B 11. Meanings of symbols: (s) = solid; (l) = liquid; (g) = gas. Unless otherwise indicated, choose values according to the natural state of the fuel; for example, benzene is normally a liquid—therefore, use values opposite (l). In every case, the CO_2 is in a gaseous state. Where applicable, the latent heat of vaporization of the fuel is q_h° in the last column minus q_h° in the fifth column.

Fuel	Formula	M	$-h_{rp}^\circ$, Btu/lb Fuel, Solid or Liquid		$-h_{rp}^\circ$, Btu/lb Fuel, Gaseous Fuel	
			Lower q_l°, H_2O(g)	Higher q_h°, H_2O(l)	Lower q_l°, H_2O(g)	Higher q_h°, H_2O(l)
SOLID (s)						
Anthracite coal*			13,330	13,540		
Bituminous coal*			13,100	13,600		
Carbon, graphite (to CO_2)	C	12.01	14,097			
Carbon graphite (to CO)	C	12.01	3,960			
Coke, beehive			12,450	12,530		
Lignite*			6,700	7,350		
Sulfur	S	32.06	3,980			
Wood, air-dried oak*			8,000			
NORMALLY LIQUID (l)						
Benzene	C_6H_6	78.108	17,259	17,986	17,446	18,172
n-Decane	$C_{10}H_{22}$	142.276	19,020	20,483	19,175	20,638
n-Dodecane	$C_{12}H_{26}$	170.328	18,966	20,410	19,120	20,564
Ethyl alcohol	C_2H_6O	46.068	11,929	13,161		
Fuel oil*			18,500	19,700		
Gasoline*			18,800	20,200		
n-Heptane	C_7H_{16}	100.198	19,157	20,668	19,314	20,825
n-Hexadecane	$C_{16}H_{34}$	226.432	18,898	20,318	19,052	20,472
Kerosene*			18,500	19,900		
Methyl alcohol	CH_4O	32.042	9,078	10,259		
Nonane	C_9H_{20}	128.25	19,056	20,531	19,211	20,687
n-Octane	C_8H_{18}	114.224	19,100	20,591	19,256	20,747
Octene	C_8H_{16}	112.208	19,000	20,350	19,157	20,506
n-Pentane	C_5H_{12}	72.146	19,340	20,914	19,499	21,072
NORMALLY GAS (g)						
Acetylene	C_2H_2	26.036			20,734	21,460
Blast-furnace gas*					1,100	1,120
n-Butane	C_4H_{10}	58.120	19,496	21,124	19,655	21,283
Carbon monoxide	CO	28.01			4,346	
Cyanogen [to CO_2 and N_2]	C_2N_2	80.052			5,890	
Ethane	C_2H_6	30.068			20,416	22,304
Ethene	C_2H_4	28.052			20,276	21,625
Hydrogen	H_2	2.016			51,605	60,998
Methane	CH_4	16.042			21,502	23,861
Natural gas*					20,500	23,000
Propane	C_3H_8	44.094	19,774	21,490	19,929	21,646
Refinery gas*					19,600	21,400

ITEM B 13   Properties of Saturated H$_2$O: Temperatures

Temp Fahr t	Abs Press. Lb per Sq In. p	Sat. Liquid v_f	Evap v_{fg}	Sat. Vapor v_g	Sat. Liquid h_f	Evap h_{fg}	Sat. Vapor h_g	Sat. Liquid s_f	Evap s_{fg}	Sat. Vapor s_g	Temp Fahr t
		Specific Volume			Enthalpy			Entropy			
32.0	0.08859	0.016022	3304.7	3304.7	−0.0179	1075.5	1075.5	0.0000	2.1873	2.1873	32.0
34.0	0.09600	0.016021	3061.9	3061.9	1.996	1074.4	1076.4	0.0041	2.1762	2.1802	34.0
36.0	0.10395	0.016020	2839.0	2839.0	4.008	1073.2	1077.2	0.0081	2.1651	2.1732	36.0
38.0	0.11249	0.016019	2634.1	2634.2	6.018	1072.1	1078.1	0.0122	2.1541	2.1663	38.0
40.0	0.12163	0.016019	2445.8	2445.8	8.027	1071.0	1079.0	0.0162	2.1432	2.1594	40.0
42.0	0.13143	0.016019	2272.4	2272.4	10.035	1069.8	1079.9	0.0202	2.1325	2.1527	42.0
44.0	0.14192	0.016019	2112.8	2112.8	12.041	1068.7	1080.7	0.0242	2.1217	2.1459	44.0
46.0	0.15314	0.016020	1965.7	1965.7	14.047	1067.6	1081.6	0.0282	2.1111	2.1393	46.0
48.0	0.16514	0.016021	1830.0	1830.0	16.051	1066.4	1082.5	0.0321	2.1006	2.1327	48.0
50.0	0.17796	0.016023	1704.8	1704.8	18.054	1065.3	1083.4	0.0361	2.0901	2.1262	50.0
52.0	0.19165	0.016024	1589.2	1589.2	20.057	1064.2	1084.2	0.0400	2.0798	2.1197	52.0
54.0	0.20625	0.016026	1482.4	1482.4	22.058	1063.1	1085.1	0.0439	2.0695	2.1134	54.0
56.0	0.22183	0.016028	1383.6	1383.6	24.059	1061.9	1086.0	0.0478	2.0593	2.1070	56.0
58.0	0.23843	0.016031	1292.2	1292.2	26.060	1060.8	1086.9	0.0516	2.0491	2.1008	58.0
60.0	0.25611	0.016033	1207.6	1207.6	28.060	1059.7	1087.7	0.0555	2.0391	2.0946	60.0
62.0	0.27494	0.016036	1129.2	1129.2	30.059	1058.5	1088.6	0.0593	2.0291	2.0885	62.0
64.0	0.29497	0.016039	1056.5	1056.5	32.058	1057.4	1089.5	0.0632	2.0192	2.0824	64.0
66.0	0.31626	0.016043	989.0	989.1	34.056	1056.3	1090.4	0.0670	2.0094	2.0764	66.0
68.0	0.33889	0.016046	926.5	926.5	36.054	1055.2	1091.2	0.0708	1.9996	2.0704	68.0
70.0	0.36292	0.016050	868.3	868.4	38.052	1054.0	1092.1	0.0745	1.9900	2.0645	70.0
72.0	0.38844	0.016054	814.3	814.3	40.049	1052.9	1093.0	0.0783	1.9804	2.0587	72.0
74.0	0.41550	0.016058	764.1	764.1	42.046	1051.8	1093.8	0.0821	1.9708	2.0529	74.0
76.0	0.44420	0.016063	717.4	717.4	44.043	1050.7	1094.7	0.0858	1.9614	2.0472	76.0
78.0	0.47461	0.016067	673.8	673.9	46.040	1049.5	1095.6	0.0895	1.9520	2.0415	78.0
80.0	0.50683	0.016072	633.3	633.3	48.037	1048.4	1096.4	0.0932	1.9426	2.0359	80.0
82.0	0.54093	0.016077	595.5	595.5	50.033	1047.3	1097.3	0.0969	1.9334	2.0303	82.0
84.0	0.57702	0.016082	560.3	560.3	52.029	1046.1	1098.2	0.1006	1.9242	2.0248	84.0
86.0	0.61518	0.016087	527.5	527.5	54.026	1045.0	1099.0	0.1043	1.9151	2.0193	86.0
88.0	0.65551	0.016093	496.8	496.8	56.022	1043.9	1099.9	0.1079	1.9060	2.0139	88.0
90.0	0.69813	0.016099	468.1	468.1	58.018	1042.7	1100.8	0.1115	1.8970	2.0086	90.0
92.0	0.74313	0.016105	441.3	441.3	60.014	1041.6	1101.6	0.1152	1.8881	2.0033	92.0
94.0	0.79062	0.016111	416.3	416.3	62.010	1040.5	1102.5	0.1188	1.8792	1.9980	94.0
96.0	0.84072	0.016117	392.8	392.9	64.006	1039.3	1103.3	0.1224	1.8704	1.9928	96.0
98.0	0.89356	0.016123	370.9	370.9	66.003	1038.2	1104.2	0.1260	1.8617	1.9876	98.0
100.0	0.94924	0.016130	350.4	350.4	67.999	1037.1	1105.1	0.1295	1.8530	1.9825	100.0
102.0	1.00789	0.016137	331.1	331.1	69.995	1035.9	1105.9	0.1331	1.8444	1.9775	102.0
104.0	1.06965	0.016144	313.1	313.1	71.992	1034.8	1106.8	0.1366	1.8358	1.9725	104.0
106.0	1.1347	0.016151	296.16	296.18	73.99	1033.6	1107.6	0.1402	1.8273	1.9675	106.0
108.0	1.2030	0.016158	280.28	280.30	75.98	1032.5	1108.5	0.1437	1.8188	1.9626	108.0
110.0	1.2750	0.016165	265.37	265.39	77.98	1031.4	1109.3	0.1472	1.8105	1.9577	110.0
112.0	1.3505	0.016173	251.37	251.38	79.98	1030.2	1110.2	0.1507	1.8021	1.9528	112.0
114.0	1.4299	0.016180	238.21	238.22	81.97	1029.1	1111.0	0.1542	1.7938	1.9480	114.0
116.0	1.5133	0.016188	225.84	225.85	83.97	1027.9	1111.9	0.1577	1.7856	1.9433	116.0
118.0	1.6009	0.016196	214.20	214.21	85.97	1026.8	1112.7	0.1611	1.7774	1.9386	118.0
120.0	1.6927	0.016204	203.25	203.26	87.97	1025.6	1113.6	0.1646	1.7693	1.9339	120.0
122.0	1.7891	0.016213	192.94	192.95	89.96	1024.5	1114.4	0.1680	1.7613	1.9293	122.0
124.0	1.8901	0.016221	183.23	183.24	91.96	1023.3	1115.3	0.1715	1.7533	1.9247	124.0
126.0	1.9959	0.016229	174.08	174.09	93.96	1022.2	1116.1	0.1749	1.7453	1.9202	126.0
128.0	2.1068	0.016238	165.45	165.47	95.96	1021.0	1117.0	0.1783	1.7374	1.9157	128.0
130.0	2.2230	0.016247	157.32	157.33	97.96	1019.8	1117.8	0.1817	1.7295	1.9112	130.0
132.0	2.3445	0.016256	149.64	149.66	99.95	1018.7	1118.6	0.1851	1.7217	1.9068	132.0
134.0	2.4717	0.016265	142.40	142.41	101.95	1017.5	1119.5	0.1884	1.7140	1.9024	134.0
136.0	2.6047	0.016274	135.55	135.57	103.95	1016.4	1120.3	0.1918	1.7063	1.8980	136.0
138.0	2.7438	0.016284	129.09	129.11	105.95	1015.2	1121.1	0.1951	1.6986	1.8937	138.0
140.0	2.8892	0.016293	122.98	123.00	107.95	1014.0	1122.0	0.1985	1.6910	1.8895	140.0
142.0	3.0411	0.016303	117.21	117.22	109.95	1012.9	1122.8	0.2018	1.6834	1.8852	142.0
144.0	3.1997	0.016312	111.74	111.76	111.95	1011.7	1123.6	0.2051	1.6759	1.8810	144.0
146.0	3.3653	0.016322	106.58	106.59	113.95	1010.5	1124.5	0.2084	1.6684	1.8769	146.0
148.0	3.5381	0.016332	101.68	101.70	115.95	1009.3	1125.3	0.2117	1.6610	1.8727	148.0
150.0	3.7184	0.016343	97.05	97.07	117.95	1008.2	1126.1	0.2150	1.6536	1.8686	150.0
152.0	3.9065	0.016353	92.66	92.68	119.95	1007.0	1126.9	0.2183	1.6463	1.8646	152.0
154.0	4.1025	0.016363	88.50	88.52	121.95	1005.8	1127.7	0.2216	1.6390	1.8606	154.0
156.0	4.3068	0.016374	84.56	84.57	123.95	1004.6	1128.6	0.2248	1.6318	1.8566	156.0
158.0	4.5197	0.016384	80.82	80.83	125.96	1003.4	1129.4	0.2281	1.6245	1.8526	158.0
160.0	4.7414	0.016395	77.27	77.29	127.96	1002.2	1130.2	0.2313	1.6174	1.8487	160.0
162.0	4.9722	0.016406	73.90	73.92	129.96	1001.0	1131.0	0.2345	1.6103	1.8448	162.0
164.0	5.2124	0.016417	70.70	70.72	131.96	999.8	1131.8	0.2377	1.6032	1.8409	164.0
166.0	5.4623	0.016428	67.67	67.68	133.97	998.6	1132.6	0.2409	1.5961	1.8371	166.0
168.0	5.7223	0.016440	64.78	64.80	135.97	997.4	1133.4	0.2441	1.5892	1.8333	168.0
170.0	5.9926	0.016451	62.04	62.06	137.97	996.2	1134.2	0.2473	1.5822	1.8295	170.0
172.0	6.2736	0.016463	59.43	59.45	139.98	995.0	1135.0	0.2505	1.5753	1.8258	172.0
174.0	6.5656	0.016474	56.95	56.97	141.98	993.8	1135.8	0.2537	1.5684	1.8221	174.0
176.0	6.8690	0.016486	54.59	54.61	143.99	992.6	1136.6	0.2568	1.5616	1.8184	176.0
178.0	7.1840	0.016498	52.35	52.36	145.99	991.4	1137.4	0.2600	1.5548	1.8147	178.0

ITEM B 13 Properties of Saturated H₂O: Temperatures (continued)

Temp Fahr t	Abs Press. Lb per Sq In. p	Specific Volume Sat. Liquid v_f	Evap v_{fg}	Sat. Vapor v_g	Enthalpy Sat. Liquid h_f	Evap h_{fg}	Sat. Vapor h_g	Entropy Sat. Liquid s_f	Evap s_{fg}	Sat. Vapor s_g	Temp Fahr t
180.0	7.5110	0.016510	50.21	50.22	148.00	990.2	1138.2	0.2631	1.5480	1.8111	180.0
182.0	7.850	0.016522	48.172	48.189	150.01	989.0	1139.0	0.2662	1.5413	1.8075	182.0
184.0	8.203	0.016534	46.232	46.249	152.01	987.8	1139.8	0.2694	1.5346	1.8040	184.0
186.0	8.568	0.016547	44.383	44.400	154.02	986.5	1140.5	0.2725	1.5279	1.8004	186.0
188.0	8.947	0.016559	42.621	42.638	156.03	985.3	1141.3	0.2756	1.5213	1.7969	188.0
190.0	9.340	0.016572	40.941	40.957	158.04	984.1	1142.1	0.2787	1.5148	1.7934	190.0
192.0	9.747	0.016585	39.337	39.354	160.05	982.8	1142.9	0.2818	1.5082	1.7900	192.0
194.0	10.168	0.016598	37.808	37.824	162.05	981.6	1143.7	0.2848	1.5017	1.7865	194.0
196.0	10.605	0.016611	36.348	36.364	164.06	980.4	1144.4	0.2879	1.4952	1.7831	196.0
198.0	11.058	0.016624	34.954	34.970	166.08	979.1	1145.2	0.2910	1.4888	1.7798	198.0
200.0	11.526	0.016637	33.622	33.639	168.09	977.9	1146.0	0.2940	1.4824	1.7764	200.0
204.0	12.512	0.016664	31.135	31.151	172.11	975.4	1147.5	0.3001	1.4697	1.7698	204.0
208.0	13.568	0.016691	28.862	28.878	176.14	972.8	1149.0	0.3061	1.4571	1.7632	208.0
212.0	14.696	0.016719	26.782	26.799	180.17	970.3	1150.5	0.3121	1.4447	1.7568	212.0
216.0	15.901	0.016747	24.878	24.894	184.20	967.8	1152.0	0.3181	1.4323	1.7505	216.0
220.0	17.186	0.016775	23.131	23.148	188.23	965.2	1153.4	0.3241	1.4201	1.7442	220.0
224.0	18.556	0.016805	21.529	21.545	192.27	962.6	1154.9	0.3300	1.4081	1.7380	224.0
228.0	20.015	0.016834	20.056	20.073	196.31	960.0	1156.3	0.3359	1.3961	1.7320	228.0
232.0	21.567	0.016864	18.701	18.718	200.35	957.4	1157.8	0.3417	1.3842	1.7260	232.0
236.0	23.216	0.016895	17.454	17.471	204.40	954.8	1159.2	0.3476	1.3725	1.7201	236.0
240.0	24.968	0.016926	16.304	16.321	208.45	952.1	1160.6	0.3533	1.3609	1.7142	240.0
244.0	26.826	0.016958	15.243	15.260	212.50	949.5	1162.0	0.3591	1.3494	1.7085	244.0
248.0	28.796	0.016990	14.264	14.281	216.56	946.8	1163.4	0.3649	1.3379	1.7028	248.0
252.0	30.883	0.017022	13.358	13.375	220.62	944.1	1164.7	0.3706	1.3266	1.6972	252.0
256.0	33.091	0.017055	12.520	12.538	224.69	941.4	1166.1	0.3763	1.3154	1.6917	256.0
260.0	35.427	0.017089	11.745	11.762	228.76	938.6	1167.4	0.3819	1.3043	1.6862	260.0
264.0	37.894	0.017123	11.025	11.042	232.83	935.9	1168.7	0.3876	1.2933	1.6808	264.0
268.0	40.500	0.017157	10.358	10.375	236.91	933.1	1170.0	0.3932	1.2823	1.6755	268.0
272.0	43.249	0.017193	9.738	9.755	240.99	930.3	1171.3	0.3987	1.2715	1.6702	272.0
276.0	46.147	0.017228	9.162	9.180	245.08	927.5	1172.5	0.4043	1.2607	1.6650	276.0
280.0	49.200	0.017264	8.627	8.644	249.17	924.6	1173.8	0.4098	1.2501	1.6599	280.0
284.0	52.414	0.01730	8.1280	8.1453	253.3	921.7	1175.0	0.4154	1.2395	1.6548	284.0
288.0	55.795	0.01734	7.6634	7.6807	257.4	918.8	1176.2	0.4208	1.2290	1.6498	288.0
292.0	59.350	0.01738	7.2301	7.2475	261.5	915.9	1177.4	0.4263	1.2186	1.6449	292.0
296.0	63.084	0.01741	6.8259	6.8433	265.6	913.0	1178.6	0.4317	1.2082	1.6400	296.0
300.0	67.005	0.01745	6.4483	6.4658	269.7	910.0	1179.7	0.4372	1.1979	1.6351	300.0
304.0	71.119	0.01749	6.0955	6.1130	273.8	907.0	1180.9	0.4426	1.1877	1.6303	304.0
308.0	75.433	0.01753	5.7655	5.7830	278.0	904.0	1182.0	0.4479	1.1776	1.6256	308.0
312.0	79.953	0.01757	5.4566	5.4742	282.1	901.0	1183.1	0.4533	1.1676	1.6209	312.0
316.0	84.688	0.01761	5.1673	5.1849	286.3	897.9	1184.1	0.4586	1.1576	1.6162	316.0
320.0	89.643	0.01766	4.8961	4.9138	290.4	894.8	1185.2	0.4640	1.1477	1.6116	320.0
324.0	94.826	0.01770	4.6418	4.6595	294.6	891.6	1186.2	0.4692	1.1378	1.6071	324.0
328.0	100.245	0.01774	4.4030	4.4208	298.7	888.5	1187.2	0.4745	1.1280	1.6025	328.0
332.0	105.907	0.01779	4.1788	4.1966	302.9	885.3	1188.2	0.4798	1.1183	1.5981	332.0
336.0	111.820	0.01783	3.9681	3.9859	307.1	882.1	1189.1	0.4850	1.1086	1.5936	336.0
340.0	117.992	0.01787	3.7699	3.7878	311.3	878.8	1190.1	0.4902	1.0990	1.5892	340.0
344.0	124.430	0.01792	3.5834	3.6013	315.5	875.5	1191.0	0.4954	1.0894	1.5849	344.0
348.0	131.142	0.01797	3.4078	3.4258	319.7	872.2	1191.1	0.5006	1.0799	1.5806	348.0
352.0	138.138	0.01801	3.2423	3.2603	323.9	868.9	1192.7	0.5058	1.0705	1.5763	352.0
356.0	145.424	0.01806	3.0863	3.1044	328.1	865.5	1193.6	0.5110	1.0611	1.5721	356.0
360.0	153.010	0.01811	2.9392	2.9573	332.3	862.1	1194.4	0.5161	1.0517	1.5678	360.0
364.0	160.903	0.01816	2.8002	2.8184	336.5	858.6	1195.2	0.5212	1.0424	1.5637	364.0
368.0	169.113	0.01821	2.6691	2.6873	340.8	855.1	1195.9	0.5263	1.0332	1.5595	368.0
372.0	177.648	0.01826	2.5451	2.5633	345.0	851.6	1196.7	0.5314	1.0240	1.5554	372.0
376.0	186.517	0.01831	2.4279	2.4462	349.3	848.1	1197.4	0.5365	1.0148	1.5513	376.0
380.0	195.729	0.01836	2.3170	2.3353	353.6	844.5	1198.0	0.5416	1.0057	1.5473	380.0
384.0	205.294	0.01842	2.2120	2.2304	357.9	840.8	1198.7	0.5466	0.9966	1.5432	384.0
388.0	215.220	0.01847	2.1126	2.1311	362.2	837.2	1199.3	0.5516	0.9876	1.5392	388.0
392.0	225.516	0.01853	2.0184	2.0369	366.5	833.4	1199.9	0.5567	0.9786	1.5352	392.0
396.0	236.193	0.01858	1.9291	1.9477	370.8	829.7	1200.4	0.5617	0.9696	1.5313	396.0
400.0	247.259	0.01864	1.8444	1.8630	375.1	825.9	1201.0	0.5667	0.9607	1.5274	400.0
404.0	258.725	0.01870	1.7640	1.7827	379.4	822.0	1201.5	0.5717	0.9518	1.5234	404.0
408.0	270.600	0.01875	1.6877	1.7064	383.8	818.2	1201.9	0.5766	0.9429	1.5195	408.0
412.0	282.894	0.01881	1.6152	1.6340	388.1	814.2	1202.4	0.5816	0.9341	1.5157	412.0
416.0	295.617	0.01887	1.5463	1.5651	392.5	810.2	1202.8	0.5866	0.9253	1.5118	416.0
420.0	308.780	0.01894	1.4808	1.4997	396.9	806.2	1203.1	0.5915	0.9165	1.5080	420.0
424.0	322.391	0.01900	1.4184	1.4374	401.3	802.2	1203.5	0.5964	0.9077	1.5042	424.0
428.0	336.463	0.01906	1.3591	1.3782	405.7	798.0	1203.7	0.6014	0.8990	1.5004	428.0
432.0	351.00	0.01913	1.30266	1.32179	410.1	793.9	1204.0	0.6063	0.8903	1.4966	432.0
436.0	366.03	0.01919	1.24887	1.26806	414.6	789.7	1204.2	0.6112	0.8816	1.4928	436.0
440.0	381.54	0.01926	1.19761	1.21687	419.0	785.4	1204.4	0.6161	0.8730	1.4890	440.0
444.0	397.56	0.01933	1.14874	1.16806	423.5	781.1	1204.6	0.6210	0.8643	1.4853	444.0
448.0	414.09	0.01940	1.10212	1.12152	428.0	776.7	1204.7	0.6259	0.8557	1.4815	448.0
452.0	431.14	0.01947	1.05764	1.07711	432.5	772.3	1204.8	0.6308	0.8471	1.4778	452.0
456.0	448.73	0.01954	1.01518	1.03472	437.0	767.8	1204.8	0.6356	0.8385	1.4741	456.0

ITEM B 13 Properties of Saturated H₂O: Temperatures (concluded)

Temp Fahr t	Abs Press. Lb per Sq In. p	Specific Volume Sat. Liquid v_f	Evap v_{fg}	Sat. Vapor v_g	Enthalpy Sat Liquid h_f	Evap h_{fg}	Sat Vapor h_g	Entropy Sat. Liquid s_f	Evap s_{fg}	Sat. Vapor s_g	Temp Fahr t
460.0	466.87	0.01961	0.97463	0.99424	441.5	763.2	1204.8	0.6405	0.8299	1.4704	460.0
464.0	485.56	0.01969	0.93588	0.95557	446.1	758.6	1204.7	0.6454	0.8213	1.4667	464.0
468.0	504.83	0.01976	0.89885	0.91862	450.7	754.0	1204.6	0.6502	0.8127	1.4629	468.0
472.0	524.67	0.01984	0.86345	0.88329	455.2	749.3	1204.5	0.6551	0.8042	1.4592	472.0
476.0	545.11	0.01992	0.82958	0.84950	459.9	744.5	1204.3	0.6599	0.7956	1.4555	476.0
480.0	566.15	0.02000	0.79716	0.81717	464.5	739.6	1204.1	0.6648	0.7871	1.4518	480.0
484.0	587.81	0.02009	0.76613	0.78622	469.1	734.7	1203.8	0.6696	0.7785	1.4481	484.0
488.0	610.10	0.02017	0.73641	0.75658	473.8	729.7	1203.5	0.6745	0.7700	1.4444	488.0
492.0	633.03	0.02026	0.70794	0.72820	478.5	724.6	1203.1	0.6793	0.7614	1.4407	492.0
496.0	656.61	0.02034	0.68065	0.70100	483.2	719.5	1202.7	0.6842	0.7528	1.4370	496.0
500.0	680.86	0.02043	0.65448	0.67492	487.9	714.3	1202.2	0.6890	0.7443	1.4333	500.0
504.0	705.78	0.02053	0.62938	0.64991	492.7	709.0	1201.7	0.6939	0.7357	1.4296	504.0
508.0	731.40	0.02062	0.60530	0.62592	497.5	703.7	1201.1	0.6987	0.7271	1.4258	508.0
512.0	757.72	0.02072	0.58218	0.60289	502.3	698.2	1200.5	0.7036	0.7185	1.4221	512.0
516.0	784.76	0.02081	0.55997	0.58079	507.1	692.7	1199.8	0.7085	0.7099	1.4183	516.0
520.0	812.53	0.02091	0.53864	0.55956	512.0	687.0	1199.0	0.7133	0.7013	1.4146	520.0
524.0	841.04	0.02102	0.51814	0.53916	516.9	681.3	1198.2	0.7182	0.6926	1.4108	524.0
528.0	870.31	0.02112	0.49843	0.51955	521.8	675.5	1197.3	0.7231	0.6839	1.4070	528.0
532.0	900.34	0.02123	0.47947	0.50070	526.8	669.6	1196.4	0.7280	0.6752	1.4032	532.0
536.0	931.17	0.02134	0.46123	0.48257	531.7	663.6	1195.4	0.7329	0.6665	1.3993	536.0
540.0	962.79	0.02146	0.44367	0.46513	536.8	657.5	1194.3	0.7378	0.6577	1.3954	540.0
544.0	995.22	0.02157	0.42677	0.44834	541.8	651.3	1193.1	0.7427	0.6489	1.3915	544.0
548.0	1028.49	0.02169	0.41048	0.43217	546.9	645.0	1191.9	0.7476	0.6400	1.3876	548.0
552.0	1062.59	0.02182	0.39479	0.41660	552.0	638.5	1190.6	0.7525	0.6311	1.3837	552.0
556.0	1097.55	0.02194	0.37966	0.40160	557.2	632.0	1189.2	0.7575	0.6222	1.3797	556.0
560.0	1133.38	0.02207	0.36507	0.38714	562.4	625.3	1187.7	0.7625	0.6132	1.3757	560.0
564.0	1170.10	0.02221	0.35099	0.37320	567.6	618.5	1186.1	0.7674	0.6041	1.3716	564.0
568.0	1207.72	0.02235	0.33741	0.35975	572.9	611.5	1184.5	0.7725	0.5950	1.3675	568.0
572.0	1246.26	0.02249	0.32429	0.34678	578.3	604.5	1182.7	0.7775	0.5859	1.3634	572.0
576.0	1285.74	0.02264	0.31162	0.33426	583.7	597.2	1180.9	0.7825	0.5766	1.3592	576.0
580.0	1326.17	0.02279	0.29937	0.32216	589.1	589.9	1179.0	0.7876	0.5673	1.3550	580.0
584.0	1367.7	0.02295	0.28753	0.31048	594.6	582.4	1176.9	0.7927	0.5580	1.3507	584.0
588.0	1410.0	0.02311	0.27608	0.29919	600.1	574.7	1174.8	0.7978	0.5485	1.3464	588.0
592.0	1453.3	0.02328	0.26499	0.28827	605.7	566.8	1172.6	0.8030	0.5390	1.3420	592.0
596.0	1497.8	0.02345	0.25425	0.27770	611.4	558.8	1170.2	0.8082	0.5293	1.3375	596.0
600.0	1543.2	0.02364	0.24384	0.26747	617.1	550.6	1167.7	0.8134	0.5196	1.3330	600.0
604.0	1589.7	0.02382	0.23374	0.25757	622.9	542.2	1165.1	0.8187	0.5097	1.3284	604.0
608.0	1637.3	0.02402	0.22394	0.24796	628.8	533.6	1162.4	0.8240	0.4997	1.3238	608.0
612.0	1686.1	0.02422	0.21442	0.23865	634.8	524.7	1159.5	0.8294	0.4896	1.3190	612.0
616.6	1735.9	0.02444	0.20516	0.22960	640.8	515.6	1156.4	0.8348	0.4794	1.3141	616.0
620.0	1786.9	0.02466	0.19615	0.22081	646.9	506.3	1153.2	0.8403	0.4689	1.3092	620.0
624.0	1839.0	0.02489	0.18737	0.21226	653.1	496.6	1149.8	0.8458	0.4583	1.3041	624.0
628.0	1892.4	0.02514	0.17880	0.20394	659.5	486.7	1146.1	0.8514	0.4474	1.2988	628.0
632.0	1947.0	0.02539	0.17044	0.19583	665.9	476.4	1142.2	0.8571	0.4364	1.2934	632.0
636.0	2002.8	0.02566	0.16226	0.18792	672.4	465.7	1138.1	0.8628	0.4251	1.2879	636.0
640.0	2059.9	0.02595	0.15427	0.18021	679.1	454.6	1133.7	0.8686	0.4134	1.2821	640.0
644.0	2118.3	0.02625	0.14644	0.17269	685.9	443.1	1129.0	0.8746	0.4015	1.2761	644.0
648.0	2178.1	0.02657	0.13876	0.16534	692.9	431.1	1124.0	0.8806	0.3893	1.2699	648.0
652.0	2239.2	0.02691	0.13124	0.15816	700.0	418.7	1118.7	0.8868	0.3767	1.2634	652.0
656.0	2301.7	0.02728	0.12387	0.15115	707.4	405.7	1113.1	0.8931	0.3637	1.2567	656.0
660.0	2365.7	0.02768	0.11663	0.14431	714.9	392.1	1107.0	0.8995	0.3502	1.2498	660.0
664.0	2431.1	0.02811	0.10947	0.13757	722.9	377.7	1100.6	0.9064	0.3361	1.2425	664.0
668.0	2498.1	0.02858	0.10229	0.13087	731.5	362.1	1093.5	0.9137	0.3210	1.2347	668.0
672.0	2566.6	0.02911	0.09514	0.12424	740.2	345.7	1085.9	0.9212	0.3054	1.2266	672.0
676.0	2636.8	0.02970	0.08799	0.11769	749.2	328.5	1077.6	0.9287	0.2892	1.2179	676.0
680.0	2708.6	0.03037	0.08080	0.11117	758.5	310.1	1068.5	0.9365	0.2720	1.2086	680.0
684.0	2782.1	0.03114	0.07349	0.10463	768.2	290.2	1058.4	0.9447	0.2537	1.1984	684.0
688.0	2857.4	0.03204	0.06595	0.09799	778.8	268.2	1047.0	0.9535	0.2337	1.1872	688.0
692.0	2934.5	0.03313	0.05797	0.09110	790.5	243.1	1033.6	0.9634	0.2110	1.1744	692.0
696.0	3013.4	0.03455	0.04916	0.08371	804.4	212.8	1017.2	0.9749	0.1841	1.1591	696.0
700.0	3094.3	0.03662	0.03857	0.07519	822.4	172.7	995.2	0.9901	0.1490	1.1390	700.0
702.0	3135.5	0.03824	0.03173	0.06997	835.0	144.7	979.7	1.0006	0.1246	1.1252	702.0
704.0	3177.2	0.04108	0.02192	0.06300	854.2	102.0	956.2	1.0169	0.0876	1.1046	704.0
705.0	3198.3	0.04427	0.01304	0.05730	873.0	61.4	934.4	1.0329	0.0527	1.0856	705.0
705.47*	3208.2	0.05078	0.00000	0.05078	906.0	0.0	906.0	1.0612	0.0000	1.0612	705.47*

*Critical temperature

ITEM B 14 Properties of Saturated H_2O: Pressures

Abs Press. Lb/Sq In. p	Temp Fahr t	Specific Volume			Enthalpy			Entropy			Abs Press. Lb/Sq In. p
		Sat. Liquid v_f	Evap v_{fg}	Sat. Vapor v_g	Sat. Liquid h_f	Evap h_{tg}	Sat. Vapor h_g	Sat. Liquid s_f	Evap s_{fg}	Sat. Vapor s_g	
0.08865	32.018	0.016022	3302.4	3302.4	0.0003	1075.5	1075.5	0.0000	2.1872	2.1872	0.08865
0.25	59.323	0.016032	1235.5	1235.5	27.382	1060.1	1087.4	0.0542	2.0425	2.0967	0.25
0.50	79.586	0.016071	641.5	641.5	47.623	1048.6	1096.3	0.0925	1.9446	2.0370	0.50
1.0	101.74	0.016136	333.59	333.60	69.73	1036.1	1105.8	0.1326	1.8455	1.9781	1.0
5.0	162.24	0.016407	73.515	73.532	130.20	1000.9	1131.1	0.2349	1.6094	1.8443	5.0
10.0	193.21	0.016592	38.404	38.420	161.26	982.1	1143.3	0.2836	1.5043	1.7879	10.0
14.696	212.00	0.016719	26.782	26.799	180.17	970.3	1150.5	0.3121	1.4447	1.7568	14.696
15.0	213.03	0.016726	26.274	26.290	181.21	969.7	1150.9	0.3137	1.4415	1.7552	15.0
20.0	227.96	0.016834	20.070	20.087	196.27	960.1	1156.3	0.3358	1.3962	1.7320	20.0
30.0	250.34	0.017009	13.7266	13.7436	218.9	945.2	1164.1	0.3682	1.3313	1.6995	30.0
40.0	267.25	0.017151	10.4794	10.4965	236.1	933.6	1169.8	0.3921	1.2844	1.6765	40.0
50.0	281.02	0.017274	8.4967	8.5140	250.2	923.9	1174.1	0.4112	1.2474	1.6586	50.0
60.0	292.71	0.017383	7.1562	7.1736	262.2	915.4	1177.6	0.4273	1.2167	1.6440	60.0
70.0	302.93	0.017482	6.1875	6.2050	272.7	907.8	1180.6	0.4411	1.1905	1.6316	70.0
80.0	312.04	0.017573	5.4536	5.4711	282.1	900.9	1183.1	0.4534	1.1675	1.6208	80.0
90.0	320.28	0.017659	4.8779	4.8953	290.7	894.6	1185.3	0.4643	1.1470	1.6113	90.0
100.0	327.82	0.017740	4.4133	4.4310	298.5	888.6	1187.2	0.4743	1.1284	1.6027	100.0
110.0	334.79	0.01782	4.0306	4.0484	305.8	883.1	1188.9	0.4834	1.1115	1.5950	110.0
120.0	341.27	0.01789	3.7097	3.7275	312.6	877.8	1190.4	0.4919	1.0960	1.5879	120.0
130.0	347.33	0.01796	3.4364	3.4544	319.0	872.8	1191.7	0.4998	1.0815	1.5813	130.0
140.0	353.04	0.01803	3.2010	3.2190	325.0	868.0	1193.0	0.5071	1.0681	1.5752	140.0
150.0	358.43	0.01809	2.9958	3.0139	330.6	863.4	1194.1	0.5141	1.0554	1.5695	150.0
160.0	363.55	0.01815	2.8155	2.8336	336.1	859.0	1195.1	0.5206	1.0435	1.5641	160.0
170.0	368.42	0.01821	2.6556	2.6738	341.2	854.8	1196.0	0.5269	1.0322	1.5591	170.0
180.0	373.08	0.01827	2.5129	2.5312	346.2	850.7	1196.9	0.5328	1.0215	1.5543	180.0
190.0	377.53	0.01833	2.3847	2.4030	350.9	846.7	1197.6	0.5384	1.0113	1.5498	190.0
200.0	381.80	0.01839	2.2689	2.2873	355.5	842.8	1198.3	0.5438	1.0016	1.5454	200.0
210.0	385.91	0.01844	2.16373	2.18217	359.9	839.1	1199.0	0.5490	0.9923	1.5413	210.0
220.0	389.88	0.01850	2.06779	2.08629	364.2	835.4	1199.6	0.5540	0.9834	1.5374	220.0
230.0	393.70	0.01855	1.97991	1.99846	368.3	831.8	1200.1	0.5588	0.9748	1.5336	230.0
240.0	397.39	0.01860	1.89909	1.91769	372.3	828.4	1200.6	0.5634	0.9665	1.5299	240.0
250.0	400.97	0.01865	1.82452	1.84317	376.1	825.0	1201.1	0.5679	0.9585	1.5264	250.0
260.0	404.44	0.01870	1.75548	1.77418	379.9	821.6	1201.5	0.5722	0.9508	1.5230	260.0
270.0	407.80	0.01875	1.69137	1.71013	383.6	818.3	1201.9	0.5764	0.9433	1.5197	270.0
280.0	411.07	0.01880	1.63169	1.65049	387.1	815.1	1202.3	0.5805	0.9361	1.5166	280.0
290.0	414.25	0.01885	1.57597	1.59482	390.6	812.0	1202.6	0.5844	0.9291	1.5135	290.0
300.0	417.35	0.01889	1.52384	1.54274	394.0	808.9	1202.9	0.5882	0.9223	1.5105	300.0
350.0	431.73	0.01912	1.30642	1.32554	409.8	794.2	1204.0	0.6059	0.8909	1.4968	350.0
400.0	444.60	0.01934	1.14162	1.16095	424.2	780.4	1204.6	0.6217	0.8630	1.4847	400.0
450.0	456.28	0.01954	1.01224	1.03179	437.3	767.5	1204.8	0.6360	0.8378	1.4738	450.0
500.0	467.01	0.01975	0.90787	0.92762	449.5	755.1	1204.7	0.6490	0.8148	1.4639	500.0
550.0	476.94	0.01994	0.82183	0.84177	460.9	743.3	1204.3	0.6611	0.7936	1.4547	550.0
600.0	486.20	0.02013	0.74962	0.76975	471.7	732.0	1203.7	0.6723	0.7738	1.4461	600.0
650.0	494.89	0.02032	0.68811	0.70843	481.9	720.9	1202.8	0.6828	0.7552	1.4381	650.0
700.0	503.08	0.02050	0.63505	0.65556	491.6	710.2	1201.8	0.6928	0.7377	1.4304	700.0
750.0	510.84	0.02069	0.58880	0.60949	500.9	699.8	1200.7	0.7022	0.7210	1.4232	750.0
800.0	518.21	0.02087	0.54809	0.56896	509.8	689.6	1199.4	0.7111	0.7051	1.4163	800.0
850.0	525.24	0.02105	0.51197	0.53302	518.4	679.5	1198.0	0.7197	0.6899	1.4096	850.0
900.0	531.95	0.02123	0.47968	0.50091	526.7	669.7	1196.4	0.7279	0.6753	1.4032	900.0
950.0	538.39	0.02141	0.45064	0.47205	534.7	660.0	1194.7	0.7358	0.6612	1.3970	950.0
1000.0	544.58	0.02159	0.42436	0.44596	542.6	650.4	1192.9	0.7434	0.6476	1.3910	1000.0
1050.0	550.53	0.02177	0.40047	0.42224	550.1	640.9	1191.0	0.7507	0.6344	1.3851	1050.0
1100.0	556.28	0.02195	0.37863	0.40058	557.5	631.5	1189.1	0.7578	0.6216	1.3794	1100.0
1150.0	561.82	0.02214	0.35859	0.38073	564.8	622.2	1187.0	0.7647	0.6091	1.3738	1150.0
1200.0	567.19	0.02232	0.34013	0.36245	571.9	613.0	1184.8	0.7714	0.5969	1.3683	1200.0
1250.0	572.38	0.02250	0.32306	0.34556	578.8	603.8	1182.6	0.7780	0.5850	1.3630	1250.0
1300.0	577.42	0.02269	0.30722	0.32991	585.6	594.6	1180.2	0.7843	0.5733	1.3577	1300.0
1350.0	582.32	0.02288	0.29250	0.31537	592.3	585.4	1177.8	0.7906	0.5620	1.3525	1350.0
1400.0	587.07	0.02307	0.27871	0.30178	598.8	576.5	1175.3	0.7966	0.5507	1.3474	1400.0
1450.0	591.70	0.02327	0.26584	0.28911	605.3	567.4	1172.8	0.8026	0.5397	1.3423	1450.0
1500.0	596.20	0.02346	0.25372	0.27719	611.7	558.4	1170.1	0.8085	0.5288	1.3373	1500.0
1550.0	600.59	0.02366	0.24235	0.26601	618.0	549.4	1167.4	0.8142	0.5182	1.3324	1550.0
1600.0	604.87	0.02387	0.23159	0.25545	624.2	540.3	1164.5	0.8199	0.5076	1.3274	1600.0
1650.0	609.05	0.02407	0.22143	0.24551	630.4	531.3	1161.6	0.8254	0.4971	1.3225	1650.0
1700.0	613.13	0.02428	0.21178	0.23607	636.5	522.2	1158.6	0.8309	0.4867	1.3176	1700.0
1750.0	617.12	0.02450	0.20263	0.22713	642.5	513.1	1155.6	0.8363	0.4765	1.3128	1750.0
1800.0	621.02	0.02472	0.19390	0.21861	648.5	503.8	1152.3	0.8417	0.4662	1.3079	1800.0
1850.0	624.83	0.02495	0.18558	0.21052	654.5	494.6	1149.0	0.8470	0.4561	1.3030	1850.0
1900.0	628.56	0.02517	0.17761	0.20278	660.4	485.2	1145.6	0.8522	0.4459	1.2981	1900.0
1950.0	632.22	0.02541	0.16999	0.19540	666.3	475.8	1142.0	0.8574	0.4358	1.2931	1950.0
2000.0	635.80	0.02565	0.16266	0.18831	672.1	466.2	1138.3	0.8625	0.4256	1.2881	2000.0
2100.0	642.76	0.02615	0.14885	0.17501	683.8	446.7	1130.5	0.8727	0.4053	1.2780	2100.0
2200.0	649.45	0.02669	0.13603	0.16272	695.5	426.7	1122.2	0.8828	0.3848	1.2676	2200.0
2300.0	655.89	0.02727	0.12406	0.15133	707.2	406.0	1113.2	0.8929	0.3640	1.2569	2300.0
2400.0	662.11	0.02790	0.11287	0.14076	719.0	384.8	1103.7	0.9031	0.3430	1.2460	2400.0
2500.0	668.11	0.02859	0.10209	0.13068	731.7	361.6	1093.3	0.9139	0.3206	1.2345	2500.0
2600.0	673.91	0.02938	0.09172	0.12110	744.5	337.6	1082.0	0.9247	0.2977	1.2225	2600.0
2700.0	679.53	0.03029	0.08165	0.11194	757.3	312.3	1069.7	0.9356	0.2741	1.2097	2700.0
2800.0	684.96	0.03134	0.07171	0.10305	770.7	285.1	1055.8	0.9468	0.2491	1.1958	2800.0
2900.0	690.22	0.03262	0.06158	0.09420	785.1	254.7	1039.8	0.9588	0.2215	1.1803	2900.0
3000.0	695.33	0.03428	0.05073	0.08500	801.8	218.4	1020.3	0.9728	0.1891	1.1619	3000.0
3100.0	700.28	0.03681	0.03771	0.07452	824.0	169.3	993.3	0.9914	0.1460	1.1373	3100.0
3200.0	705.08	0.04472	0.01191	0.05663	875.5	56.1	931.6	1.0351	0.0482	1.0832	3200.0
3208.2*	705.47	0.05078	0.00000	0.05078	906.0	0.0	906.0	1.0612	0.0000	1.0612	3208.2*

*Critical pressure

ITEM B 15 Properties of Superheated Steam

Abs Press. Lb/Sq In. (Sat. Temp)		Sat. Water	Sat. Steam	200	250	300	350	400	450	500	600	700	800	900	1000	1100	1200
1 (101.74)	Sh			98.26	148.26	198.26	248.26	298.26	348.26	398.26	498.26	598.26	698.26	798.26	898.26	998.26	1098.26
	v	0.01614	333.6	392.5	422.4	452.3	482.1	511.9	541.7	571.5	631.1	690.7	750.2	809.8	869.4	929.1	988.7
	h	69.73	1105.8	1150.2	1172.9	1195.7	1218.7	1241.8	1265.1	1288.6	1336.1	1384.5	1431.0	1480.8	1531.4	1583.0	1635.4
	s	0.1326	1.9781	2.0509	2.0841	2.1152	2.1445	2.1722	2.1985	2.2237	2.2708	2.3144	2.3512	2.3892	2.4251	2.4592	2.4918
5 (162.24)	Sh			37.76	87.76	137.76	187.76	237.76	287.76	337.76	437.76	537.76	637.76	737.76	837.76	937.76	1037.76
	v	0.01641	73.53	78.14	84.21	90.24	96.25	102.24	108.23	114.21	126.15	138.08	150.01	161.94	173.86	185.78	197.70
	h	130.20	1131.1	1148.6	1171.7	1194.8	1218.0	1241.3	1264.7	1288.2	1335.9	1384.3	1433.6	1483.7	1534.7	1586.7	1639.6
	s	0.2349	1.8443	1.8716	1.9054	1.9369	1.9664	1.9943	2.0208	2.0460	2.0932	2.1369	2.1776	2.2159	2.2521	2.2866	2.3194
10 (193.21)	Sh			6.79	56.79	106.79	156.79	206.79	256.79	306.79	406.79	506.79	606.79	706.79	806.79	906.79	1006.79
	v	0.01659	38.42	38.84	41.93	44.98	48.02	51.03	54.04	57.04	63.03	69.00	74.98	80.94	86.91	92.87	98.84
	h	161.26	1143.3	1146.6	1170.2	1193.7	1217.1	1240.6	1264.1	1287.8	1335.5	1384.0	1433.4	1483.5	1534.6	1586.6	1639.5
	s	0.2836	1.7879	1.7928	1.8273	1.8593	1.8892	1.9173	1.9439	1.9692	2.0166	2.0603	2.1011	2.1394	2.1757	2.2101	2.2430
14.696 (212.00)	Sh				38.00	88.00	138.00	188.00	238.00	288.00	388.00	488.00	588.00	688.00	788.00	888.00	988.00
	v	0.0167	26.828		28.44	30.52	32.61	34.65	36.73	38.75	42.83	46.91	50.97	55.03	59.09	63.19	67.25
	h	180.07	1150.4		1169.2	1192.0	1215.4	1238.9	1262.1	1285.4	1333.0	1381.4	1430.5	1480.4	1531.1	1582.7	1635.1
	s	0.3120	1.7566		1.7838	1.8148	1.8446	1.8727	1.8989	1.9238	1.9709	2.0145	2.0551	2.0932	2.1292	2.1634	2.1960
15 (213.03)	Sh				36.97	86.97	136.97	186.97	236.97	286.97	386.97	486.97	586.97	686.97	786.97	886.97	986.97
	v	0.01673	26.290		27.837	29.899	31.939	33.963	35.977	37.985	41.986	45.978	49.964	53.946	57.926	61.905	65.882
	h	181.21	1150.9		1168.7	1192.5	1216.2	1239.9	1263.6	1287.3	1335.2	1383.8	1433.2	1483.4	1534.5	1586.5	1639.4
	s	0.3137	1.7552		1.7809	1.8134	1.8437	1.8720	1.8988	1.9242	1.9717	2.0155	2.0563	2.0946	2.1309	2.1653	2.1982
20 (227.96)	Sh				22.04	72.04	122.04	172.04	222.04	272.04	372.04	472.04	572.04	672.04	772.04	872.04	972.04
	v	0.01683	20.087		20.788	22.356	23.900	25.428	26.946	28.457	31.466	34.465	37.458	40.447	43.435	46.420	49.405
	h	196.27	1156.3		1167.1	1191.4	1215.4	1239.2	1263.0	1286.9	1334.9	1383.5	1432.9	1483.2	1534.3	1586.3	1639.3
	s	0.3358	1.7320		1.7475	1.7805	1.8111	1.8397	1.8666	1.8921	1.9397	1.9836	2.0244	2.0628	2.0991	2.1336	2.1665
25 (240.07)	Sh				9.93	59.93	109.93	159.93	209.93	259.93	359.93	459.93	559.93	659.93	759.93	859.93	959.93
	v	0.01693	16.301		16.558	17.829	19.076	20.307	21.527	22.740	25.153	27.557	29.954	32.348	34.740	37.130	39.518
	h	208.52	1160.6		1165.6	1190.2	1214.5	1238.5	1262.5	1286.1	1334.6	1383.3	1432.7	1483.0	1534.2	1586.2	1639.2
	s	0.3535	1.7141		1.7212	1.7547	1.7856	1.8145	1.8415	1.8672	1.9149	1.9588	1.9997	2.0381	2.0744	2.1089	2.1418
30 (250.34)	Sh					49.66	99.66	149.66	199.66	249.66	349.66	449.66	549.66	649.66	749.66	849.66	949.66
	v	0.01701	13.744			14.810	15.859	16.892	17.914	18.929	20.945	22.951	24.952	26.949	28.943	30.936	32.927
	h	218.93	1164.1			1189.0	1213.6	1237.8	1261.9	1286.0	1334.2	1383.0	1432.5	1482.8	1534.0	1586.1	1639.0
	s	0.3682	1.6995			1.7334	1.7647	1.7937	1.8210	1.8467	1.8946	1.9386	1.9795	2.0179	2.0543	2.0888	2.1217
35 (259.29)	Sh					40.71	90.71	140.71	190.71	240.71	340.71	440.71	540.71	640.71	740.71	840.71	940.71
	v	0.01708	11.896			12.654	13.562	14.453	15.334	16.207	17.939	19.662	21.379	23.092	24.803	26.512	28.220
	h	228.03	1167.1			1187.8	1212.7	1237.1	1261.3	1285.5	1333.9	1382.8	1432.3	1482.7	1533.9	1586.0	1638.9
	s	0.3809	1.6872			1.7152	1.7468	1.7761	1.8035	1.8294	1.8774	1.9214	1.9624	2.0009	2.0372	2.0717	2.1046
40 (267.25)	Sh					32.75	82.75	132.75	182.75	232.75	332.75	432.75	532.75	632.75	732.75	832.75	932.75
	v	0.01715	10.497			11.036	11.838	12.624	13.398	14.165	15.685	17.195	18.699	20.199	21.697	23.194	24.689
	h	236.14	1169.8			1186.6	1211.7	1236.4	1260.8	1285.0	1333.6	1382.5	1432.1	1482.5	1533.7	1585.8	1638.8
	s	0.3921	1.6765			1.6992	1.7312	1.7608	1.7883	1.8143	1.8624	1.9065	1.9476	1.9860	2.0224	2.0569	2.0899
45 (274.43)	Sh					25.57	75.57	125.57	175.57	225.57	325.57	425.57	525.57	625.57	725.57	825.57	925.57
	v	0.01722	9.403			9.782	10.503	11.206	11.897	12.584	13.939	15.284	16.623	17.959	19.292	20.623	21.954
	h	243.47	1172.1			1185.4	1210.8	1235.7	1260.2	1284.6	1333.3	1382.3	1432.0	1482.4	1533.6	1585.7	1638.8
	s	0.4021	1.6671			1.6949	1.7174	1.7472	1.7749	1.8010	1.8492	1.8934	1.9345	1.9730	2.0094	2.0439	2.0769
50 (281.02)	Sh					18.98	68.98	118.98	168.98	218.98	318.98	418.98	518.98	618.98	718.98	818.98	918.98
	v	0.1727	8.514			8.769	9.424	10.062	10.688	11.306	12.529	13.741	14.947	16.150	17.350	18.549	19.746
	h	250.21	1174.1			1184.1	1209.9	1234.9	1259.6	1284.1	1332.9	1382.0	1431.7	1482.2	1533.4	1585.6	1638.6
	s	0.4112	1.6586			1.6720	1.7048	1.7349	1.7628	1.7890	1.8374	1.8816	1.9227	1.9613	1.9977	2.0322	2.0652
55 (287.07)	Sh					12.93	62.93	112.93	162.93	212.93	312.93	412.93	512.93	612.93	712.93	812.93	912.93
	v	0.01733	7.787			7.947	8.550	9.134	9.706	10.270	11.385	12.489	13.587	14.682	15.775	16.865	17.954
	h	256.42	1176.0			1182.9	1208.9	1234.3	1259.1	1283.6	1332.6	1381.8	1431.6	1482.0	1533.3	1585.5	1638.5
	s	0.4196	1.6510			1.6602	1.6934	1.7238	1.7518	1.7781	1.8267	1.8710	1.9123	1.9507	1.9871	2.0217	2.0546
60 (292.71)	Sh					7.29	57.29	107.29	157.29	207.29	307.29	407.29	507.29	607.29	707.29	807.29	907.29
	v	0.1738	7.174			7.257	7.815	8.354	8.881	9.400	10.425	11.438	12.446	13.450	14.452	15.452	16.450
	h	262.21	1177.6			1181.6	1208.0	1233.5	1258.5	1283.2	1332.3	1381.5	1431.3	1481.8	1533.2	1585.3	1638.4
	s	0.4273	1.6440			1.6492	**1.6830**	1.7134	1.7417	1.7681	1.8168	1.8612	1.9024	1.9410	1.9774	2.0120	2.0450
65 (297.98)	Sh					2.02	52.02	102.02	152.02	202.02	302.02	402.02	502.02	602.02	702.02	802.02	902.02
	v	0.01743	6.653			6.675	7.195	7.697	8.186	8.667	9.615	10.552	11.484	12.412	13.337	14.261	15.183
	h	267.63	1179.1			1180.3	1207.0	1232.7	1257.9	1282.7	1331.9	1381.3	1431.1	1481.6	1533.0	1585.2	1638.3
	s	0.4344	1.6375			1.6390	1.6731	1.7040	1.7324	1.7590	1.8077	1.8522	1.8935	1.9321	1.9685	2.0031	2.0361
70 (302.93)	Sh						47.07	97.07	147.07	197.07	297.07	397.07	497.07	597.07	697.07	797.07	897.07
	v	0.01748	6.205				6.664	7.133	7.590	8.039	8.922	9.793	10.659	11.522	12.382	13.240	14.097
	h	272.74	1180.6				1206.0	1232.0	1257.3	1282.2	1331.6	1381.0	1430.9	1481.5	1532.9	1585.1	1638.2
	s	0.4411	1.6316				1.6640	1.6951	1.7237	1.7504	1.7993	1.8439	1.8852	1.9238	1.9603	1.9949	2.0279
75 (307.61)	Sh						42.39	92.39	142.39	192.39	292.39	392.39	492.39	592.39	692.39	792.39	892.39
	v	0.01753	5.814				6.204	6.645	7.074	7.494	8.320	9.135	9.945	10.750	11.553	12.355	13.155
	h	277.56	1181.9				1205.0	1231.2	1256.7	1281.7	1331.3	1380.7	1430.7	1481.3	1532.7	1585.0	1638.1
	s	0.4474	1.6260				1.6554	1.6868	1.7156	1.7424	1.7915	1.8361	1.8774	1.9161	1.9526	1.9872	2.0202

Sh = superheat, F
v = specific volume, cu ft per lb
h = enthalpy, Btu per lb
s = entropy, Btu per F per lb

*Values from STEAM TABLES, Properties of Saturated and Superheated Steam Published by COMBUSTION ENGINEERING, INC., Copyright 1940
**Values interpolated from ASME STEAM TABLES

ITEM B 15 Properties of Superheated Steam (continued)

Abs Press. Lb/Sq In (Sat. Temp)		Sat Water	Sat Steam	*350	400	450	500	550	600	700	800	900	1000	1100	1200	1300	1400
80 (312.04)	Sh			37.96	87.96	137.96	187.96	237.96	287.96	387.96	487.96	587.96	687.96	787.96	887.96	987.96	1087.96
	v	0.01757	5.471	5.801	6.218	6.622	7.018	7.408	7.794	8.560	9.319	10.075	10.829	11.581	12.331	13.081	13.829
	h	282.15	1183.1	1204.0	1230.5	1256.1	1281.3	1306.2	1330.9	1380.5	1430.5	1481.1	1532.6	1584.9	1638.0	1692.0	1746.8
	s	0.4534	1.6208	1.6473	1.6790	1.7080	1.7349	1.7602	1.7842	1.8289	1.8702	1.9089	1.9454	1.9800	2.0131	2.0446	2.0750
85 (316.26)	Sh			33.74	83.74	133.74	183.74	233.74	283.74	383.74	483.74	583.74	683.74	783.74	883.74	983.74	1083.74
	v	0.01762	5.167	5.445	5.840	6.223	6.597	6.966	7.330	8.052	8.768	9.480	10.190	10.898	11.604	12.310	13.014
	h	286.52	1184.2	1203.0	1229.7	1255.5	1280.8	1305.8	1330.6	1380.2	1430.3	1481.0	1532.4	1584.7	1637.9	1691.9	1746.8
	s	0.4590	1.6159	1.6396	1.6716	1.7008	1.7279	1.7532	1.7772	1.8220	1.8634	1.9021	1.9386	1.9733	2.0063	2.0379	2.0682
90 (320.28)	Sh			29.72	79.72	129.72	179.72	229.72	279.72	379.72	479.72	579.72	679.72	779.72	879.72	979.72	1079.72
	v	0.01766	4.895	5.128	5.505	5.869	6.223	6.572	6.917	7.600	8.277	8.950	9.621	10.290	10.958	11.625	12.290
	h	290.69	1185.3	1202.0	1228.9	1254.9	1280.3	1305.4	1330.2	1380.0	1430.1	1480.8	1532.3	1584.6	1637.8	1691.8	1746.7
	s	0.4643	1.6113	1.6323	1.6646	1.6940	1.7212	1.7467	1.7707	1.8156	1.8570	1.8957	1.9323	1.9669	2.0000	2.0316	2.0619
95 (324.13)	Sh			25.87	75.87	125.87	175.87	225.87	275.87	375.87	475.87	575.87	675.87	775.87	875.87	975.87	1075.87
	v	0.01770	4.651	4.845	5.205	5.551	5.889	6.221	6.548	7.196	7.838	8.477	9.113	9.747	10.380	11.012	11.643
	h	294.70	1186.2	1200.9	1228.1	1254.3	1279.8	1305.0	1329.9	1379.7	1429.9	1480.6	1532.1	1584.5	1637.7	1691.7	1746.6
	s	0.4694	1.6069	1.6253	1.6580	1.6876	1.7149	1.7404	1.7645	1.8094	1.8509	1.8897	1.9262	1.9609	1.9940	2.0256	2.0559
100 (327.82)	Sh			22.18	72.18	122.18	172.18	222.18	272.18	372.18	472.18	572.18	672.18	772.18	872.18	972.18	1072.18
	v	0.01774	4.431	4.590	4.935	5.266	5.588	5.904	6.216	6.833	7.443	8.050	8.655	9.258	9.860	10.460	11.060
	h	298.54	1187.2	1199.9	1227.4	1253.7	1279.3	1304.6	1329.6	1379.5	1429.7	1480.4	1532.0	1584.4	1637.6	1691.6	1746.5
	s	0.4743	1.6027	1.6187	1.6516	1.6814	1.7088	1.7344	1.7586	1.8036	1.8451	1.8839	1.9205	1.9552	1.9883	2.0199	2.0502
105 (331.37)	Sh			18.63	68.63	118.63	168.63	218.63	268.63	368.63	468.63	568.63	668.63	768.63	868.63	968.63	1068.63
	v	0.01778	4.231	4.359	4.690	5.007	5.315	5.617	5.915	6.504	7.086	7.665	8.241	8.816	9.389	9.961	10.532
	h	302.24	1188.0	1198.8	1226.6	1253.1	1278.8	1304.2	1329.2	1379.2	1429.4	1480.3	1531.8	1584.2	1637.5	1691.5	1746.4
	s	0.4790	1.5988	1.6122	1.6455	1.6755	1.7031	1.7288	1.7530	1.7981	1.8396	1.8785	1.9151	1.9498	1.9828	2.0145	2.0448
110 (334.79)	Sh			15.21	65.21	115.21	165.21	215.21	265.21	365.21	465.21	565.21	665.21	765.21	865.21	965.21	1065.21
	v	0.01782	4.048	4.149	4.468	4.772	5.068	5.357	5.642	6.205	6.761	7.314	7.865	8.413	8.961	9.507	10.053
	h	305.80	1188.9	1197.7	1225.8	1252.5	1278.3	1303.8	1328.9	1379.0	1429.2	1480.1	1531.7	1584.1	1637.4	1691.4	1746.4
	s	0.4834	1.5950	1.6061	1.6396	1.6698	1.6975	1.7233	1.7476	1.7928	1.8344	1.8732	1.9099	1.9446	1.9777	2.0093	2.0397
115 (338.08)	Sh			11.92	61.92	111.92	161.92	211.92	261.92	361.92	461.92	561.92	661.92	761.92	861.92	961.92	1061.92
	v	0.01785	3.881	3.957	4.265	4.558	4.841	5.119	5.392	5.932	6.465	6.994	7.521	8.046	8.570	9.093	9.615
	h	309.25	1189.6	1196.7	1225.0	1251.8	1277.9	1303.3	1328.6	1378.7	1429.0	1479.9	1531.6	1584.0	1637.2	1691.4	1746.3
	s	0.4877	1.5913	1.6001	1.6340	1.6644	1.6922	1.7181	1.7425	1.7877	1.8294	1.8682	1.9049	1.9396	1.9727	2.0044	2.0347
120 (341.27)	Sh			8.73	58.73	108.73	158.73	208.73	258.73	358.73	458.73	558.73	658.73	758.73	858.73	958.73	1058.73
	v	0.01789	3.7275	3.7815	4.0786	4.3610	4.6341	4.9009	5.1637	5.6813	6.1928	6.7006	7.2060	7.7096	8.2119	8.7130	9.2134
	h	312.58	1190.4	1195.6	1224.1	1251.2	1277.4	1302.9	1328.2	1378.4	1428.8	1479.8	1531.4	1583.9	1637.1	1691.3	1746.2
	s	0.4919	1.5879	1.5943	1.6286	1.6592	1.6872	1.7132	1.7376	1.7829	1.8246	1.8635	1.9001	1.9349	1.9680	1.9996	2.0300
130 (347.33)	Sh			2.67	52.67	102.67	152.67	202.67	252.67	352.67	452.67	552.67	652.67	752.67	852.67	952.67	1052.67
	v	0.01796	3.4544	3.4699	3.7489	4.0129	4.2672	4.5151	4.7589	5.2384	5.7118	6.1814	6.6486	7.1140	7.5781	8.0411	8.5033
	h	318.95	1191.7	1193.4	1222.5	1249.9	1276.4	1302.1	1327.5	1377.9	1428.4	1479.4	1531.1	1583.6	1636.9	1691.1	1746.1
	s	0.4998	1.5813	1.5833	1.6182	1.6493	1.6775	1.7037	1.7283	1.7737	1.8155	1.8545	1.8911	1.9259	1.9591	1.9907	2.0211
140 (353.04)	Sh				46.96	96.96	146.96	196.96	246.96	346.96	446.96	546.96	646.96	746.96	846.96	946.96	1046.96
	v	0.01803	3.2190		3.4661	3.7143	3.9526	4.1844	4.4119	4.8588	5.2995	5.7364	6.1709	6.6036	7.0349	7.4652	7.8946
	h	324.96	1193.0		1220.8	1248.7	1275.3	1301.3	1326.8	1377.4	1428.0	1479.1	1530.8	1583.4	1636.7	1690.9	1745.9
	s	0.5071	1.5752		1.6085	1.6400	1.6686	1.6949	1.7196	1.7652	1.8071	1.8461	1.8828	1.9176	1.9508	1.9825	2.0129
150 (358.43)	Sh				41.57	91.57	141.57	191.57	241.57	341.57	441.57	541.57	641.57	741.57	841.57	941.57	1041.57
	v		3.0139		3.2208	3.4555	3.6799	3.8898	4.1112	4.5298	4.9421	5.3507	5.7568	6.1612	6.5642	6.9661	7.3671
	h	330.65	1194.1		1219.1	1247.4	1274.3	1300.5	1326.1	1376.9	1427.6	1478.7	1530.5	1583.1	1636.5	1690.7	1745.7
	s	0.5141	1.5695		1.5993	1.6313	1.6602	1.6867	1.7115	1.7573	1.7992	1.8383	1.8751	1.9099	1.9431	1.9748	2.0052
160 (363.55)	Sh				36.45	86.45	136.45	186.45	236.45	336.45	436.45	536.45	636.45	736.45	836.45	936.45	1036.45
	v	0.01815	2.8336		3.0060	3.2288	3.4413	3.6649	3.8480	4.2420	4.6295	5.0132	5.3945	5.7741	6.1522	6.5293	6.9055
	h	336.07	1195.1		1217.4	1246.0	1273.3	1299.6	1325.4	1376.4	1427.2	1478.4	1530.3	1582.9	1636.3	1690.5	1745.6
	s	0.5206	1.5641		1.5906	1.6231	1.6522	1.6790	1.7039	1.7499	1.7919	1.8310	1.8678	1.9027	1.9359	1.9676	1.9980
170 (368.42)	Sh				31.58	81.58	131.58	181.58	231.58	331.58	431.58	531.58	631.58	731.58	831.58	931.58	1031.58
	v	0.01821	2.6738		2.8162	3.0288	3.2306	3.4255	3.6158	3.9879	4.3536	4.7155	5.0749	5.4325	5.7888	6.1440	6.4983
	h	341.24	1196.0		1215.6	1244.7	1272.2	1298.8	1324.7	1375.8	1426.8	1478.0	1530.0	1582.6	1636.1	1690.4	1745.4
	s	0.5269	1.5591		1.5823	1.6152	1.6447	1.6717	1.6968	1.7428	1.7850	1.8241	1.8610	1.8959	1.9291	1.9608	1.9913
180 (373.08)	Sh				26.92	76.92	126.92	176.92	226.92	326.92	426.92	526.92	626.92	726.92	826.92	926.92	1026.92
	v	0.01827	2.5312		2.6474	2.8508	3.0433	3.2286	3.4093	3.7621	4.1084	4.4508	4.7907	5.1289	5.4657	5.8014	6.1363
	h	346.19	1196.9		1213.8	1243.4	1271.2	1297.9	1324.0	1375.3	1426.3	1477.7	1529.7	1582.4	1635.9	1690.2	1745.3
	s	0.5328	1.5543		1.5743	1.6078	1.6376	1.6647	1.6900	1.7362	1.7784	1.8176	1.8545	1.8894	1.9227	1.9545	1.9849
190 (377.53)	Sh				22.47	72.47	122.47	172.47	222.47	322.47	422.47	522.47	622.47	722.47	822.47	922.47	1022.47
	v	0.01833	2.4030		2.4961	2.6915	2.8756	3.0525	3.2246	3.5601	3.8889	4.2140	4.5365	4.8572	5.1766	5.4949	5.8124
	h	350.94	1197.6		1212.0	1242.0	1270.1	1297.1	1323.3	1374.8	1425.9	1477.4	1529.4	1582.1	1635.7	1690.0	1745.1
	s	0.5384	1.5498		1.5667	1.6006	1.6307	1.6581	1.6835	1.7299	1.7722	1.8115	1.8484	1.8834	1.9166	1.9484	1.9789
200 (381.80)	Sh				18.20	68.20	118.20	168.20	218.20	318.20	418.20	518.20	618.20	718.20	818.20	918.20	1018.20
	v	0.01839	2.2873		2.3598	2.5480	2.7247	2.8939	3.0583	3.3783	3.6915	4.0008	4.3077	4.6128	4.9165	5.2191	5.5209
	h	355.51	1198.3		1210.1	1240.6	1269.0	1296.2	1322.6	1374.3	1425.5	1477.0	1529.1	1581.9	1635.4	1689.8	1745.0
	s	0.5438	1.5454		1.5593	1.5938	1.6242	1.6518	1.6773	1.7239	1.7663	1.8057	1.8426	1.8776	1.9109	1.9427	1.9732

Sh = superheat, F
v = specific volume, cu ft per lb
h = enthalpy, Btu per lb
s = entropy, Btu per F per lb

ITEM B 15 Properties of Superheated Steam (continued)

Abs Press. Lb/Sq In. (Sat. Temp)		Sat. Water	Sat. Steam	Temperature — Degrees Fahrenheit													
				400	450	500	550	600	700	800	900	1000	1100	1200	1300	1400	1500
210 (385.91)	Sh			14.09	64.09	114.09	164.09	214.09	314.09	414.09	514.09	614.09	714.09	814.09	914.09	1014.09	1114.09
	v	0.01844	2.1822	2.2364	2.4181	2.5880	2.7504	2.9078	3.2137	3.5128	3.8080	4.1007	4.3915	4.6811	4.9695	5.2571	5.5440
	h	359.91	1199.0	1208.02	1239.2	1268.0	1295.3	1321.9	1373.7	1425.1	1476.7	1528.8	1581.6	1635.2	1689.6	1744.8	1800.8
	s	0.5490	1.5413	1.5522	1.5872	1.6180	1.6458	1.6715	1.7182	1.7607	1.8001	1.8371	1.8721	1.9054	1.9372	1.9677	1.9970
220 (389.88)	Sh			10.12	60.12	110.12	160.12	210.12	310.12	410.12	510.12	610.12	710.12	810.12	910.12	1010.12	1110.12
	v	0.01850	2.0863	2.1240	2.2999	2.4638	2.6199	2.7710	3.0642	3.3504	3.6327	3.9125	4.1905	4.4671	4.7426	5.0173	5.2913
	h	364.17	1199.6	1206.3	1237.8	1266.9	1294.5	1321.2	1373.2	1424.7	1476.3	1528.5	1581.4	1635.0	1689.4	1744.7	1800.6
	s	0.5540	1.5374	1.5453	1.5808	1.6120	1.6400	1.6658	1.7128	1.7553	1.7948	1.8318	1.8668	1.9002	1.9320	1.9625	1.9919
230 (393.70)	Sh			6.30	56.30	106.30	156.30	206.30	306.30	406.30	506.30	606.30	706.30	806.30	906.30	1006.30	1106.30
	v	0.01855	1.9985	2.0130	2.1919	2.3503	2.5008	2.6461	2.9276	3.2020	3.4726	3.7406	4.0068	4.2717	4.5355	4.7984	5.0606
	h	368.28	1200.1	1204.4	1236.3	1265.7	1293.6	1320.4	1372.7	1424.2	1476.0	1528.2	1581.1	1634.8	1689.3	1744.5	1800.5
	s	0.5588	1.5336	1.5385	1.5748	1.6062	1.6344	1.6604	1.7075	1.7502	1.7897	1.8268	1.8618	1.8952	1.9270	1.9576	1.9869
240 (397.39)	Sh			2.61	52.61	102.61	152.61	202.61	302.61	402.61	502.61	602.61	702.61	802.61	902.61	1002.61	1102.61
	v	0.01860	1.9177	1.9268	2.0928	2.2462	2.3915	2.5316	2.8024	3.0661	3.3259	3.5831	3.8385	4.0926	4.3456	4.5977	4.8492
	h	372.27	1200.6	1202.4	1234.9	1264.6	1292.7	1319.7	1372.1	1423.8	1475.6	1527.9	1580.9	1634.6	1689.1	1744.3	1800.4
	s	0.5634	1.5299	1.5320	1.5687	1.6006	1.6291	1.6552	1.7025	1.7452	1.7848	1.8219	1.8570	1.8904	1.9223	1.9528	1.9822
250 (400.97)	Sh				49.03	99.03	149.03	199.03	299.03	399.03	499.03	599.03	699.03	799.03	899.03	999.03	1099.03
	v	0.01865	1.8432		2.0016	2.1504	2.2909	2.4262	2.6872	2.9410	3.1909	3.4382	3.6837	3.9278	4.1709	4.4131	4.6546
	h	376.14	1201.1		1233.4	1263.5	1291.8	1319.0	1371.6	1423.4	1475.3	1527.6	1580.6	1634.4	1688.9	1744.2	1800.2
	s	0.5679	1.5264		1.5629	1.5951	1.6239	1.6502	1.6976	1.7405	1.7801	1.8173	1.8524	1.8858	1.9177	1.9482	1.9776
260 (404.44)	Sh				45.56	95.56	145.56	195.56	295.56	395.56	495.56	595.56	695.56	795.56	895.56	995.56	1095.56
	v	0.01870	1.7742		1.9173	2.0619	2.1981	2.3289	2.5808	2.8256	3.0663	3.3044	3.5408	3.7758	4.0097	4.2427	4.4750
	h	379.90	1201.5		1231.9	1262.4	1290.9	1318.2	1371.1	1423.0	1474.9	1527.3	1580.4	1634.2	1688.7	1744.0	1800.1
	s	0.5722	1.5230		1.5573	1.5899	1.6189	1.6453	1.6930	1.7359	1.7756	1.8128	1.8480	1.8814	1.9133	1.9439	1.9732
270 (407.80)	Sh				42.20	92.20	142.20	192.20	292.20	392.20	492.20	592.20	692.20	792.20	892.20	992.20	1092.20
	v	0.01875	1.7101		1.8391	1.9799	2.1121	2.2388	2.4824	2.7186	2.9509	3.1806	3.4084	3.6349	3.8603	4.0849	4.3087
	h	383.56	1201.9		1230.4	1261.2	1290.0	1317.5	1370.5	1422.6	1474.6	1527.1	1580.1	1634.0	1688.5	1743.9	1800.0
	s	0.5764	1.5197		1.5518	1.5848	1.6140	1.6405	1.6884	1.7315	1.7713	1.8085	1.8437	1.8771	1.9090	1.9396	1.9690
280 (411.07)	Sh				38.93	88.93	138.93	188.93	288.93	388.93	488.93	588.93	688.93	788.93	888.93	988.93	1088.93
	v	0.01880	1.6505		1.7665	1.9037	2.0322	2.1551	2.3909	2.6194	2.8437	3.0655	3.2855	3.5042	3.7217	3.9384	4.1543
	h	387.12	1202.3		1228.8	1260.0	1289.1	1316.8	1370.0	1422.1	1474.2	1526.8	1579.9	1633.8	1688.4	1743.7	1799.8
	s	0.5805	1.5166		1.5464	1.5798	1.6093	1.6361	1.6841	1.7273	1.7671	1.8043	1.8395	1.8730	1.9050	1.9356	1.9649
290 (414.25)	Sh				35.75	85.75	135.75	185.75	285.75	385.75	485.75	585.75	685.75	785.75	885.75	985.75	1085.75
	v	0.01885	1.5948		1.6988	1.8327	1.9578	2.0772	2.3058	2.5269	2.7440	2.9585	3.1711	3.3824	3.5926	3.8019	4.0106
	h	390.60	1202.6		1227.3	1258.9	1288.1	1316.0	1369.5	1421.7	1473.9	1526.5	1579.6	1633.5	1688.2	1743.6	1799.7
	s	0.5844	1.5135		1.5412	1.5750	1.6048	1.6317	1.6799	1.7232	1.7630	1.8003	1.8356	1.8690	1.9010	1.9316	1.9610
300 (417.35)	Sh				32.65	82.65	132.65	182.65	282.65	382.65	482.65	582.65	682.65	782.65	882.65	982.65	1082.65
	v	0.01889	1.5427		1.6356	1.7665	1.8883	2.0044	2.2263	2.4407	2.6509	2.8585	3.0643	3.2688	3.4721	3.6746	3.8764
	h	393.99	1202.9		1225.7	1257.7	1287.2	1315.2	1368.9	1421.3	1473.6	1526.2	1579.4	1633.3	1688.0	1743.4	1799.6
	s	0.5882	1.5105		1.5361	1.5703	1.6003	1.6274	1.6758	1.7192	1.7591	1.7964	1.8317	1.8652	1.8972	1.9278	1.9572
310 (420.36)	Sh				29.64	79.64	129.64	179.64	279.64	379.64	479.64	579.64	679.64	779.64	879.64	979.64	1079.64
	v	0.01894	1.4939		1.5763	1.7044	1.8233	1.9363	2.1520	2.3600	2.5638	2.7650	2.9644	3.1625	3.3594	3.5555	3.7509
	h	397.30	1203.2		1224.1	1256.5	1286.3	1314.5	1368.4	1420.9	1473.2	1525.9	1579.2	1633.1	1687.8	1743.3	1799.4
	s	0.5920	1.5076		1.5311	1.5657	1.5960	1.6233	1.6719	1.7153	1.7553	1.7927	1.8280	1.8615	1.8935	1.9241	1.9536
320 (423.31)	Sh				26.69	76.69	126.69	176.69	276.69	376.69	476.69	576.69	676.69	776.69	876.69	976.69	1076.69
	v	0.01899	1.4480		1.5207	1.6462	1.7623	1.8725	2.0823	2.2843	2.4821	2.6774	2.8708	3.0628	3.2538	3.4438	3.6332
	h	400.53	1203.4		1222.5	1255.2	1285.3	1313.7	1367.8	1420.5	1472.9	1525.6	1578.9	1632.9	1687.6	1743.1	1799.3
	s	0.5956	1.5048		1.5261	1.5612	1.5918	1.6192	1.6680	1.7116	1.7516	1.7890	1.8243	1.8579	1.8899	1.9206	1.9500
330 (426.18)	Sh				23.82	73.82	123.82	173.82	273.82	373.82	473.82	573.82	673.82	773.82	873.82	973.82	1073.82
	v	0.01903	1.4048		1.4684	1.5915	1.7050	1.8125	2.0168	2.2132	2.4054	2.5950	2.7828	2.9692	3.1545	3.3389	3.5227
	h	403.70	1203.6		1220.9	1254.0	1284.4	1313.0	1367.3	1420.0	1472.5	1525.3	1578.7	1632.7	1687.5	1742.9	1799.2
	s	0.5991	1.5021		1.5213	1.5568	1.5876	1.6153	1.6643	1.7080	1.7480	1.7855	1.8208	1.8544	1.8864	1.9171	1.9466
340 (428.99)	Sh				21.01	71.01	121.01	171.01	271.01	371.01	471.01	571.01	671.01	771.01	871.01	971.01	1071.01
	v	0.01908	1.3640		1.4191	1.5399	1.6511	1.7561	1.9552	2.1463	2.3333	2.5175	2.7000	2.8811	3.0611	3.2402	3.4186
	h	406.80	1203.8		1219.2	1252.8	1283.4	1312.2	1366.7	1419.6	1472.2	1525.0	1578.4	1632.5	1687.3	1742.8	1799.0
	s	0.6026	1.4994		1.5165	1.5525	1.5836	1.6114	1.6606	1.7044	1.7445	1.7820	1.8174	1.8510	1.8831	1.9138	1.9432
350 (431.73)	Sh				18.27	68.27	118.27	168.27	268.27	368.27	468.27	568.27	668.27	768.27	868.27	968.27	1068.27
	v	0.01912	1.3255		1.3725	1.4913	1.6002	1.7028	1.8970	2.0832	2.2652	2.4445	2.6219	2.7980	2.9730	3.1471	3.3205
	h	409.83	1204.0		1217.5	1251.5	1282.4	1311.4	1366.2	1419.2	1471.8	1524.7	1578.2	1632.3	1687.1	1742.6	1798.9
	s	0.6059	1.4968		1.5119	1.5483	1.5797	1.6077	1.6571	1.7009	1.7411	1.7787	1.8141	1.8477	1.8798	1.9105	1.9400
360 (434.41)	Sh				15.59	65.59	115.59	165.59	265.59	365.59	465.59	565.59	665.59	765.59	865.59	965.59	1065.59
	v	0.01917	1.2891		1.3285	1.4454	1.5521	1.6525	1.8421	2.0237	2.2009	2.3755	2.5482	2.7196	2.8898	3.0592	3.2279
	h	412.81	1204.1		1215.8	1250.3	1281.5	1310.6	1365.6	1418.7	1471.5	1524.4	1577.9	1632.1	1686.9	1742.5	1798.8
	s	0.6092	1.4943		1.5073	1.5441	1.5758	1.6040	1.6536	1.6976	1.7379	1.7754	1.8109	1.8445	1.8766	1.9073	1.9368
380 (439.61)	Sh				10.39	60.39	110.39	160.39	260.39	360.39	460.39	560.39	660.39	760.39	860.39	960.39	1060.39
	v	0.01925	1.2218		1.2472	1.3606	1.4635	1.5598	1.7410	1.9139	2.0825	2.2484	2.4124	2.5750	2.7366	2.8973	3.0572
	h	418.59	1204.4		1212.4	1247.7	1279.5	1309.0	1364.5	1417.9	1470.8	1523.8	1577.4	1631.6	1686.5	1742.2	1798.5
	s	0.6156	1.4894		1.4982	1.5360	1.5683	1.5969	1.6470	1.6911	1.7315	1.7692	1.8047	1.8384	1.8705	1.9012	1.9307

Sh = superheat, F
v = specific volume, cu ft per lb

h = enthalpy, Btu per lb
s = entropy, Btu per F per lb

ITEM B 15 Properties of Superheated Steam (continued)

Abs Press. Lb/Sq In. (Sat. Temp)		Sat. Water	Sat. Steam	Temperature — Degrees Fahrenheit 450	500	550	600	650	700	800	900	1000	1100	1200	1300	1400	1500
400 (444.60)	Sh			5.40	55.40	105.40	155.40	205.40	255.40	355.40	455.40	555.40	655.40	755.40	855.40	955.40	1055.40
	v	0.01934	1.1610	1.1738	1.2841	1.3836	1.4763	1.5646	1.6499	1.8151	1.9759	2.1339	2.2901	2.4450	2.5987	2.7515	2.9037
	h	424.17	1204.6	1208.8	1245.1	1277.5	1307.4	1335.9	1363.4	1417.0	1470.1	1523.3	1576.9	1631.2	1686.2	1741.9	1798.2
	s	0.6217	1.4847	1.4894	1.5282	1.5611	1.5901	1.6163	1.6406	1.6850	1.7255	1.7632	1.7988	1.8325	1.8647	1.8955	1.9250
420 (449.40)	Sh			.60	50.60	100.60	150.60	200.60	250.60	350.60	450.60	550.60	650.60	750.60	850.60	950.60	1050.60
	v	0.01942	1.1057	1.1071	1.2148	1.3113	1.4007	1.4856	1.5676	1.7258	1.8795	2.0304	2.1795	2.3273	2.4739	2.6196	2.7647
	h	429.56	1204.7	1205.2	1242.4	1275.4	1305.8	1334.5	1362.3	1416.2	1469.4	1522.7	1576.4	1630.8	1685.8	1741.6	1798.0
	s	0.6276	1.4802	1.4808	1.5206	1.5542	1.5835	1.6100	1.6345	1.6791	1.7197	1.7575	1.7932	1.8269	1.8591	1.8899	1.9195
440 (454.03)	Sh				45.97	95.97	145.97	195.97	245.97	345.97	445.97	545.97	645.97	745.97	845.97	945.97	1045.97
	v	0.01950	1.0554		1.1517	1.2454	1.3319	1.4138	1.4926	1.6445	1.7918	1.9363	2.0790	2.2203	2.3605	2.4998	2.6384
	h	434.77	1204.8		1239.7	1273.4	1304.2	1333.2	1361.1	1415.3	1468.7	1522.1	1575.9	1630.4	1685.5	1741.2	1797.7
	s	0.6332	1.4759		1.5132	1.5474	1.5772	1.6040	1.6286	1.6734	1.7142	1.7521	1.7878	1.8216	1.8538	1.8847	1.9143
460 (458.50)	Sh				41.50	91.50	141.50	191.50	241.50	341.50	441.50	541.50	641.50	741.50	841.50	941.50	1041.50
	v	0.01959	1.0092		1.0939	1.1852	1.2691	1.3482	1.4242	1.5703	1.7117	1.8504	1.9872	2.1226	2.2569	2.3903	2.5230
	h	439.83	1204.8		1236.9	1271.3	1302.5	1331.8	1360.0	1414.4	1468.0	1521.5	1575.4	1629.9	1685.1	1740.9	1797.4
	s	0.6387	1.4718		1.5060	1.5409	1.5711	1.5982	1.6230	1.6680	1.7089	1.7469	1.7826	1.8165	1.8488	1.8797	1.9093
480 (462.82)	Sh				37.18	87.18	137.18	187.18	237.18	337.18	437.18	537.18	637.18	737.18	837.18	937.18	1037.18
	v	0.01967	0.9668		1.0409	1.1300	1.2115	1.2881	1.3615	1.5023	1.6384	1.7716	1.9030	2.0330	2.1619	2.2900	2.4173
	h	444.75	1204.8		1234.1	1269.1	1300.8	1330.5	1358.8	1413.6	1467.3	1520.9	1574.9	1629.5	1684.7	1740.6	1797.2
	s	0.6439	1.4677		1.4990	1.5346	1.5652	1.5925	1.6176	1.6628	1.7038	1.7419	1.7777	1.8116	1.8439	1.8748	1.9045
500 (467.01)	Sh				32.99	82.99	132.99	182.99	232.99	332.99	432.99	532.99	632.99	732.99	832.99	932.99	1032.99
	v	0.01975	0.9276		0.9919	1.0791	1.1584	1.2327	1.3037	1.4397	1.5708	1.6992	1.8256	1.9507	2.0746	2.1977	2.3200
	h	449.52	1204.7		1231.2	1267.0	1299.1	1329.1	1357.7	1412.7	1466.6	1520.3	1574.4	1629.1	1684.4	1740.3	1796.9
	s	0.6490	1.4639		1.4921	1.5284	1.5595	1.5871	1.6123	1.6578	1.6990	1.7371	1.7730	1.8069	1.8393	1.8702	1.8998
520 (471.07)	Sh				28.93	78.93	128.93	178.93	228.93	328.93	428.93	528.93	628.93	728.93	828.93	928.93	1028.93
	v	0.01982	0.8914		0.9466	1.0321	1.1094	1.1816	1.2504	1.3819	1.5085	1.6323	1.7542	1.8746	1.9940	2.1125	2.2302
	h	454.18	1204.5		1228.3	1264.8	1297.4	1327.7	1356.5	1411.8	1465.9	1519.7	1573.9	1628.7	1684.0	1740.0	1796.7
	s	0.6540	1.4601		1.4853	1.5223	1.5539	1.5818	1.6072	1.6530	1.6943	1.7325	1.7684	1.8024	1.8348	1.8657	1.8954
540 (475.01)	Sh				24.99	74.99	124.99	174.99	224.99	324.99	424.99	524.99	624.99	724.99	824.99	924.99	1024.99
	v	0.01990	0.8577		0.9045	0.9884	1.0640	1.1342	1.2010	1.3284	1.4508	1.5704	1.6880	1.8042	1.9193	2.0336	2.1471
	h	458.71	1204.4		1225.3	1262.5	1295.7	1326.3	1355.3	1410.9	1465.1	1519.1	1573.4	1628.2	1683.6	1739.7	1796.4
	s	0.6587	1.4565		1.4786	1.5164	1.5485	1.5767	1.6023	1.6483	1.6897	1.7280	1.7640	1.7980	1.8305	1.8615	1.8911
560 (478.84)	Sh				21.16	71.16	121.16	171.16	221.16	321.16	421.16	521.16	621.16	721.16	821.16	921.16	1021.16
	v	0.01998	0.8264		0.8653	0.9479	1.0217	1.0902	1.1552	1.2787	1.3972	1.5129	1.6266	1.7388	1.8500	1.9603	2.0699
	h	463.14	1204.2		1222.2	1260.3	1293.9	1324.9	1354.2	1410.0	1464.4	1518.6	1572.9	1627.8	1683.3	1739.4	1796.1
	s	0.6634	1.4529		1.4720	1.5106	1.5431	1.5717	1.5975	1.6438	1.6853	1.7237	1.7598	1.7939	1.8263	1.8573	1.8870
580 (482.57)	Sh				17.43	67.43	117.43	167.43	217.43	317.43	417.43	517.43	617.43	717.43	817.43	917.43	1017.43
	v	0.02006	0.7971		0.8287	0.9100	0.9824	1.0492	1.1125	1.2324	1.3473	1.4593	1.5693	1.6780	1.7855	1.8921	1.9980
	h	467.47	1203.9		1219.1	1258.0	1292.1	1323.4	1353.0	1409.2	1463.7	1518.0	1572.4	1627.4	1682.9	1739.1	1795.9
	s	0.6679	1.4495		1.4654	1.5049	1.5380	1.5668	1.5929	1.6394	1.6811	1.7196	1.7556	1.7898	1.8223	1.8533	1.8831
600 (486.20)	Sh				13.80	63.80	113.80	163.80	213.80	313.80	413.80	513.80	613.80	713.80	813.80	913.80	1013.80
	v	0.02013	0.7697		0.7944	0.8746	0.9456	1.0109	1.0726	1.1892	1.3008	1.4093	1.5160	1.6211	1.7252	1.8284	1.9309
	h	471.70	1203.7		1215.9	1255.6	1290.3	1322.0	1351.8	1408.3	1463.0	1517.4	1571.9	1627.0	1682.6	1738.8	1795.6
	s	0.6723	1.4461		1.4590	1.4993	1.5329	1.5621	1.5884	1.6351	1.6769	1.7155	1.7517	1.7859	1.8184	1.8494	1.8792
650 (494.89)	Sh				5.11	55.11	105.11	155.11	205.11	305.11	405.11	505.11	605.11	705.11	805.11	905.11	1005.11
	v	0.02032	0.7084		0.7173	0.7954	0.8634	0.9254	0.9835	1.0929	1.1969	1.2979	1.3969	1.4944	1.5909	1.6864	1.7813
	h	481.89	1202.8		1207.6	1249.6	1285.7	1318.3	1348.7	1406.0	1461.2	1515.9	1570.7	1625.9	1681.6	1738.0	1794.9
	s	1.6828	1.4381		1.4430	1.4858	1.5207	1.5507	1.5775	1.6249	1.6671	1.7059	1.7422	1.7765	1.8092	1.8403	1.8701
700 (503.08)	Sh					46.92	96.92	146.92	196.92	296.92	396.92	496.92	596.92	696.92	796.92	896.92	996.92
	v	0.02050	0.6556			0.7271	0.7928	0.8520	0.9072	1.0102	1.1078	1.2023	1.2948	1.3858	1.4757	1.5647	1.6530
	h	491.60	1201.8			1243.4	1281.0	1314.6	1345.6	1403.7	1459.4	1514.4	1569.4	1624.8	1680.7	1737.2	1794.3
	s	0.6928	1.4304			1.4726	1.5090	1.5399	1.5673	1.6154	1.6580	1.6970	1.7335	1.7679	1.8006	1.8318	1.8617
750 (510.84)	Sh					39.16	89.16	139.16	189.16	289.16	389.16	489.16	589.16	689.16	789.16	889.16	989.16
	v	0.02069	0.6095			0.6676	0.7313	0.7882	0.8409	0.9386	1.0306	1.1195	1.2063	1.2916	1.3759	1.4592	1.5419
	h	500.89	1200.7			1236.9	1276.1	1310.7	1342.5	1401.5	1457.6	1512.9	1568.2	1623.8	1679.8	1736.4	1793.6
	s	0.7022	1.4232			1.4598	1.4977	1.5296	1.5577	1.6065	1.6494	1.6886	1.7252	1.7598	1.7926	1.8239	1.8538
800 (518.21)	Sh					31.79	81.79	131.79	181.79	281.79	381.79	481.79	581.79	681.79	781.79	881.79	981.79
	v	0.02087	0.5690			0.6151	0.6774	0.7323	0.7828	0.8759	0.9631	1.0470	1.1289	1.2093	1.2885	1.3669	1.4446
	h	509.81	1199.4			1230.1	1271.1	1306.8	1339.3	1399.1	1455.8	1511.4	1566.9	1622.7	1678.9	1735.7	1792.9
	s	0.7111	1.4163			1.4472	1.4869	1.5198	1.5484	1.5980	1.6413	1.6807	1.7175	1.7522	1.7851	1.8164	1.8464
850 (525.24)	Sh					24.76	74.76	124.76	174.76	274.76	374.76	474.76	574.76	674.76	774.76	874.76	974.76
	v	0.02105	0.5330			0.5683	0.6296	0.6829	0.7315	0.8205	0.9034	0.9830	1.0606	1.1366	1.2115	1.2855	1.3588
	h	518.40	1198.0			1223.0	1265.9	1302.8	1336.0	1396.8	1454.0	1510.0	1565.7	1621.6	1678.0	1734.9	1792.3
	s	0.7197	1.4096			1.4347	1.4763	1.5102	1.5396	1.5899	1.6336	1.6733	1.7102	1.7450	1.7780	1.8094	1.8395
900 (531.95)	Sh					18.05	68.05	118.05	168.05	268.05	368.05	468.05	568.05	668.05	768.05	868.05	968.05
	v	0.02123	0.5009			0.5263	0.5869	0.6388	0.6858	0.7713	0.8504	0.9262	0.9998	1.0720	1.1430	1.2131	1.2825
	h	526.70	1196.4			1215.5	1260.6	1298.6	1332.7	1394.4	1452.2	1508.5	1564.5	1620.6	1677.1	1734.1	1791.6
	s	0.7279	1.4032			1.4223	1.4659	1.5010	1.5311	1.5822	1.6263	1.6662	1.7033	1.7382	1.7713	1.8028	1.8329

Sh = superheat, F
v = specific volume, cu ft per lb

h = enthalpy, Btu per lb
s = entropy, Btu per F per lb

ITEM B 15 Properties of Superheated Steam (continued)

Abs Press. Lb/Sq In. (Sat. Temp)		Sat. Water	Sat. Steam	550	600	650	700	750	800	850	900	1000	1100	1200	1300	1400	1500
950 (538.39)	Sh			11.61	61.61	111.61	161.61	211.61	261.61	311.61	361.61	461.61	561.61	661.61	761.61	861.61	961.61
	v	0.02141	0.4721	0.4883	0.5485	0.5993	0.6449	0.6871	0.7272	0.7656	0.8030	0.8753	0.9455	1.0142	1.0817	1.1484	1.2143
	h	534.74	1194.7	1207.6	1255.1	1294.4	1329.3	1361.5	1392.0	1421.5	1450.3	1507.0	1563.2	1619.5	1676.2	1733.3	1791.0
	s	0.7358	1.3970	1.4098	1.4557	1.4921	1.5228	1.5500	1.5748	1.5977	1.6193	1.6595	1.6967	1.7317	1.7649	1.7965	1.8267
1000 (544.58)	Sh			5.42	55.42	105.42	155.42	205.42	255.42	305.42	355.42	455.42	555.42	655.42	755.42	855.42	955.42
	v	0.02159	0.4460	0.4535	0.5137	0.5636	0.6080	0.6489	0.6875	0.7245	0.7603	0.8295	0.8966	0.9622	1.0266	1.0901	1.1529
	h	542.55	1192.9	1199.3	1249.3	1290.1	1325.9	1358.7	1389.6	1419.4	1448.5	1505.4	1561.9	1618.4	1675.3	1732.5	1790.3
	s	0.7434	1.3910	1.3973	1.4457	1.4833	1.5149	1.5426	1.5677	1.5908	1.6126	1.6530	1.6905	1.7256	1.7589	1.7905	1.8207
1050 (550.53)	Sh				49.47	99.47	149.47	199.47	249.47	299.47	349.47	449.47	549.47	649.47	749.47	849.47	949.47
	v	0.02177	0.4222		0.4821	0.5312	0.5745	0.6142	0.6515	0.6872	0.7216	0.7881	0.8524	0.9151	0.9767	1.0373	1.0973
	h	550.15	1191.0		1243.4	1285.7	1322.4	1355.8	1387.2	1417.3	1446.6	1503.9	1560.7	1617.4	1674.4	1731.8	1789.6
	s	0.7507	1.3851		1.4358	1.4748	1.5072	1.5354	1.5608	1.5842	1.6062	1.6469	1.6845	1.7197	1.7531	1.7848	1.8151
1100 (556.28)	Sh				43.72	93.72	143.72	193.72	243.72	293.72	343.72	443.72	543.72	643.72	743.72	843.72	943.72
	v	0.02195	0.4006		0.4531	0.5017	0.5440	0.5826	0.6188	0.6533	0.6865	0.7505	0.8121	0.8723	0.9313	0.9894	1.0468
	h	557.55	1189.1		1237.3	1281.2	1318.8	1352.9	1384.7	1415.2	1444.7	1502.4	1559.4	1616.3	1673.5	1731.0	1789.0
	s	0.7578	1.3794		1.4259	1.4664	1.4996	1.5284	1.5542	1.5779	1.6000	1.6410	1.6787	1.7141	1.7475	1.7793	1.8097
1150 (561.82)	Sh				39.18	89.18	139.18	189.18	239.18	289.18	339.18	439.18	539.18	639.18	739.18	839.18	939.18
	v	0.02214	0.3807		0.4263	0.4746	0.5162	0.5538	0.5889	0.6223	0.6544	0.7161	0.7754	0.8332	0.8899	0.9456	1.0007
	h	564.78	1187.0		1230.9	1276.6	1315.2	1349.9	1382.0	1413.0	1442.8	1500.9	1558.1	1615.2	1672.6	1730.2	1788.3
	s	0.7647	1.3738		1.4160	1.4582	1.4923	1.5216	1.5478	1.5717	1.5941	1.6353	1.6732	1.7087	1.7422	1.7741	1.8045
1200 (567.19)	Sh				32.81	82.81	132.81	182.81	232.81	282.81	332.81	432.81	532.81	632.81	732.81	832.81	932.81
	v	0.02232	0.3624		0.4016	0.4497	0.4905	0.5273	0.5615	0.5939	0.6250	0.6845	0.7418	0.7974	0.8519	0.9055	0.9584
	h	571.85	1184.8		1224.2	1271.8	1311.5	1346.9	1379.7	1410.8	1440.9	1499.4	1556.9	1614.2	1671.6	1729.4	1787.6
	s	0.7714	1.3683		1.4061	1.4501	1.4851	1.5150	1.5415	1.5658	1.5883	1.6298	1.6679	1.7035	1.7371	1.7691	1.7996
1300 (577.42)	Sh				22.58	72.58	122.58	172.58	222.58	272.58	322.58	422.58	522.58	622.58	722.58	822.58	922.58
	v	0.02269	0.3299		0.3570	0.4052	0.4451	0.4804	0.5129	0.5436	0.5729	0.6287	0.6822	0.7341	0.7847	0.8345	0.8836
	h	585.58	1180.2		1209.9	1261.9	1303.9	1340.8	1374.6	1406.4	1437.1	1496.3	1554.3	1612.0	1669.8	1727.9	1786.3
	s	0.7843	1.3577		1.3860	1.4340	1.4711	1.5022	1.5296	1.5544	1.5773	1.6194	1.6578	1.6937	1.7275	1.7596	1.7902
1400 (587.07)	Sh				12.93	62.93	112.93	162.93	212.93	262.93	312.93	412.93	512.93	612.93	712.93	812.93	912.93
	v	0.02307	0.3018		0.3176	0.3667	0.4059	0.4400	0.4712	0.5004	0.5282	0.5809	0.6311	0.6798	0.7272	0.7737	0.8195
	h	598.83	1175.3		1194.1	1251.4	1296.1	1334.5	1369.3	1402.0	1433.2	1493.2	1551.8	1609.9	1668.0	1726.3	1785.0
	s	0.7966	1.3474		1.3652	1.4181	1.4575	1.4900	1.5182	1.5436	1.5670	1.6096	1.6484	1.6845	1.7185	1.7508	1.7815
1500 (596.20)	Sh				3.80	53.80	103.80	153.80	203.80	253.80	303.80	403.80	503.80	603.80	703.80	803.80	903.80
	v	0.02346	0.2772		0.2820	0.3328	0.3717	0.4049	0.4350	0.4629	0.4894	0.5394	0.5869	0.6327	0.6773	0.7210	0.7639
	h	611.68	1170.1		1176.3	1240.2	1287.9	1328.0	1364.0	1397.4	1429.2	1490.1	1549.2	1607.7	1666.2	1724.8	1783.7
	s	0.8085	1.3373		1.3431	1.4022	1.4443	1.4782	1.5073	1.5333	1.5572	1.6004	1.6395	1.6759	1.7101	1.7425	1.7734
1600 (604.87)	Sh					45.13	95.13	145.13	195.13	245.13	295.13	395.13	495.13	595.13	695.13	795.13	895.13
	v	0.02387	0.2555			0.3026	0.3415	0.3741	0.4032	0.4301	0.4555	0.5031	0.5482	0.5915	0.6336	0.6748	0.7153
	h	624.20	1164.5			1228.3	1279.4	1321.4	1358.5	1392.8	1425.2	1486.9	1546.6	1605.6	1664.3	1723.2	1782.3
	s	0.8199	1.3274			1.3861	1.4312	1.4667	1.4968	1.5235	1.5478	1.5916	1.6312	1.6678	1.7022	1.7347	1.7657
1700 (613.13)	Sh					36.87	86.87	136.87	186.87	236.87	286.87	386.87	486.87	586.87	686.87	786.87	886.87
	v	0.02428	0.2361			0.2754	0.3147	0.3468	0.3751	0.4011	0.4255	0.4711	0.5140	0.5552	0.5951	0.6341	0.6724
	h	636.45	1158.6			1215.3	1270.5	1314.5	1352.9	1388.1	1421.2	1483.8	1544.0	1603.4	1662.5	1721.7	1781.0
	s	0.8309	1.3176			1.3697	1.4183	1.4555	1.4867	1.5140	1.5388	1.5833	1.6232	1.6601	1.6947	1.7274	1.7585
1800 (621.02)	Sh					28.98	78.98	128.98	178.98	228.98	278.98	378.98	478.98	578.98	678.98	778.98	878.98
	v	0.02472	0.2186			0.2505	0.2906	0.3223	0.3500	0.3752	0.3988	0.4426	0.4836	0.5229	0.5609	0.5980	0.6343
	h	648.49	1152.3			1201.2	1261.1	1307.4	1347.2	1383.3	1417.1	1480.6	1541.4	1601.2	1660.7	1720.1	1779.7
	s	0.8417	1.3079			1.3526	1.4054	1.4446	1.4768	1.5049	1.5302	1.5753	1.6156	1.6528	1.6876	1.7204	1.7516
1900 (628.56)	Sh					21.44	71.44	121.44	171.44	221.44	271.44	371.44	471.44	571.44	671.44	771.44	871.44
	v	0.02517	0.2028			0.2274	0.2687	0.3004	0.3275	0.3521	0.3749	0.4171	0.4565	0.4940	0.5303	0.5656	0.6002
	h	660.36	1145.6			1185.7	1251.3	1300.2	1341.4	1378.4	1412.9	1477.4	1538.8	1599.1	1658.8	1718.6	1778.4
	s	0.8522	1.2981			1.3346	1.3925	1.4338	1.4672	1.4960	1.5219	1.5677	1.6084	1.6458	1.6808	1.7138	1.7451
2000 (635.80)	Sh					14.20	64.20	114.20	164.20	214.20	264.20	364.20	464.20	564.20	664.20	764.20	864.20
	v	0.02565	0.1883			0.2056	0.2488	0.2805	0.3072	0.3312	0.3534	0.3942	0.4320	0.4680	0.5027	0.5365	0.5695
	h	672.11	1138.3			1168.3	1240.9	1292.6	1335.4	1373.5	1408.7	1474.1	1536.2	1596.9	1657.0	1717.0	1771.1
	s	0.8625	1.2881			1.3154	1.3794	1.4231	1.4578	1.4874	1.5138	1.5603	1.6014	1.6391	1.6743	1.7075	1.7389
2100 (642.76)	Sh					7.24	57.24	107.24	157.24	207.24	257.24	357.24	457.24	557.24	657.24	757.24	857.24
	v	0.02615	0.1750			0.1847	0.2304	0.2624	0.2888	0.3123	0.3339	0.3734	0.4099	0.4445	0.4778	0.5101	0.5418
	h	683.79	1130.5			1148.5	1229.8	1284.9	1329.3	1368.4	1404.4	1470.9	1533.6	1594.7	1655.2	1715.4	1775.7
	s	0.8727	1.2780			1.2942	1.3661	1.4125	1.4486	1.4790	1.5060	1.5532	1.5948	1.6327	1.6681	1.7014	1.7330
2200 (649.45)	Sh					.55	50.55	100.55	150.55	200.55	250.55	350.55	450.55	550.55	650.55	750.55	850.55
	v	0.02669	0.1627			0.1636	0.2134	0.2458	0.2720	0.2950	0.3161	0.3545	0.3897	0.4231	0.4551	0.4862	0.5165
	h	695.46	1122.2			1123.9	1218.0	1276.8	1323.1	1363.3	1400.0	1467.6	1530.9	1592.5	1653.3	1713.9	1774.4
	s	0.8828	1.2676			1.2691	1.3523	1.4020	1.4395	1.4708	1.4984	1.5463	1.5883	1.6266	1.6622	1.6956	1.7273
2300 (655.89)	Sh						44.11	94.11	144.11	194.11	244.11	344.11	444.11	544.11	644.11	744.11	844.11
	v	0.02727	0.1513				0.1975	0.2305	0.2566	0.2793	0.2999	0.3372	0.3714	0.4035	0.4344	0.4643	0.4935
	h	707.18	1113.2				1205.3	1268.4	1316.7	1358.1	1395.7	1464.2	1528.3	1590.3	1651.5	1712.3	1773.1
	s	0.8929	1.2569				1.3381	1.3914	1.4305	1.4628	1.4910	1.5397	1.5821	1.6207	1.6565	1.6901	1.7219

Sh = superheat, F
v = specific volume, cu ft per lb
h = enthalpy, Btu per lb
s = entropy, Btu per F per lb

ITEM B 15   Properties of Superheated Steam (continued)

Abs. Press. Lb/Sq In. (Sat. Temp)		Sat Water	Sat Steam	700	750	800	850	900	950	1000	1050	1100	1150	1200	1300	1400	1500
2400 (662.11)	Sh			37.89	87.89	137.89	187.89	237.89	287.89	337.89	387.89	437.89	487.89	537.89	637.89	737.89	837.89
	v	0.02790	0.1408	0.1824	0.2164	0.2424	0.2648	0.2850	0.3037	0.3214	0.3382	0.3545	0.3703	0.3856	0.4155	0.4443	0.4724
	h	718.95	1103.7	1191.6	1259.7	1310.1	1352.8	1391.2	1426.9	1460.9	1493.7	1525.6	1557.0	1588.1	1649.6	1710.8	1771.8
	s	0.9031	1.2460	1.3232	1.3808	1.4217	1.4549	1.4837	1.5095	1.5332	1.5553	1.5761	1.5959	1.6149	1.6509	1.6847	1.7167
2500 (668.11)	Sh			31.89	81.89	131.89	181.89	231.89	281.89	331.89	381.89	431.89	481.89	531.89	631.89	731.89	831.89
	v	0.02859	0.1307	0.1681	0.2032	0.2293	0.2514	0.2712	0.2896	0.3068	0.3232	0.3390	0.3543	0.3692	0.3980	0.4259	0.4529
	h	731.71	1093.3	1176.7	1250.6	1303.4	1347.4	1386.7	1423.1	1457.5	1490.7	1522.9	1554.6	1585.9	1647.8	1709.2	1770.4
	s	0.9139	1.2345	1.3076	1.3701	1.4129	1.4472	1.4766	1.5029	1.5269	1.5492	1.5703	1.5903	1.6094	1.6456	1.6796	1.7116
2600 (673.91)	Sh			26.09	76.09	126.09	176.09	226.09	276.09	326.09	376.09	426.09	476.09	526.09	626.09	726.09	826.09
	v	0.02938	0.1211	0.1544	0.1909	0.2171	0.2390	0.2585	0.2765	0.2933	0.3093	0.3247	0.3395	0.3540	0.3819	0.4088	0.4350
	h	744.47	1082.0	1160.2	1241.1	1296.5	1341.9	1382.1	1419.2	1454.1	1487.7	1520.2	1552.2	1583.7	1646.0	1707.7	1769.1
	s	0.9247	1.2225	1.2908	1.3592	1.4042	1.4395	1.4696	1.4964	1.5208	1.5434	1.5646	1.5848	1.6040	1.6405	1.6746	1.7068
2700 (679.53)	Sh			20.47	70.47	120.47	170.47	220.47	270.47	320.47	370.47	420.47	470.47	520.47	620.47	720.47	820.47
	v	0.03029	0.1119	0.1411	0.1794	0.2058	0.2275	0.2468	0.2644	0.2809	0.2965	0.3114	0.3259	0.3399	0.3670	0.3931	0.4184
	h	757.34	1069.7	1142.0	1231.1	1289.5	1336.3	1377.5	1415.2	1450.7	1484.6	1517.5	1549.8	1581.5	1644.1	1706.1	1767.8
	s	0.9356	1.2097	1.2727	1.3481	1.3954	1.4319	1.4628	1.4900	1.5148	1.5376	1.5591	1.5794	1.5988	1.6355	1.6697	1.7021
2800 (684.96)	Sh			15.04	65.04	115.04	165.04	215.04	265.04	315.04	365.04	415.04	465.04	515.04	615.04	715.04	815.04
	v	0.03134	0.1030	0.1278	0.1685	0.1952	0.2168	0.2358	0.2531	0.2693	0.2845	0.2991	0.3132	0.3268	0.3532	0.3785	0.4030
	h	770.69	1055.8	1121.2	1220.6	1282.2	1330.7	1372.8	1411.2	1447.2	1481.6	1514.8	1547.3	1579.3	1642.2	1704.5	1766.5
	s	0.9468	1.1958	1.2527	1.3368	1.3867	1.4245	1.4561	1.4838	1.5089	1.5321	1.5537	1.5742	1.5938	1.6306	1.6651	1.6975
2900 (690.22)	Sh			9.78	59.78	109.78	159.78	209.78	259.78	309.78	359.78	409.78	459.78	509.78	609.78	709.78	809.78
	v	0.03262	0.0942	0.1138	0.1581	0.1853	0.2068	0.2256	0.2427	0.2585	0.2734	0.2877	0.3014	0.3147	0.3403	0.3649	0.3887
	h	785.13	1039.8	1095.3	1209.6	1274.7	1324.9	1368.0	1407.2	1443.7	1478.5	1512.1	1544.9	1577.0	1640.4	1703.0	1765.2
	s	0.9588	1.1803	1.2283	1.3251	1.3780	1.4171	1.4494	1.4777	1.5032	1.5266	1.5485	1.5692	1.5889	1.6259	1.6605	1.6931
3000 (695.33)	Sh			4.67	54.67	104.67	154.67	204.67	254.67	304.67	354.67	404.67	454.67	504.67	604.67	704.67	804.67
	v	0.03428	0.0850	0.0982	0.1483	0.1759	0.1975	0.2161	0.2329	0.2484	0.2630	0.2770	0.2904	0.3033	0.3282	0.3522	0.3753
	h	801.84	1020.3	1060.5	1197.9	1267.0	1319.0	1363.2	1403.1	1440.2	1475.4	1509.4	1542.4	1574.8	1638.5	1701.4	1763.8
	s	0.9728	1.1619	1.1966	1.3131	1.3692	1.4097	1.4429	1.4717	1.4976	1.5213	1.5434	1.5642	1.5841	1.6214	1.6561	1.6888
3100 (700.28)	Sh				49.72	99.72	149.72	199.72	249.72	299.72	349.72	399.72	449.72	499.72	599.72	699.72	799.72
	v	0.03681	0.0745		0.1389	0.1671	0.1887	0.2071	0.2237	0.2390	0.2533	0.2670	0.2800	0.2927	0.3170	0.3403	0.3628
	h	823.97	993.3		1185.4	1259.1	1313.0	1358.4	1399.0	1436.7	1472.3	1506.6	1539.9	1572.6	1636.7	1699.8	1762.5
	s	0.9914	1.1373		1.3007	1.3604	1.4024	1.4364	1.4658	1.4920	1.5161	1.5384	1.5594	1.5794	1.6169	1.6518	1.6847
3200 (705.08)	Sh				44.92	94.92	144.92	194.92	244.92	294.92	344.92	394.92	444.92	494.92	594.92	694.92	794.92
	v	0.04472	0.0566		0.1300	0.1588	0.1804	0.1987	0.2151	0.2301	0.2442	0.2576	0.2704	0.2827	0.3065	0.3291	0.3510
	h	875.54	931.6		1172.3	1250.9	1306.9	1353.4	1394.9	1433.1	1469.2	1503.8	1537.4	1570.3	1634.8	1698.3	1761.2
	s	1.0351	1.0832		1.2877	1.3515	1.3951	1.4300	1.4600	1.4866	1.5110	1.5335	1.5547	1.5749	1.6126	1.6477	1.6806
3300	Sh																
	v			0.1213	0.1510	0.1727	0.1908	0.2070	0.2218	0.2357	0.2488	0.2613	0.2734		0.2966	0.3187	0.3400
	h			1158.2	1242.5	1300.7	1348.4	1390.7	1429.5	1466.1	1501.0	1534.9	1568.1		1632.9	1696.7	1759.9
	s			1.2742	1.3425	1.3879	1.4237	1.4542	1.4813	1.5059	1.5287	1.5501	1.5704		1.6084	1.6436	1.6767
3400	Sh																
	v			0.1129	0.1435	0.1653	0.1834	0.1994	0.2140	0.2276	0.2405	0.2528	0.2646		0.2872	0.3088	0.3296
	h			1143.2	1233.7	1294.3	1343.4	1386.4	1425.9	1462.9	1498.3	1532.4	1565.8		1631.1	1695.1	1758.5
	s			1.2600	1.3334	1.3807	1.4174	1.4486	1.4761	1.5010	1.5240	1.5456	1.5660		1.6042	1.6396	1.6728
3500	Sh																
	v			0.1048	0.1364	0.1583	0.1764	0.1922	0.2066	0.2200	0.2326	0.2447	0.2563		0.2784	0.2995	0.3198
	h			1127.1	1224.6	1287.8	1338.2	1382.2	1422.2	1459.7	1495.5	1529.9	1563.6		1629.2	1693.6	1757.2
	s			1.2450	1.3242	1.3734	1.4112	1.4430	1.4709	1.4962	1.5194	1.5412	1.5618		1.6002	1.6358	1.6691
3600	Sh																
	v			0.0966	0.1296	0.1517	0.1697	0.1854	0.1996	0.2128	0.2252	0.2371	0.2485		0.2702	0.2908	0.3106
	h			1108.6	1215.3	1281.2	1333.0	1377.9	1418.6	1456.5	1492.6	1527.4	1561.3		1627.3	1692.0	1755.9
	s			1.2281	1.3148	1.3662	1.4050	1.4374	1.4658	1.4914	1.5149	1.5369	1.5576		1.5962	1.6320	1.6654
3800	Sh																
	v			0.0799	0.1169	0.1395	0.1574	0.1729	0.1868	0.1996	0.2116	0.2231	0.2340		0.2549	0.2746	0.2936
	h			1064.2	1195.5	1267.6	1322.4	1369.1	1411.2	1450.1	1487.0	1522.4	1556.8		1623.6	1688.9	1753.2
	s			1.1888	1.2955	1.3517	1.3928	1.4265	1.4558	1.4821	1.5061	1.5284	1.5495		1.5886	1.6247	1.6584
4000	Sh																
	v			0.0631	0.1052	0.1284	0.1463	0.1616	0.1752	0.1877	0.1994	0.2105	0.2210		0.2411	0.2601	0.2783
	h			1007.4	1174.3	1253.4	1311.6	1360.2	1403.6	1443.6	1481.3	1517.3	1552.2		1619.8	1685.7	1750.6
	s			1.1396	1.2754	1.3371	1.3807	1.4158	1.4461	1.4730	1.4976	1.5203	1.5417		1.5812	1.6177	1.6516
4200	Sh																
	v			0.0498	0.0945	0.1183	0.1362	0.1513	0.1647	0.1769	0.1883	0.1991	0.2093		0.2287	0.2470	0.2645
	h			950.1	1151.6	1238.6	1300.4	1351.2	1396.0	1437.1	1475.5	1512.2	1547.6		1616.1	1682.6	1748.0
	s			1.0905	1.2544	1.3223	1.3686	1.4053	1.4366	1.4642	1.4893	1.5124	1.5341		1.5742	1.6109	1.6452
4400	Sh																
	v			0.0421	0.0846	0.1090	0.1270	0.1420	0.1552	0.1671	0.1782	0.1887	0.1986		0.2174	0.2351	0.2519
	h			909.5	1127.3	1223.3	1289.0	1342.0	1388.3	1430.4	1469.7	1507.1	1543.0		1612.3	1679.4	1745.3
	s			1.0556	1.2325	1.3073	1.3566	1.3949	1.4272	1.4556	1.4812	1.5048	1.5268		1.5673	1.6044	1.6389

Sh = superheat, F
v = specific volume, cu ft per lb

h = enthalpy, Btu per lb
s = entropy, Btu per F per lb

ITEM B 15 Properties of Superheated Steam (continued)

Abs Press. Lb/Sq In. (Sat. Temp)		Sat. Water	Sat. Steam	750	800	850	900	950	1000	1050	1100	1150	1200	1250	1300	1400	1500
4600	Sh																
	v			0.0380	0.0751	0.1005	0.1186	0.1335	0.1465	0.1582	0.1691	0.1792	0.1889	0.1982	0.2071	0.2242	0.2404
	h			883.8	1100.0	1207.3	1277.2	1332.6	1380.5	1423.7	1463.9	1501.9	1538.4	1573.8	1608.5	1676.3	1742.7
	s			1.0331	1.2084	1.2922	1.3446	1.3847	1.4181	1.4472	1.4734	1.4974	1.5197	1.5407	1.5607	1.5982	1.6330
4800	Sh																
	v			0.0355	0.0665	0.0927	0.1109	0.1257	0.1385	0.1500	0.1606	0.1706	0.1800	0.1890	0.1977	0.2142	0.2299
	h			866.9	1071.2	1190.7	1265.2	1323.1	1372.6	1417.0	1458.0	1496.7	1533.8	1569.7	1604.7	1673.1	1740.0
	s			1.0180	1.1835	1.2768	1.3327	1.3745	1.4090	1.4390	1.4657	1.4901	1.5128	1.5341	1.5543	1.5921	1.6272
5000	Sh																
	v			0.0338	0.0591	0.0855	0.1038	0.1185	0.1312	0.1425	0.1529	0.1626	0.1718	0.1806	0.1890	0.2050	0.2203
	h			854.9	1042.9	1173.6	1252.9	1313.5	1364.6	1410.2	1452.1	1491.5	1529.1	1565.5	1600.9	1670.0	1737.4
	s			1.0070	1.1593	1.2612	1.3207	1.3645	1.4001	1.4309	1.4582	1.4831	1.5061	1.5277	1.5481	1.5863	1.6216
5200	Sh																
	v			0.0326	0.0531	0.0789	0.0973	0.1119	0.1244	0.1356	0.1458	0.1553	0.1642	0.1728	0.1810	0.1966	0.2114
	h			845.8	1016.9	1156.0	1240.4	1303.7	1356.6	1403.4	1446.2	1486.3	1524.5	1561.3	1597.2	1666.8	1734.7
	s			0.9985	1.1370	1.2455	1.3088	1.3545	1.3914	1.4229	1.4509	1.4762	1.4995	1.5214	1.5420	1.5806	1.6161
5400	Sh																
	v			0.0317	0.0483	0.0728	0.0912	0.1058	0.1182	0.1292	0.1392	0.1485	0.1572	0.1656	0.1736	0.1888	0.2031
	h			838.5	994.3	1138.1	1227.7	1293.7	1348.4	1396.5	1440.3	1481.1	1519.8	1557.1	1593.4	1663.7	1732.1
	s			0.9915	1.1175	1.2296	1.2969	1.3446	1.3827	1.4151	1.4437	1.4694	1.4931	1.5153	1.5362	1.5750	1.6109
5600	Sh																
	v			0.0309	0.0447	0.0672	0.0856	0.1001	0.1124	0.1232	0.1331	0.1422	0.1508	0.1589	0.1667	0.1815	0.1954
	h			832.4	975.0	1119.9	1214.8	1283.7	1340.2	1389.6	1434.3	1475.9	1515.2	1552.9	1589.6	1660.5	1729.5
	s			0.9855	1.1008	1.2137	1.2850	1.3348	1.3742	1.4075	1.4366	1.4628	1.4869	1.5093	1.5304	1.5697	1.6058
5800	Sh																
	v			0.0303	0.0419	0.0622	0.0805	0.0949	0.1070	0.1177	0.1274	0.1363	0.1447	0.1527	0.1603	0.1747	0.1883
	h			827.3	958.8	1101.8	1201.8	1273.6	1332.0	1382.6	1428.3	1470.6	1510.5	1548.7	1585.8	1657.4	1726.8
	s			0.9803	1.0867	1.1981	1.2732	1.3250	1.3658	1.3999	1.4297	1.4564	1.4808	1.5035	1.5248	1.5644	1.6008
6000	Sh																
	v			0.0298	0.0397	0.0579	0.0757	0.0900	0.1020	0.1126	0.1221	0.1309	0.1391	0.1469	0.1544	0.1684	0.1817
	h			822.9	945.1	1084.6	1188.8	1263.4	1323.6	1375.7	1422.3	1465.4	1505.9	1544.6	1582.0	1654.2	1724.2
	s			0.9758	1.0746	1.1833	1.2615	1.3154	1.3574	1.3925	1.4229	1.4500	1.4748	1.4978	1.5194	1.5593	1.5960
6500	Sh																
	v			0.0287	0.0358	0.0495	0.0655	0.0793	0.0909	0.1012	0.1104	0.1188	0.1266	0.1340	0.1411	0.1544	0.1669
	h			813.9	919.5	1046.7	1156.3	1237.8	1302.7	1358.1	1407.3	1452.2	1494.2	1534.1	1572.5	1646.4	1717.6
	s			0.9661	1.0515	1.1506	1.2328	1.2917	1.3370	1.3743	1.4064	1.4347	1.4604	1.4841	1.5062	1.5471	1.5844
7000	Sh																
	v			0.0279	0.0334	0.0438	0.0573	0.0704	0.0816	0.0915	0.1004	0.1085	0.1160	0.1231	0.1298	0.1424	0.1542
	h			806.9	901.8	1016.5	1124.9	1212.6	1281.7	1340.5	1392.2	1439.1	1482.6	1523.7	1563.1	1638.6	1711.1
	s			0.9582	1.0350	1.1243	1.2055	1.2689	1.3171	1.3567	1.3904	1.4200	1.4466	1.4710	1.4938	1.5355	1.5735
7500	Sh																
	v			0.0272	0.0318	0.0399	0.0512	0.0631	0.0737	0.0833	0.0918	0.0996	0.1068	0.1136	0.1200	0.1321	0.1433
	h			801.3	889.0	992.9	1097.7	1188.3	1261.0	1322.9	1377.2	1426.0	1471.0	1513.3	1553.7	1630.8	1704.6
	s			0.9514	1.0224	1.1033	1.1818	1.2473	1.2980	1.3397	1.3751	1.4059	1.4335	1.4586	1.4819	1.5245	1.5632
8000	Sh																
	v			0.0267	0.0306	0.0371	0.0465	0.0571	0.0671	0.0762	0.0845	0.0920	0.0989	0.1054	0.1115	0.1230	0.1338
	h			796.6	879.1	974.4	1074.3	1165.4	1241.0	1305.5	1362.2	1413.0	1459.6	1503.1	1544.5	1623.1	1698.1
	s			0.9455	1.0122	1.0864	1.1613	1.2271	1.2798	1.3233	1.3603	1.3924	1.4208	1.4467	1.4705	1.5140	1.5533
8500	Sh																
	v			0.0262	0.0296	0.0350	0.0429	0.0522	0.0615	0.0701	0.0780	0.0853	0.0919	0.0982	0.1041	0.1151	0.1254
	h			792.7	871.2	959.8	1054.5	1144.0	1221.9	1288.5	1347.5	1400.2	1448.2	1492.9	1535.3	1615.4	1691.7
	s			0.9402	1.0037	1.0727	1.1437	1.2084	1.2627	1.3076	1.3460	1.3793	1.4087	1.4352	1.4597	1.5040	1.5439
9000	Sh																
	v			0.0258	0.0288	0.0335	0.0402	0.0483	0.0568	0.0649	0.0724	0.0794	0.0858	0.0918	0.0975	0.1081	0.1179
	h			789.3	864.7	948.0	1037.6	1125.4	1204.1	1272.1	1333.0	1387.5	1437.1	1482.9	1526.3	1607.9	1685.3
	s			0.9354	0.9964	1.0613	1.1285	1.1918	1.2468	1.2926	1.3323	1.3667	1.3970	1.4243	1.4492	1.4944	1.5349
9500	Sh																
	v			0.0254	0.0282	0.0322	0.0380	0.0451	0.0528	0.0603	0.0675	0.0742	0.0804	0.0862	0.0917	0.1019	0.1113
	h			786.4	859.2	938.3	1023.4	1108.9	1187.7	1256.6	1318.9	1375.1	1426.1	1473.1	1517.3	1600.4	1679.0
	s			0.9310	0.9900	1.0516	1.1153	1.1771	1.2320	1.2785	1.3191	1.3546	1.3858	1.4137	1.4392	1.4851	1.5263
10000	Sh																
	v			0.0251	0.0276	0.0312	0.0362	0.0425	0.0495	0.0565	0.0633	0.0697	0.0757	0.0812	0.0865	0.0963	0.1054
	h			783.8	854.5	930.2	1011.3	1094.2	1172.6	1242.0	1305.3	1362.9	1415.3	1463.4	1508.6	1593.1	1672.8
	s			0.9270	0.9842	1.0432	1.1039	1.1638	1.2185	1.2652	1.3065	1.3429	1.3749	1.4035	1.4295	1.4763	1.5180
10500	Sh																
	v			0.0248	0.0271	0.0303	0.0347	0.0404	0.0467	0.0532	0.0595	0.0656	0.0714	0.0768	0.0818	0.0913	0.1001
	h			781.5	850.5	923.4	1001.0	1081.3	1158.9	1228.4	1292.4	1351.1	1404.7	1453.9	1500.0	1585.8	1666.7
	s			0.9232	0.9790	1.0358	1.0939	1.1519	1.2060	1.2529	1.2946	1.3371	1.3644	1.3937	1.4202	1.4677	1.5100

Sh = superheat, F
v = specific volume, cu ft per lb

h = enthalpy, Btu per lb
s = entropy, Btu per F per lb

ITEM B 15 Properties of Superheated Steam (concluded)

Abs Press. Lb/Sq In. (Sat. Temp)		Sat. Water	Sat. Steam	750	800	850	900	950	1000	1050	1100	1150	1200	1250	1300	1400	1500
				temp													
11000	v			0.0245	0.0267	0.0296	0.0335	0.0386	0.0443	0.0503	0.0562	0.0620	0.0676	0.0727	0.0776	0.0868	0.0952
	h			779.5	846.9	917.5	992.1	1069.9	1146.3	1215.9	1280.2	1339.7	1394.4	1444.6	1491.5	1578.7	1660.6
	s			0.9196	0.9742	1.0292	1.0851	1.1412	1.1945	1.2414	1.2833	1.3209	1.3544	1.3842	1.4112	1.4595	1.5023
11500	v			0.0243	0.0263	0.0290	0.0325	0.0370	0.0423	0.0478	0.0534	0.0588	0.0641	0.0691	0.0739	0.0827	0.0909
	h			777.7	843.8	912.4	984.5	1059.8	1134.9	1204.3	1268.7	1328.8	1384.4	1435.5	1483.2	1571.8	1654.7
	s			0.9163	0.9698	1.0232	1.0772	1.1316	1.1840	1.2308	1.2727	1.3107	1.3446	1.3750	1.4025	1.4515	1.4949
12000	v			0.0241	0.0260	0.0284	0.0317	0.0357	0.0405	0.0456	0.0508	0.0560	0.0610	0.0659	0.0704	0.0790	0.0869
	h			776.1	841.0	907.9	977.8	1050.9	1124.5	1193.7	1258.0	1318.5	1374.7	1426.6	1475.1	1564.9	1648.8
	s			0.9131	0.9657	1.0177	1.0701	1.1229	1.1742	1.2209	1.2627	1.3010	1.3353	1.3662	1.3941	1.4438	1.4877
12500	v			0.0238	0.0256	0.0279	0.0309	0.0346	0.0390	0.0437	0.0486	0.0535	0.0583	0.0629	0.0673	0.0756	0.0832
	h			774.7	838.6	903.9	971.9	1043.1	1115.2	1184.1	1247.9	1308.8	1365.4	1418.0	1467.2	1558.2	1643.1
	s			0.9101	0.9618	1.0127	1.0637	1.1151	1.1653	1.2117	1.2534	1.2918	1.3264	1.3576	1.3860	1.4363	1.4808
13000	v			0.0236	0.0253	0.0275	0.0302	0.0336	0.0376	0.0420	0.0466	0.0512	0.0558	0.0602	0.0645	0.0725	0.0799
	h			773.5	836.3	900.4	966.8	1036.2	1106.7	1174.8	1238.5	1299.6	1356.5	1409.6	1459.4	1551.6	1637.4
	s			0.9073	0.9582	1.0080	1.0578	1.1079	1.1571	1.2030	1.2445	1.2831	1.3179	1.3494	1.3781	1.4291	1.4741
13500	v			0.0235	0.0251	0.0271	0.0297	0.0328	0.0364	0.0405	0.0448	0.0492	0.0535	0.0577	0.0619	0.0696	0.0768
	h			772.3	834.4	897.2	962.2	1030.0	1099.1	1166.3	1229.7	1291.0	1348.1	1401.5	1451.8	1545.2	1631.9
	s			0.9045	0.9548	1.0037	1.0524	1.1014	1.1495	1.1948	1.2361	1.2749	1.3098	1.3415	1.3705	1.4221	1.4675
14000	v			0.0233	0.0248	0.0267	0.0291	0.0320	0.0354	0.0392	0.0432	0.0474	0.0515	0.0555	0.0595	0.0670	0.0740
	h			771.3	832.6	894.3	958.0	1024.5	1092.3	1158.5	1221.4	1283.0	1340.2	1393.8	1444.4	1538.8	1626.5
	s			0.9019	0.9515	0.9996	1.0473	1.0953	1.1426	1.1872	1.2282	1.2671	1.3021	1.3339	1.3631	1.4153	1.4612
14500	v			0.0231	0.0246	0.0264	0.0287	0.0314	0.0345	0.0380	0.0418	0.0458	0.0496	0.0534	0.0573	0.0646	0.0714
	h			770.4	831.0	891.7	954.3	1019.6	1086.2	1151.4	1213.8	1275.4	1332.9	1386.4	1437.3	1532.6	1621.1
	s			0.8994	0.9484	0.9957	1.0426	1.0897	1.1362	1.1801	1.2208	1.2597	1.2949	1.3266	1.3560	1.4087	1.4551
15000	v			0.0230	0.0244	0.0261	0.0282	0.0308	0.0337	0.0369	0.0405	0.0443	0.0479	0.0516	0.0552	0.0624	0.0690
	h			769.6	829.5	889.3	950.9	1015.1	1080.6	1144.9	1206.8	1268.1	1326.0	1379.4	1430.3	1526.4	1615.9
	s			0.8970	0.9455	0.9920	1.0382	1.0846	1.1302	1.1735	1.2139	1.2525	1.2880	1.3197	1.3491	1.4022	1.4491
15500	v			0.0228	0.0242	0.0258	0.0278	0.0302	0.0329	0.0360	0.0393	0.0429	0.0464	0.0499	0.0534	0.0603	0.0668
	h			768.9	828.2	887.2	947.8	1011.1	1075.7	1139.0	1200.3	1261.1	1319.6	1372.8	1423.6	1520.4	1610.8
	s			0.8946	0.9427	0.9886	1.0340	1.0797	1.1247	1.1674	1.2073	1.2457	1.2815	1.3131	1.3424	1.3959	1.4433

Sh = superheat, F
v = specific volume, cu ft per lb

h = enthalpy, Btu per lb
s = entropy, Btu per F per lb

ITEM B 16-A Mollier Chart for Steam (English)

Modified and greatly reduced from Keenan and Keye's *Thermodynamic Properties of Steam*, published (1936) by John Wiley and Sons, Inc. Reproduced by permission of the publishers.

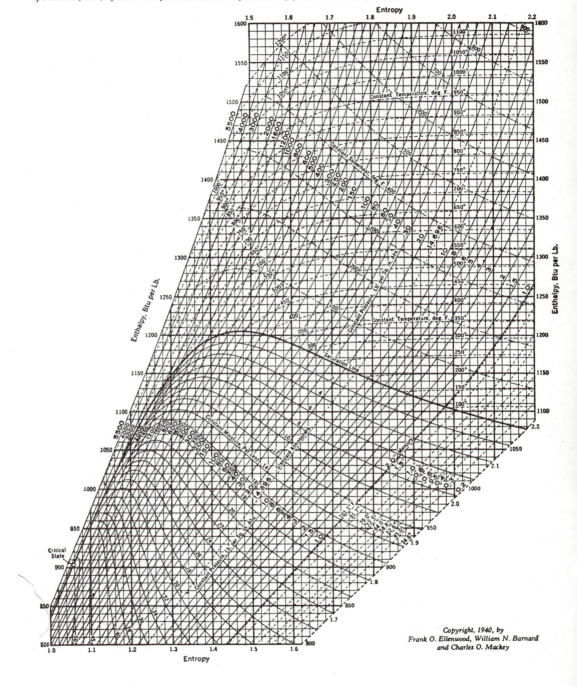

ITEM B 16-B   Mollier Chart for Steam SI (Metric)

Modified and reduced from Steam and Air Tables in SI Units, Irvine and Hartnett, published by Hemisphere Publishing Corporation 1976. Reproduced by permission of Springer-Verlag Publishing Company, owners of copyrights on chart.

(See chart on pages 174–175)

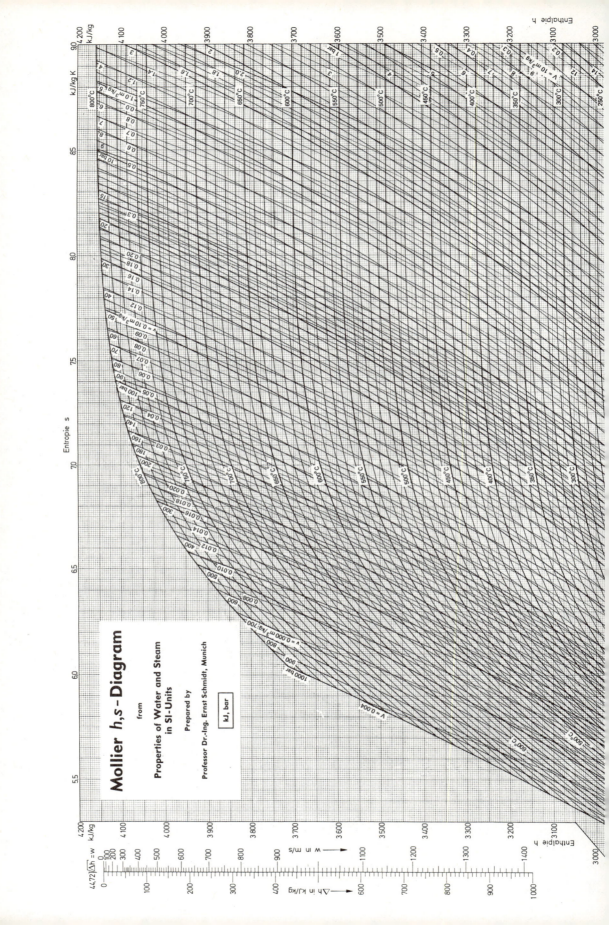

Mollier *h,s* – Diagram

from

Properties of Water and Steam in SI-Units

Prepared by

Professor Dr.-Ing. Ernst Schmidt, Munich

kJ, bar

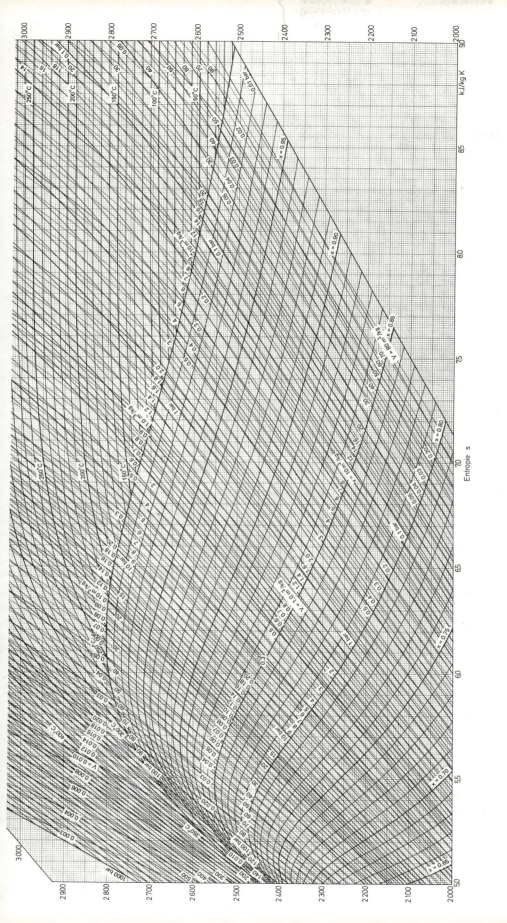

ITEM B 17 Psychrometric Chart for Air-Steam Mixtures

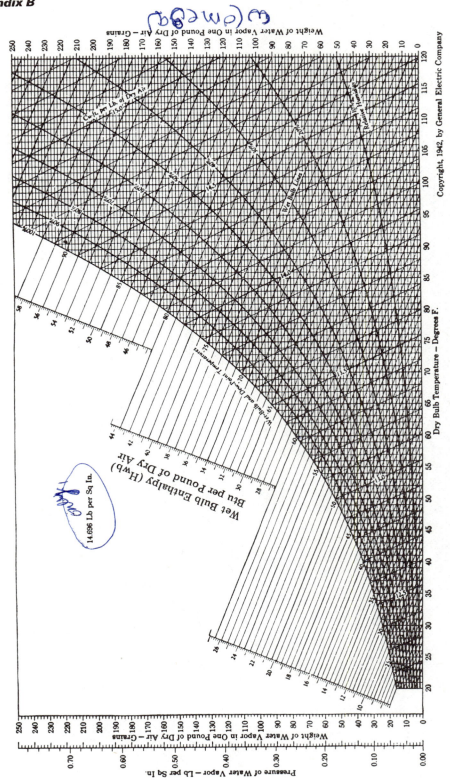

ω (omega)

14.696 Lb per Sq In.

Weight of Water Vapor in One Pound of Dry Air – Grains

Dry Bulb Temperature – Degrees F.

Copyright, 1942, by General Electric Company

Wet Bulb Enthalpy (Hwb)
Btu per Pound of Dry Air

Weight of Water Vapor in One Pound of Dry Air – Grains

Pressure of Water Vapor – Lb per Sq In.

ITEM B 18 Critical Properties and van der Waals Constants

Most of the values of T_c and p_c are adapted from the collection by Nelson and Obert[10.6]; others from International Critical Tables. Most values of $\bar{v}_c$ from reference [0.3]: others from International Critical Tables. The values of Z_c, a, and b are computed from these critical data; $a = 27R^2 T_c^2/(64 p_c)$ and $b = RT_c/(8p_c)$.

Substance	T_c, °R	p_c, atm	$\bar{v}_c$, ft³/pmole	$\bar{v}_{ci}$, ft³/pmole	$Z_c = p_c v_c / RT_c$	van der Waals a, atm $\left(\dfrac{\text{ft}^3}{\text{pmole}}\right)^2$	b ft³/pmole
Acetylene (C_2H_2)	556	62	1.80	6.55	0.274	1121	0.818
Air (equivalent)	239	37.2	1.33	4.69	0.284	345.2	0.585
Ammonia (NH_3)	730	111.3	1.16	4.79	0.242	1076	0.598
Argon (A)	271.6	48.34	1.19	4.10	0.291		
Benzene (C_6H_6)	1011	47.7	4.12	15.47	0.266	4736	1.896
n-Butane (C_4H_{10})	765	37.5	4.13	14.89	0.274	3508	1.919
Carbon dioxide (CO_2)	548	72.9	1.51	5.49	0.276	926	0.686
Carbon monoxide (CO)	239	34.5	1.49	5.06	0.294	372	0.632
Freon 12 (CCl_2F_2)	692	39.6	3.55	12.76	0.273	2718	1.595
Ethane (C_2H_6)	550	48.2	2.29	8.33	0.284	1410	1.041
Ethylene (C_2H_4)	510	50.5	1.98	7.37	0.270	1158	0.922
Helium (He)	9.33	2.26	0.93	3.01	0.300	8.66	0.376
n-Heptane (C_7H_{16})	972	27	6.86	8.31	0.26	7866	3.298
Hydrogen (H_2)	59.8	12.8	1.04	34.1	0.304	62.8	0.426
Methane (CH_4)	344	45.8	1.59	5.48	0.290	581	0.685
Methyl chloride (CH_3Cl)	749	65.8	2.18	8.31	0.262	1917	1.040
Neon (Ne)	80.3	25.9	0.668	2.26	0.295		
Nitrogen (N_2)	227	33.5	1.44	4.59	0.291	346	0.618
Nonane (C_9H_{20})	1071	22.86	8.86	34.2	0.250		
n-Octane (C_8H_{18})	1025	24.6	7.82	30.42	0.258	9601	3.76
Oxygen (O_2)	278	50.1	1.19	5.05	0.290	348	0.506
Propane (C_3H_8)	666	42.1	3.13	11.55	0.276	2368	1.445
Sulfur dioxide (SO_2)	775	77.7	1.99	7.28	0.268	1738	0.911
Water (H_2O)	1165	218.3	0.896	3.898	0.230	1400	0.488

ITEM B 19   Compressibility Factors Z, Low Pressures

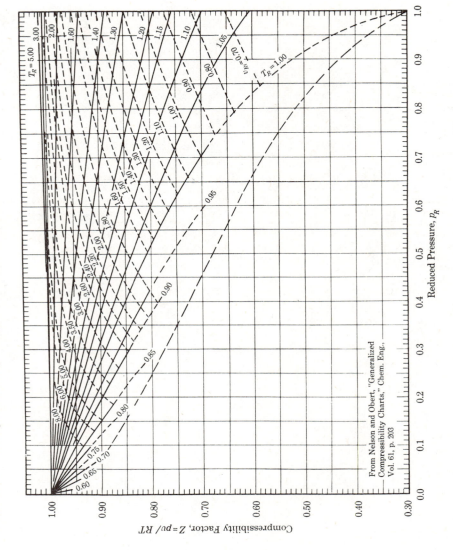

ITEM B 20 Compressibility Factors Z, Intermediate Pressures

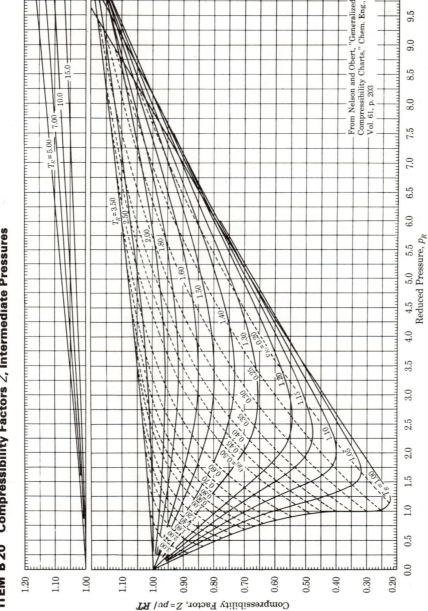

From Nelson and Obert, "Generalized Compressibility Charts," Chem. Eng., Vol. 61, p. 203

ITEM B 21 Compressibility Factors Z, High Pressures

Compressibility Factor Z = pv/RT

Reduced pressure, p_R

ITEM B 22   Enthalpy Deviation, $p_R \gtrless 1$ $(Z_c = 0.27)$.

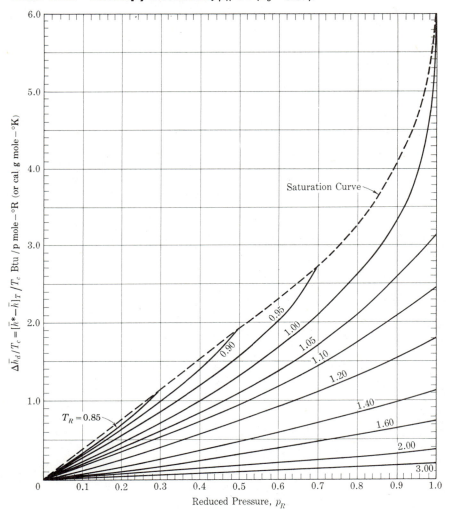

ITEM B 23   Enthalpy Deviation, $p_R > 1$ $(Z_c = 0.27)$

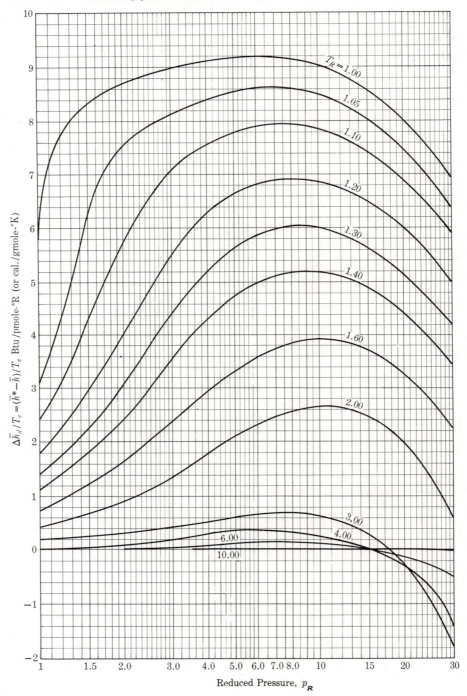

Reduced Pressure, p_R

ITEM B 24   Entropy Deviation, $p_R \lessgtr 1$ $(Z_c = 0.27)$

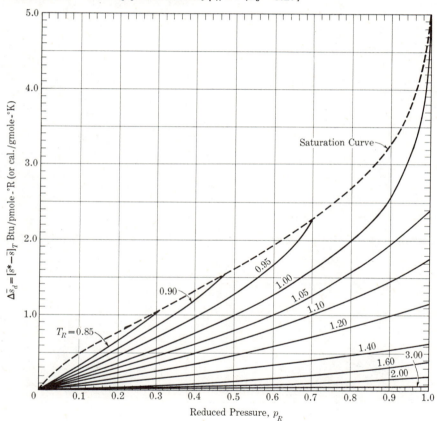

ITEM B 25   Entropy Deviation, $p_R > 1$ ($Z_c = 0.27$)

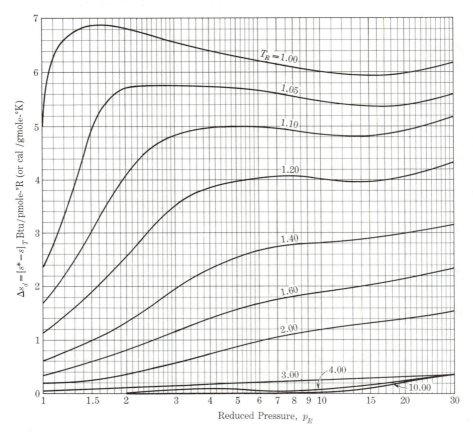

ITEM B 26 **Temperature-Entropy Chart, Air (courtesy NBS; drawn from data of Michels, Wassenaar, and Wolkers; Claitor and Crawford)**

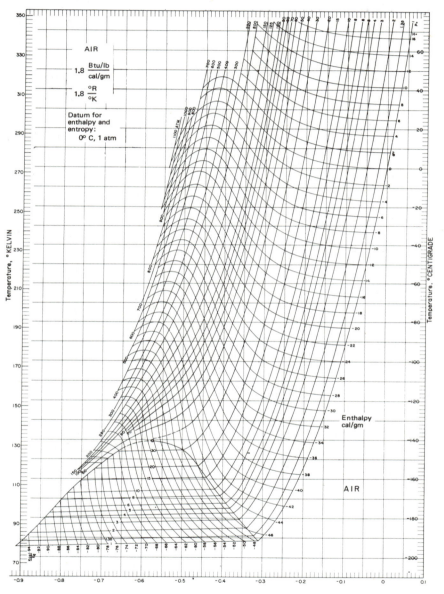

Entropy, kcal/kg - °K = Btu/lb - °R

ITEM B 27 **Temperature-Entropy Chart, Oxygen (courtesy NBS; by Richard B. Stewart, Ph.D. dissertation, Univ. of Iowa)**

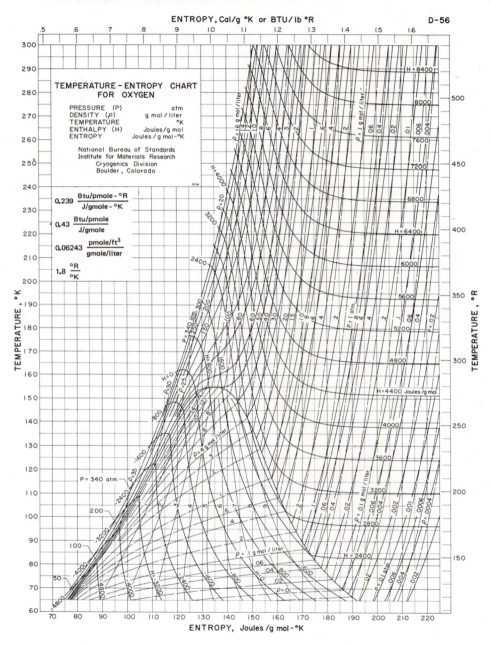

ITEM B 28   **Temperature-Entropy Chart, Hydrogen (courtesy NBS)**

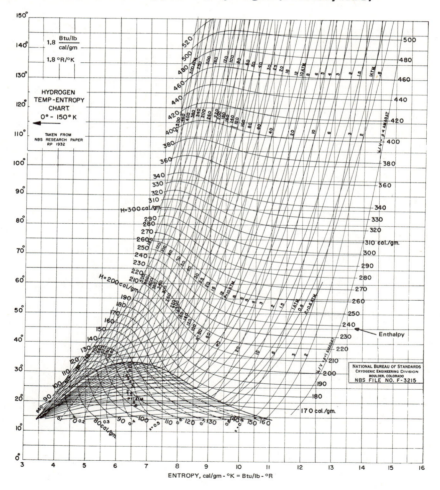

ITEM B 29   Temperature-Entropy Chart, Nitrogen (courtesy NBS; attributed to T. B. Strobridge, NBS TN 129; R. D. McCarty, L. J. Ericks)

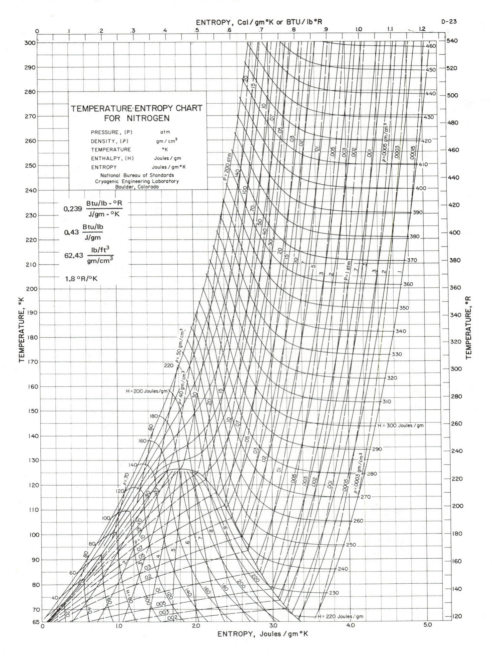

ITEM B 30 **Temperature-Entropy Chart, Helium (courtesy NBS; attributed to D. B. Mann, NBS TN 154; R. D. McCarty, L. J. Ericks)**

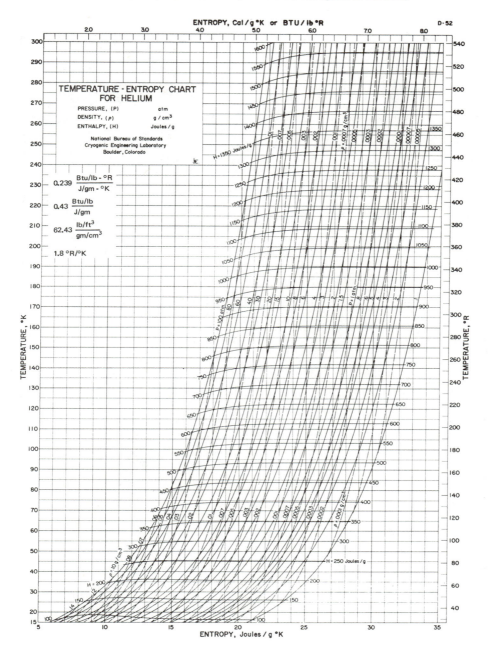

ITEM B 31   Pressure-Enthalpy Chart, Carbon Dioxide

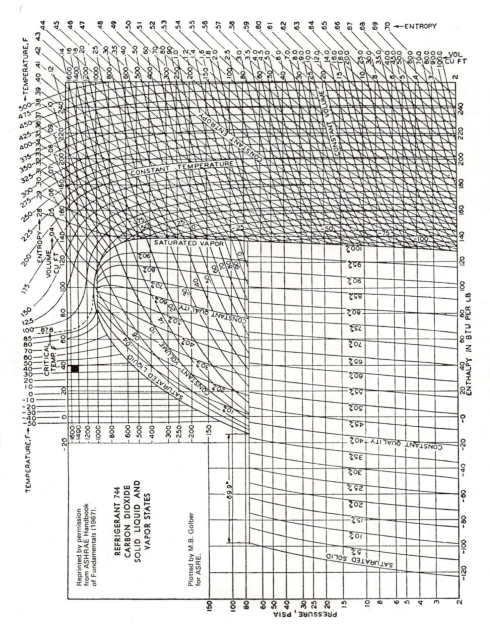

Reprinted by permission from ASHRAE Handbook of Fundamentals (1967).

REFRIGERANT 744
CARBON DIOXIDE
SOLID LIQUID AND
VAPOR STATES

Plotted by M.B. Golber for ASRE.

ITEM B 32 Values of $\log_{10} K_p$ for Certain Reactions of Gases

Taken or derived from JANAF.[0.22]

Note: Temperatures are degrees Kelvin.

Reaction → T, °K↓	$CO + \frac{1}{2}O_2$ $= CO_2$	$H_2 + \frac{1}{2}O_2$ $= H_2O$	$CO_2 + H_2$ $= CO + H_2O$	$H_2O =$ $\frac{1}{2}H_2 + OH$	$\frac{1}{2}N_2 + \frac{1}{2}O_2$ $= NO$	$\frac{1}{2}O_2 = O$	$\frac{1}{2}N_2 = N$
298	45.066	40.048	−5.018	−46.137	−15.171	−40.604	−79.800
300	44.760	39.786	−4.974	−45.832	−15.073	−40.334	−79.289
400	32.431	29.240	−3.191	−33.567	−11.142	−29.473	−58.704
600	20.087	18.633	−1.454	−21.242	−7.210	−18.574	−38.081
800	13.916	13.289	−0.627	−15.044	−5.243	−13.101	−27.744
1000	10.221	10.062	−0.159	−11.309	−4.062	−9.807	−21.528
1200	7.764	7.899	+0.135	−8.811	−3.275	−7.604	−17.377
1300	6.821	7.064	0.243	−7.848	−2.972	−6.755	−15.778
1400	6.014	6.347	0.333	−7.021	−2.712	−6.027	−14.406
1500	5.316	5.725	0.409	−6.305	−2.487	−5.395	−13.217
1600	4.706	5.180	0.474	−5.677	−2.290	−4.842	−12.175
1700	4.169	4.699	0.530	−5.124	−2.116	−4.353	−11.256
1800	3.693	4.270	0.577	−4.631	−1.962	−3.918	−10.437
1900	3.267	3.886	0.619	−4.190	−1.823	−3.529	−9.705
2000	2.884	3.540	0.656	−3.793	−1.699	−3.178	−9.046
2100	2.539	3.227	0.668	−3.434	−1.586	−2.860	−8.449
2200	2.226	2.942	0.716	−3.107	−1.484	−2.571	−7.905
2300	1.940	2.682	0.742	−2.809	−1.391	−2.307	−7.409
2400	1.679	2.443	0.764	−2.535	−1.305	−2.065	−6.954
2500	1.440	2.224	0.784	−2.284	−1.227	−1.842	−6.535
2600	1.219	2.021	0.802	−2.052	−1.154	−1.636	−6.149
2700	1.015	1.833	0.818	−1.837	−1.087	−1.446	−5.790
2800	0.825	1.658	0.833	−1.637	−1.025	−1.268	−5.457
2900	0.649	1.495	0.846	−1.451	−0.967	−1.103	−5.147
3000	0.485	1.343	0.858	−1.278	−0.913	−0.949	−4.858
3100	0.332	1.201	0.869	−1.116	−0.863	−0.805	−4.587
3200	0.189	1.067	0.878	−0.963	−0.815	−0.670	−4.332
3300	0.054	0.942	0.888	−0.821	−0.771	−0.543	−4.093
3400	−0.071	0.824	0.895	−0.687	−0.729	−0.423	−3.868
3500	−0.190	0.712	0.902	−0.559	−0.690	−0.310	−3.656
3600	−0.302	0.607	0.909	−0.440	−0.653	−0.204	−3.455
3700	−0.408	0.507	0.915	−0.327	−0.618	−0.103	−3.265
3800	−0.508	0.413	0.921	−0.220	−0.585	−0.007	−3.086
3900	−0.603	0.323	0.926	−0.120	−0.554	+0.084	−2.915
4000	−0.692	0.238	0.930	−0.022	−0.524	0.170	−2.752
4200	−0.858	+0.079	0.937	+0.158	−0.470	0.330	−2.450
4400	−1.009	−0.065	0.944	0.320	−0.420	0.475	−2.176
4600	−1.147	−0.197	0.950	0.469	−0.375	0.608	−1.924
4800	−1.272	−0.319	0.953	0.606	−0.333	0.730	−1.694
5000	−1.386	−0.430	0.956	0.731	−0.296	0.843	−1.481
5200	−1.492	−0.534	0.958	0.847	−0.261	0.946	−1.284
5400	−1.589	−0.630	0.959	0.954	−0.229	1.042	−1.102
5600	−1.679	−0.719	0.960	1.053	−0.199	1.132	−0.932
5800	−1.763	−0.803	0.960·	1.146	−0.172	1.215	−0.774
6000	−1.841	−0.880	0.961	1.232	−0.147	1.292	−0.625

ITEM B 33   Pressure-Enthalpy Chart, Ammonia

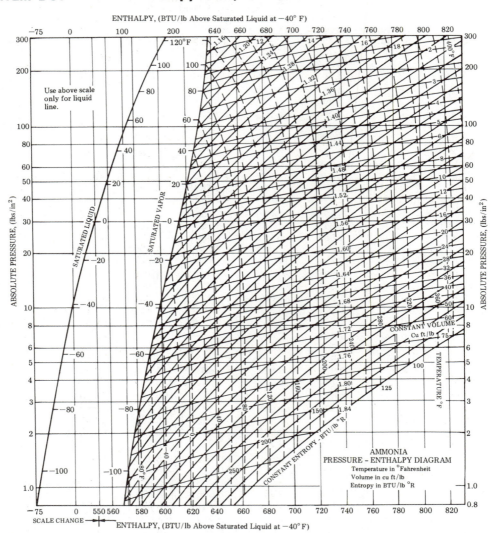

(Reprinted by permission from ASHRAE Handbook of Fundamentals 1967.)

ITEM B 34 Enthalpy-Entropy Chart, Mercury

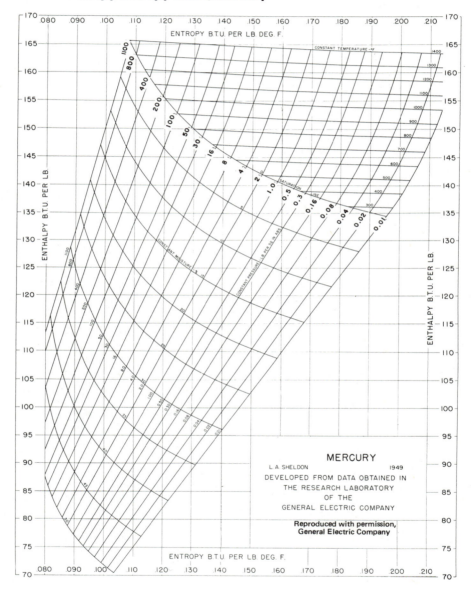

MERCURY

L.A. SHELDON   1949

DEVELOPED FROM DATA OBTAINED IN
THE RESEARCH LABORATORY
OF THE
GENERAL ELECTRIC COMPANY

**Reproduced with permission,
General Electric Company**

ITEM B 35 Pressure-Enthalpy Diagram of Freon, Refrigerant 12 (Dichlorodifluoromethane) (courtesy "Freon" Products Division, E. I. du Pont and Co., Inc., copyright 1967)

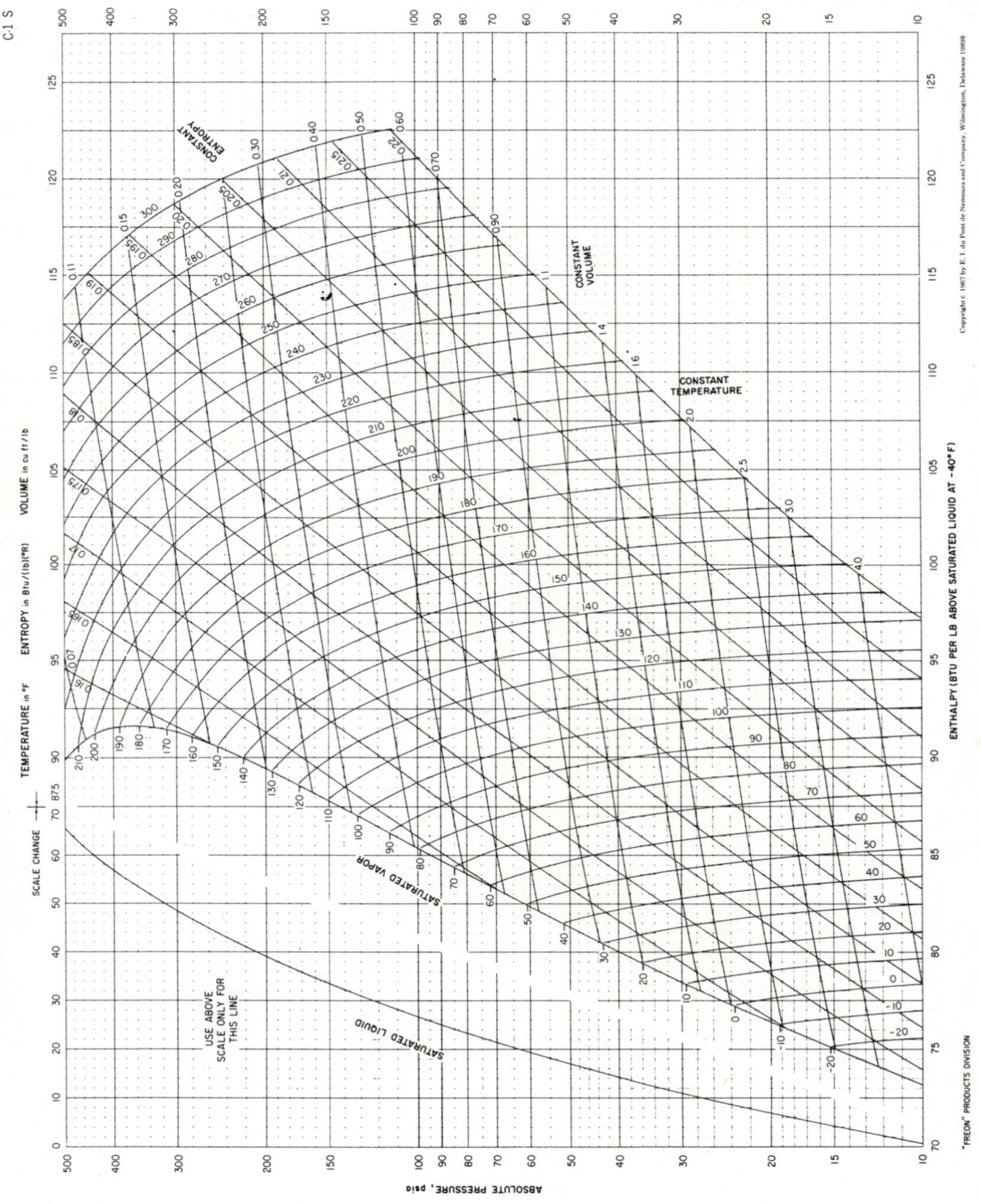

C-1 S
ABSOLUTE PRESSURE, psia
ENTHALPY (BTU PER LB ABOVE SATURATED LIQUID AT −40°F)
TEMPERATURE in °F
ENTROPY in Btu/(lb)(°R)
VOLUME in cu ft/lb
SCALE CHANGE
CONSTANT ENTROPY
CONSTANT VOLUME
CONSTANT TEMPERATURE
SATURATED VAPOR
SATURATED LIQUID
USE ABOVE SCALE ONLY FOR THIS LINE
"FREON" PRODUCTS DIVISION
Copyright © 1967 by E. I. du Pont de Nemours and Company, Wilmington, Delaware 19898

ITEM B 36   Pressure-Enthalpy Chart, Sulfur Dioxide (courtesy Shell Development Co.)

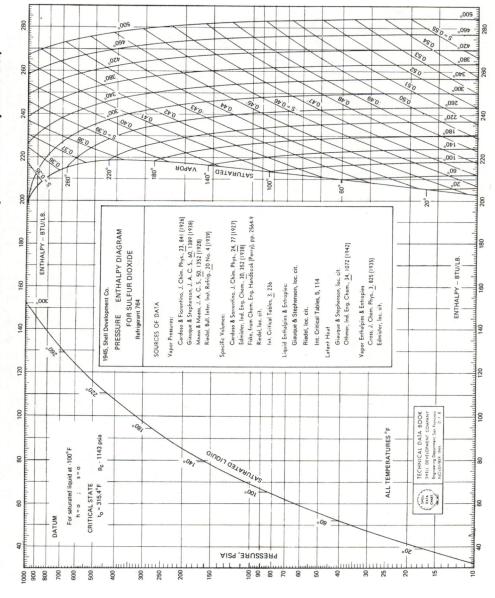

1945, Shell Development Co.

PRESSURE   ENTHALPY DIAGRAM
FOR SULFUR DIOXIDE
Refrigerant 764

SOURCES OF DATA

Vapor Pressures:
  Cardoso & Fiorentino, J. Chim. Phys., 23, 841 (1926)
  Giauque & Stephenson, J. A. C. S., 60, 1389 (1938)
  Maass & Maass, J. A. C. S., 50, 1352 (1928)
  Riedel, Bull. Inter. Int. Refrig., 20 No. 4 (1939)

Specific Volumes:
  Cardoso & Sorrentino, J. Chim. Phys., 24, 77 (1927)
  Edmister, Ind. Eng. Chem., 30, 352 (1938)
  Fiske, from Chem. Eng. Handbook (Perry), pp. 2564-9
  Riedel, loc. cit.
  Int. Critical Tables, 3, 236

Liquid Enthalpies & Entropies:
  Giauque & Stephenson, loc. cit.
  Riedel, loc. cit.
  Int. Critical Tables, 5, 114

Latent Heat
  Giauque & Stephenson, loc. cit.
  Othmer, Ind. Eng. Chem., 34, 1072 (1942)

Vapor Enthalpies & Entropies
  Cross, J. Chem. Phys., 3, 825 (1935)
  Edmister, loc. cit.

ENTHALPY — BTU/LB.

ENTHALPY — BTU/LB.

PRESSURE, PSIA

SATURATED LIQUID

SATURATED VAPOR

ALL TEMPERATURES °F

DATUM
For saturated liquid at -100° F
h = 0   ;   s = 0

CRITICAL STATE
$t_c = 315.4°F$ $p_c = 1143$ psia

TECHNICAL DATA BOOK
SHELL DEVELOPMENT COMPANY
Engineering Department, San Francisco
NOVEMBER 1944   D.1.8

ITEM B 37   Generalized Fugacity Coefficient Chart

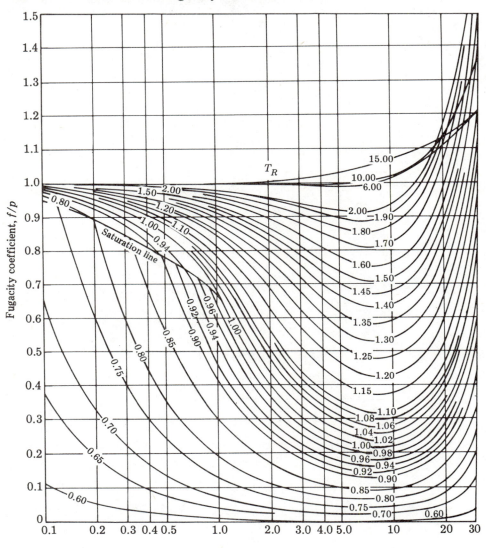

ITEM B 38 Relations of Units; Basic Constants

Where relevant, abbreviations given in *The International System of Units*, NASA SP-7012, are used. For the given conversions that are not exact by definition, additional digits may be found in the literature if greater accuracy is desired.

Abbreviations. Å = angstrom, atm = standard atmosphere, 760 mm of Hg at 0°C, cal = calorie (gram), cm = centimeter, deg = degree, gal = gallon, U.S. liquid, gm (and g) = gram, gmole = gram-mole, J = joule, kcal = kilocalorie, kg = kilogram, kJ = kilojoule, km = kilometer, kw = kilowatt, l = liter, lb = avoirdupois pound, m = meter, mi = mile (U.S.), mm = millimeter, N = newton, oz = avoirdupois ounce, pmole = pound mole, pt = pint, rad = radian, rev = revolution, s = second, ton = short U.S. ton, V = volt, wt = watt. Others are as usual; see Abbreviations in front matter.

LENGTH

$12 \dfrac{\text{in.}}{\text{ft}}$	$6080.2 \dfrac{\text{ft}}{\text{naut. mi}}$	$5280 \dfrac{\text{ft}}{\text{mi}}$	$0.3937 \dfrac{\text{in.}}{\text{cm}}$	$30.48 \dfrac{\text{cm}}{\text{ft}}$	$10^4 \dfrac{\text{microns}}{\text{cm}}$
$3 \dfrac{\text{ft}}{\text{yd}}$	$1.152 \dfrac{\text{mi}}{\text{naut. mi}}$	$10^{10} \dfrac{\text{Å}}{\text{m}}$	$2.54 \dfrac{\text{cm}}{\text{in.}}$	$3.28 \dfrac{\text{ft}}{\text{m}}$	$1.609 \dfrac{\text{km}}{\text{mi}}$

AREA

$144 \dfrac{\text{in.}^2}{\text{ft}^2}$	$43,560 \dfrac{\text{ft}^2}{\text{acre}}$	$640 \dfrac{\text{acres}}{\text{mi}^2}$	$10.76 \dfrac{\text{ft}^2}{\text{m}^2}$	$929 \dfrac{\text{cm}^2}{\text{ft}^2}$	$6.452 \dfrac{\text{cm}^2}{\text{in.}^2}$

VOLUME

$1728 \dfrac{\text{in.}^3}{\text{ft}^3}$	$7.481 \dfrac{\text{gal}}{\text{ft}^3}$	$43,560 \dfrac{\text{ft}^3}{\text{acre-ft}}$	$3.7854 \dfrac{\text{l}}{\text{gal}}$	$28.317 \dfrac{\text{l}}{\text{ft}^3}$	$35.31 \dfrac{\text{ft}^3}{\text{m}^3}$
$231 \dfrac{\text{in.}^3}{\text{gal}}$	$8 \dfrac{\text{pt}}{\text{gal}}$	$10^3 \dfrac{\text{l}}{\text{m}^3}$	$61.025 \dfrac{\text{in.}^3}{\text{l}}$	$10^3 \dfrac{\text{cm}^3}{\text{l}}$	$28,317 \dfrac{\text{cm}^3}{\text{ft}^3}$

DENSITY

$1728 \dfrac{\text{lb/ft}^3}{\text{lb/in.}^3}$	$32.174 \dfrac{\text{lb/ft}^3}{\text{slug/ft}^3}$	$0.51538 \dfrac{\text{gm/cm}^3}{\text{slug/ft}^3}$	$16.018 \dfrac{\text{kg/m}^3}{\text{lb/ft}^3}$	$1000 \dfrac{\text{kg/m}^3}{\text{gm/cm}^3}$

ANGULAR

$2\pi = 6.2832 \dfrac{\text{rad}}{\text{rev}}$	$57.3 \dfrac{\text{deg}}{\text{rad}}$	$\dfrac{1}{2\pi} \dfrac{\text{rpm}}{\text{rad/min}}$	$9.549 \dfrac{\text{rpm}}{\text{rad/sec}}$

TIME

$60 \dfrac{\text{s}}{\text{min}}$	$3600 \dfrac{\text{s}}{\text{hr}}$	$60 \dfrac{\text{min}}{\text{hr}}$	$24 \dfrac{\text{hr}}{\text{day}}$

SPEED

$88 \dfrac{\text{fpm}}{\text{mph}}$	$0.6818 \dfrac{\text{mph}}{\text{fps}}$	$0.5144 \dfrac{\text{m/s}}{\text{knot}}$	$0.3048 \dfrac{\text{m/s}}{\text{fps}}$	$0.44704 \dfrac{\text{m/s}}{\text{mph}}$
$1.467 \dfrac{\text{fps}}{\text{mph}}$	$1.152 \dfrac{\text{mph}}{\text{knot}}$	$1.689 \dfrac{\text{fps}}{\text{knot}}$	$152.4 \dfrac{\text{cm/min}}{\text{ips}}$	

FORCE, MASS

$16 \dfrac{\text{oz}}{\text{lb}_m}$	$32.174 \dfrac{\text{lb}_m}{\text{slug}}$	$444,820 \dfrac{\text{dynes}}{\text{lb}_f}$	$2.205 \dfrac{\text{lb}_m}{\text{kg}}$	$9.80665 \dfrac{\text{N}}{\text{kg}_f}$
$1000 \dfrac{\text{lb}_f}{\text{kip}}$	$32.174 \dfrac{\text{poundals}}{\text{lb}_f}$	$980.665 \dfrac{\text{dynes}}{\text{gm}_f}$	$14.594 \dfrac{\text{kg}}{\text{slug}}$	$4.4482 \dfrac{\text{N}}{\text{lb}_f}$
$2000 \dfrac{\text{lb}_m}{\text{ton}}$	$7000 \dfrac{\text{grains}}{\text{lb}_m}$	$453.6 \dfrac{\text{gm}}{\text{lb}_m}$	$10^5 \dfrac{\text{dynes}}{\text{N}}$	$1 \dfrac{\text{kilopond}}{\text{kg}}$
$14.594 \dfrac{\text{kg}}{\text{slug}}$	$28.35 \dfrac{\text{gm}}{\text{oz}}$	$453.6 \dfrac{\text{gmole}}{\text{pmole}}$	$907.18 \dfrac{\text{kg}}{\text{ton}}$	$1000 \dfrac{\text{kg}}{\text{metric ton}}$

ITEM B 38   Relations of Units; Basic Constants (continued)

PRESSURE

$14.696 \dfrac{\text{psi}}{\text{atm}}$	$101{,}325 \dfrac{\text{N/m}^2}{\text{atm}}$	$13.6 \dfrac{\text{kg}}{\text{mm Hg}(0°C)}$	$51.715 \dfrac{\text{mm Hg}(0°C)}{\text{psi}}$	$47.88 \dfrac{\text{N/m}^2}{\text{psf}}$
$29.921 \dfrac{\text{in. Hg}(0°C)}{\text{atm}}$	$10^5 \dfrac{\text{N/m}^2}{\text{bar}}$ *pascal*	$13.57 \dfrac{\text{in. H}_2\text{O}(60°F)}{\text{in. Hg}(60°F)}$	$703.07 \dfrac{\text{kg/m}^2}{\text{psi}}$	$6894.8 \dfrac{\text{N/m}^2}{\text{psi}}$ *pascal*
$33.934 \dfrac{\text{ft H}_2\text{O}(60°F)}{\text{atm}}$	$14.504 \dfrac{\text{psi}}{\text{bar}}$	$0.0361 \dfrac{\text{psi}}{\text{in. H}_2\text{O}(60°F)}$	$0.0731 \dfrac{\text{kg/cm}^2}{\text{psi}}$	$760 \dfrac{\text{torr}}{\text{atm}}$
$1.01325 \dfrac{\text{bar}}{\text{atm}}$	$10^6 \dfrac{\text{dynes/cm}^2}{\text{bar}}$	$0.4898 \dfrac{\text{psi}}{\text{in. Hg}(60°F)}$	$\dfrac{9.869}{10^7} \dfrac{\text{atm}}{\text{dyne/cm}^2}$	$133.3 \dfrac{\text{N/m}^2}{\text{torr}}$
$33.934 \dfrac{\text{ft H}_2\text{O}(60°F)}{\text{atm}}$	$760 \dfrac{\text{mm Hg}(0°C)}{\text{atm}}$	$406.79 \dfrac{\text{in. H}_2\text{O}(39.2°F)}{\text{atm}}$	$0.1 \dfrac{\text{dyne/cm}^2}{\text{N/m}^2}$	$1.0332 \dfrac{\text{kg/cm}^2}{\text{atm}}$

ENERGY AND POWER

$778.16 \dfrac{\text{ft-lb}}{\text{Btu}}$	$2544.4 \dfrac{\text{Btu}}{\text{hp-hr}}$	$252 \dfrac{\text{cal}}{\text{Btu}}$	$1 \dfrac{\text{J}}{\text{wt-s}}, \dfrac{\text{J}}{\text{N-m}}$	$0.01 \dfrac{\text{bar-dm}^3}{\text{J}}$
$550 \dfrac{\text{ft-lb}}{\text{hp-s}}$	$42.4 \dfrac{\text{Btu}}{\text{hp-min}}$	$1.8 \dfrac{\text{Btu/lb}}{\text{cal/gm}}$	$1 \dfrac{\text{kw-s}}{\text{kJ}}$	$\dfrac{16.021}{10^{12}} \dfrac{\text{J}}{\text{MeV}}$
$33{,}000 \dfrac{\text{ft-lb}}{\text{hp-min}}$	$3412.2 \dfrac{\text{Btu}}{\text{kw-hr}}$	$1800 \dfrac{\text{Btu/pmole}}{\text{kcal/gmole}}$	$1 \dfrac{\text{V-amp}}{\text{wt-s}}$	$\dfrac{1.6021}{10^{12}} \dfrac{\text{erg}}{\text{eV}}$
$737.562 \dfrac{\text{ft-lb}}{\text{kw-s}}$	$56.87 \dfrac{\text{Btu}}{\text{kw-min}}$	$2.7194 \dfrac{\text{Btu}}{\text{atm-ft}^3}$	$10^7 \dfrac{\text{ergs}}{\text{J}}$	$\dfrac{11.817}{10^{12}} \dfrac{\text{ft-lb}}{\text{MeV}}$
$1.3558 \dfrac{\text{J}}{\text{ft-lb}}$	$251.98 \dfrac{\text{cal}}{\text{Btu}}$	$4.1868 \dfrac{\text{kJ}}{\text{kcal}}$	$3600 \dfrac{\text{kJ}}{\text{kw-hr}}$	$0.746 \dfrac{\text{kw}}{\text{hp}}$
$1.055 \dfrac{\text{kJ}}{\text{Btu}}$	$101.92 \dfrac{\text{kg-m}}{\text{kJ}}$	$0.4300 \dfrac{\text{Btu/pmole}}{\text{J/gmole}}$	$860 \dfrac{\text{cal}}{\text{wt-hr}}$	$1.8 \dfrac{\text{Btu}}{\text{chu}}$

NEWTON'S PROPORTIONALITY CONSTANT k

$1 \dfrac{\text{Btu/pmole-°R}}{\text{cal/gmole-°K}}$,	$1 \dfrac{\text{Btu/lb-°R}}{\text{cal/gm-°K}}$,	$1 \dfrac{\text{Btu/lb-°R}}{\text{kcal/kg-°K}}$,	$0.2389 \dfrac{\text{Btu/pmole-°R}}{\text{J/gmole-°K}}$,	$4.187 \dfrac{\text{kJ/kg-°K}}{\text{Btu/lb-°R}}$

UNIVERSAL GAS CONSTANT

$1545.32 \dfrac{\text{ft-lb}}{\text{pmole-°R}}$	$8.3143 \dfrac{\text{kJ}}{\text{kgmole-°K}}$	$0.7302 \dfrac{\text{atm-ft}^3}{\text{pmole-°R}}$	$82.057 \dfrac{\text{atm-cm}^3}{\text{gmole-°K}}$
$1.9859 \dfrac{\text{Btu}}{\text{pmole-°R}}$	$1.9859 \dfrac{\text{cal}}{\text{gmole-°K}}$	$10.731 \dfrac{\text{psi-ft}^3}{\text{pmole-°R}}$	$83.143 \dfrac{\text{bar-cm}^3}{\text{gmole-°K}}$
$8.3143 \dfrac{\text{J}}{\text{gmole-°K}}$	$8.3149 \times 10^7 \dfrac{\text{erg}}{\text{gmole-°K}}$	$0.08206 \dfrac{\text{atm-m}^3}{\text{kgmole-°K}}$	$0.083143 \dfrac{\text{bar-l}}{\text{gmole-°K}}$

STANDARD GRAVITY g_o (as conversion unit)

$32.174 \text{ fps}^2 \left(\dfrac{\text{lb}}{\text{slug}}\right)$	$386.1 \text{ ips}^2 \left(\dfrac{\text{lb}}{\text{psin}}\right)$	$9.80665 \dfrac{\text{m}}{\text{s}^2} \left(\dfrac{\text{N}}{\text{kg}}\right)$	$980.665 \dfrac{\text{cm}}{\text{s}^2} \left(\dfrac{\text{dynes}}{\text{gm}}\right)$

MISCELLANEOUS CONSTANTS

Speed of Light	Avogadro Constant	Planck Constant
$c = 2.9979 \times 10^8 \dfrac{\text{m}}{\text{s}}$	$N_A = 6.02252 \times 10^{23} \dfrac{\text{molecules}}{\text{gmole}}$	$h = 6.6256 \times 10^{-34}$ J-s

Boltzmann Constant	Gravitational Constant	Normal mole volume
$\kappa = 1.38054 \times 10^{-23} \dfrac{\text{J}}{\text{°K}}$	$G = 6.670 \times 10^{-11} \dfrac{\text{N-m}^2}{\text{kg}^2}$	$2.24136 \times 10^{-2} \dfrac{\text{m}^3}{\text{gmole}}$

ITEM B 39 Pressures and Temperatures of Saturated Vapors

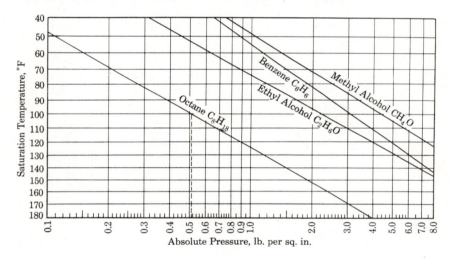

APPENDIX C:
Heat Transfer Charts

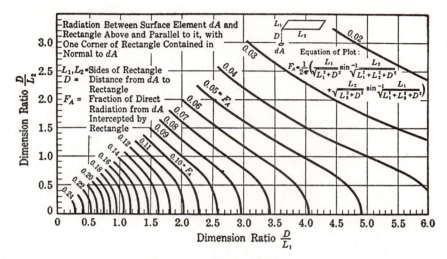

Figure 19/10.

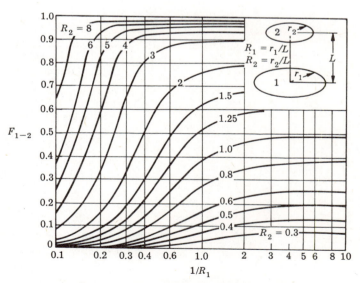

Figure *19/11   Radiation shape factor for parallel, concentric discs.* (**Chapman**[19,14])

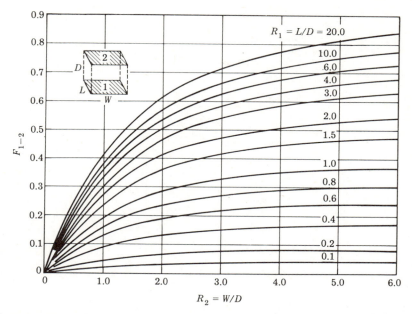

Figure 19/12 Radiation shape factor for parallel, directly opposed, rectangles. **(Chapman**[19,14]**)**

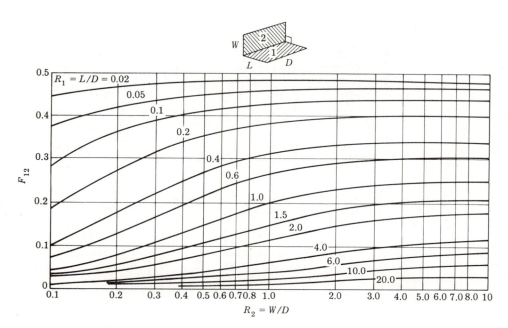

Figure 19/13   Radiation shape factor for perpendicular rectangles with a common edge. **(Chapman**[19,14]**)**

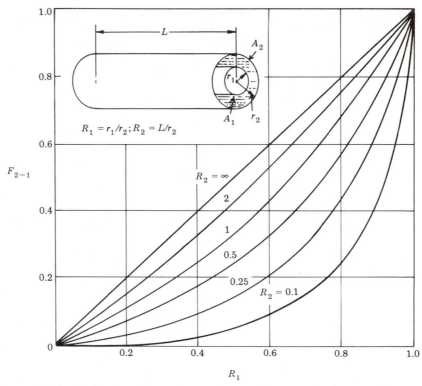

Figure 19/14 *Radiation shape factor for concentric cylinders of finite length.* (Chapman[19,14])

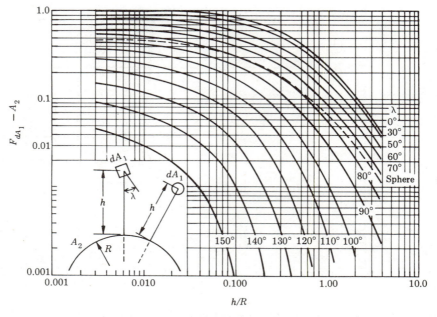

Figure 19/15 *Radiation shape factor for infinitesimal planes and spheres in the presence of a large sphere.* (Chapman[19,14])

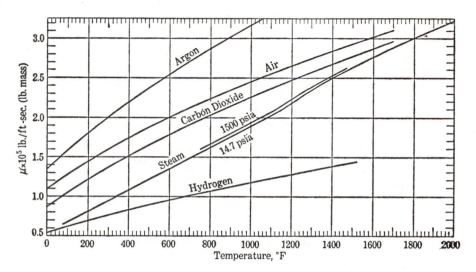

Figure 19/18 **Absolute Viscosities of Gases.**

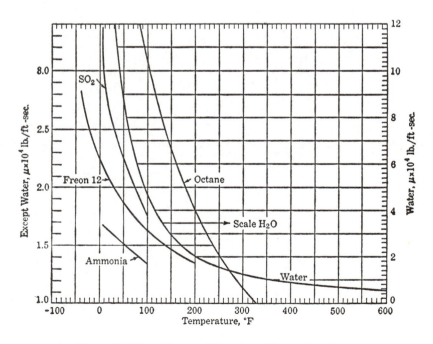

Figure 19/19 **Absolute Viscosity of Some Liquids.**

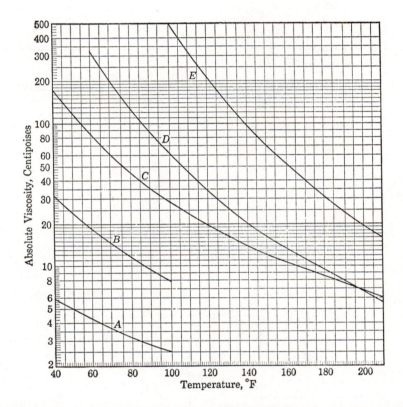

Figure 19/20   Absolute Viscosities of Selected Crude Oil specific gravities: A 0.827;
B 0.896; C 0.899; D 0.932; E 0.947.